SCIENCE, PROPHECY
AND PREDICTION

SCIENCE, PROPHECY AND PREDICTION

MAN'S EFFORTS TO FORETELL THE FUTURE— FROM BABYLON TO WALL STREET

by Richard Lewinsohn

TRANSLATED BY ARNOLD J. POMERANS

BELL PUBLISHING COMPANY, INC.

New York

This book is published in Germany under the title of
Die Enthüllung der Zukunft and in England under the
title of *Prophets and Prediction.*

This edition published by Bell Publishing Company, Inc.,
a division of Crown Publishers, Inc.
by arrangement with Harper & Row, Publishers
A B C D E F G

Library of Congress catalog card number: 61-6435

Contents

Introduction   15

Everyday Predictions 17—Experience makes us prophetic
19—Uncertainty Factors 20—Of dice and atoms 22—
Boiled Ice 25—The law of chance 27—The long and the
short of it 29—Basic forms of prediction 30—Line and
circle 33—The balance 35—Ignorance by choice 37—
Intuition, Induction, and Deduction 38—What is experience? 40—Creative Foresight 41—Utopias 42—Poets
and Dreamers 46—Take your choice 47

1. *Short History of the Art of Prophecy*   51

Mesopotamian beginnings 52—Hepatoscopy 53—Chal-
dean astrology 57—The Lo-King 60—Old Testament
Prophets 63—Egyptian mystifiers 65—The Greeks 68—
The Delphic Oracle 70—Prophetesses 72—The Romans
74—The end of the world 76—Nostradamus 82—Pascal's
Wager 87—Hypnosis 89—The decline of divination 91

2. *The Language of the Stars*   93

Symbolism triumphant 94—Lion into Crab 96—Good constellations and bad 99—Birth or Conception? 102—Political
astrology 104—Collective Horoscopes 107—The Planets
of Chance 108—The balance sheet 110—Is astrology scientific? 114—Astrological Morals 116

3. *The World of Dreams*   119

Popular Dream Books 119—Freud and prophetic dreams
122—The dream censor 124—Prophetic and creative
dreams 126—Telepathy and Clairvoyance 128—The
English dreamer 131—How to prophesy in your sleep 133
—E.S.P. 136—Is time reversible? 139—Further dimensions 141

4. *The Wheel of History* 143

History repeats itself 146—Cabbalistic numbers 148—Three stages of history 150—Marx and Darwin 153—The Decline of the West 155—Father and Son 157—War and Peace 159—Large states and small 162

5. *Wishing and Choosing* 164

Freedom of choice 164—Client motivation 165—Straw votes 167—The Gallup Poll 169—Red beans and white 171—Predicting elections today 173—The art of prediction 174—Is democracy endangered? 175

6. *Weather Prophets* 177

Astro-meteorology 117—Florentine illumination 180—The three great L's 182—The débacle of Balaclava 184—War in the air 186—Freddy, the frog 188—Doubling the scope 189—Weather-lore 192—Sunspots 193—The long summer 196

7. *Matters of Life and Death* 198

Hippocrates' teaching 199—1001 diseases 201—Infections 202—Modern difficulties 204—Surgery = Foresight 206—Pregnancy test 209—Boy or Girl? 210—Cellular sex-differentiation 212—Infection or heredity? 213—The secret of family resemblance 214

8. *Quantity and Quality* 217

Pastor Süssmilch's "divine" order 217—Malthus' forebodings 219—Depopulation by prosperity 220—Europe, 1970 223—Europe, 2000 226—The weaker sex 228—A surfeit of women 229—Comparing I.Q's 231

9. *Gambling and Safe Play* 234

The gambler's mentality 235—Gamblers par excellence 236—Gaming systems 238—Time and probability 239—State lotteries 241—Shipwreck and conflagration 242—Wagers with death 244—From the cradle to the grave 246—Subjective and objective chances 247—Predicting the improbable 249

CONTENTS

10. *The Mystery of the Business Cycle*   251

The law of income distribution 251—The discovery of
business cycles 253—Cycle research 254—Crises 255—
The Juglar-Cycle 257—Kitchins and Kondratieffs 259—Of
pigs and rubber plants 261—Trading hopes 263—Wall
Street Prophets 265—The Postman always knocks twice
267—The cycle-barometer 270—Harvard knows no crisis
272—The German barometer 273—The post-war crisis
fails to materialise 275—Models to order 276

11. *Forging the Future*   280

Re-armament plans 280—Planning the nation's economy
282—Budgeting 283—Planning by persuasion 284—
Water and land 286—Recalcitrant coffee 289—"Projections" 290—Planless planning 292—Critics of the Five-
year Plan 294—The correct proportions 295—Planning
ahead—for how long? 296—The revolt of the body 298—
Dictating and planning 300—Self-regulation 302

ENVOI The Future of Prediction   304

Specialisation without specialists 305—Collective predictions 306—Restricting chance 306

Index   309

List of Plates

opposite page

I. On their voyage to Troy, the Greeks were becalmed for some time. It was then that Palamedes is said to have invented the game of dice as an effective way of combating boredom.   48

II. Dürer's view of the end of the world (From: *Heimlich Offenbarung Johannis*, Nuremberg 1498).   49

III. Worship of the Babylonian Sun-god Shamash (*British Museum*).   64

IV. Prophecy from the intestines of an animal (Greek vase, 500 B.C.).   64

V. Gilgamesh (Babylonian seal). The Gilgamesh epic contains the oldest-known dream interpretation.   65

VI. The *Kudurru* which gave rise to the signs of the Babylonian Zodiac.   128

VII. Astrological plate from Uruk in Mesopotamia (100 B.C.).   129

VIII. The Chinese Magic Disc, Lo King, which was commonly used for divination.   129

IX. The Delphic Pythia (Greek vase).   144

X. Forecourt of Delphic Temple (400 B.C.).   144

XI. The 17th century first introduced "automation". Pascal constructed his calculating machine in 1641, when he was only 18 years old.   145

XII. Calculating machine constructed by Leibniz in 1673.   145

XIII. More complicated calculating machine constructed by J. H. Müller (1782).   145 *opposite page*

XIV. Two Tarot-cards used for fortune telling. Tarot, like so many other card games, is of Central Asian origin.   192

XV. Two of the cards used by Mlle. Lenormand (1768-1843) who allegedly predicted Napoleon's rise and fall to him.   192

XVI. A seance being conducted by the great Hanussen. The method illumination was new, the rest as old as the hills.   193

XVII. Mrs. Günther Geffers being consulted by German detectives to solve a criminal case. She always "worked" in a trance.   193

XVIII. Wheel of fortune symbolising man's rise and fall (1541 miniature).   208

Figures in Text

page

1. Mercenaries throwing dice. Woodcut by Anton von Woensam.   24

2. The zigzag line. Action and Reaction (I). Assumption: Every action is followed by a reaction in the opposite sense, which need not be equal in intensity or duration.   32

3. The circle. Recurrence of equal phenomena (II). Assumption: Historical, economic, and many other events are periodic repetitions of similar phenomena. Once the phase of a given cycle is known, the subsequent phases can be predicted.   32

4. The straight line. Rise or fall (III). Assumption: All main trends have a basic direction, though the direction may be subject to minor fluctuations. Optimists assume continuous progress, while pessimists assume a continuous decline.   32

5. The balance. Tendency toward equilibrium (IV). Assumption: All fluctuations are so many deviations from a state of perfect equilibrium, which is always restored in the end. The principle (and symbol) of justice.   33

6. Jules Verne's conception of flying. He died in 1905, shortly before the aeroplane came into its own.   45

7. Leonardo da Vinci's idea of a field gun. The cart holds 33 barrels, 11 of which are fired simultaneously.   47

8. The Babylonian god Adad was the "Lord of the Oracle", but also the god of storms, thunder, and lightning.   51

9. Head of the giant Humbaba, formed of intestines (British Museum). Humbaba played a great role in Assyrian divination.   52

11

page

10. Diagrams of coiled sheep intestines on a Babylonian clay tablet. Every turn had a special prophetic significance.   54

11. Clay model of a liver used by Babylonian diviners (British Museum).   55

12. Ancient Chinese Zodiac-plate   61

13. Bronze Liver from Piacenza. Etruscan model for hepatoscopic predictions (300-200 B.C.).   75

14. Ancient Arab Zodiac.   77

15. The end of the world as seen by Scheuchzer in his *Physica Sacra* (1734).   79

16. The 17th century combined great technical process with crude superstition. Erfurt prophecy about a bad harvest (1627) based on "celestial signs".   80

17. "Phlebotomic" figure. Every part of the body is related to a sign of the Zodiac. The stars show when a patient must be operated on or have his blood let.   81

18. In the 16th century, chemistry was an important means of prophecy. Chemical still from *Destillierkunst* (The art of distillation) by Brunswig (1547).   82

19. Geronimo Cardano, the great 16th-century physician and mathematician, was a poor astrologer.   84

20. Horoscope cast by Cardano for Edward VI of England. The horoscope proved to be completely wrong.   85

21. Nostradamus, the most famous of all 16th-century prophets. His political predictions are still in great vogue.   86

22. Zodiac from the *Lucidarius* (Augsburg, 1479). The universe was still geo-centric: sun, moon, and planets revolve about the earth.   97

23. Mercury and his children. From an English astrological calendar of 1503.   99

page

24. Saturn, the evil star, bringing mankind troubles, imprisonment, illness, and death (From *Meister des Hausbuches*). 101

25. Kepler's horoscope of Wallenstein (1608). Kepler failed to predict Wallenstein's assassination. 104

26. Zener-cards used in parapsychological research. 137

27. Ancient Mexican calendar stone showing the four suns of past ages, all of which ended in disaster, and the face of the present, the fifth, sun god. 144

28. Title page of one of many pamphlets proclaiming a flood in 1524. 179

29. Evangelista Torricelli, the inventor of the barometer (1643). 181

30. Wall Street quotations of industrial shares. A long upward trend ends with a "double top". 269

31. De Foville's General Barometer, one of the first attempts to present a pictorial analysis of economic phenomena. 271

Introduction

*A*LL OF US ARE PROPHETS, NOT SO MUCH FROM CHOICE AS
from sheer necessity. Whenever we cross a road and fail to
take into account traffic conditions, or misjudge distances and
speeds, we may have to pay dearly for our lack of foresight. The
foresight needed in this case is not on a very high level—it
resembles the instinctive reaction of animals sensing danger.
However, man is not born with it. Very small children are
incapable of dealing with even such simple situations, and can
do little more than scream at the approach of danger. Their
physical co-ordination is not yet sufficiently developed to make
good their lack of judgment. Unfortunately many adults fare
little better—their inability to estimate the immediate future
correctly is borne out by the mounting toll which traffic accidents
take of drivers and pedestrians alike. And this despite the fact
that the Highway Code prescribes a set of elementary rules,
observance of which would lead to a drastic reduction of road
accidents.

The type of foresight we are discussing consists of immediate
responses to external signals. Someone approaches me recklessly, and I must take the necessary evasive action. My response
—i.e. fear, thought, escape—is both one of the most primitive
and also one of the most persistent human reactions. Civilisation
has done little to reduce our general anxieties—it has merely
shifted their causes. The builders of the Pyramids simply had a
different set of anxieties from those of the modern motorist and
had to take different precautions. No doubt they took too few—
men have since grown a little more careful. In other words, they
have become more prophetic, or, which amounts to the same
thing, more civilised.

The foresight needed to avoid accidents is occasionally called
"presence of mind", though "mind" plays little part in it. In
essence, it involves making good use of the fraction of time

between the discovery of the source of danger and the evasive action, and acting appropriately within very circumscribed conditions. The pedestrian who wants to dodge an approaching car may have to take into account the fact that another pedestrian is approaching from the opposite direction, and the driver who wants to avoid the accident must be able to gauge at a glance the total traffic situation at that point. Even so, what he does is to judge a relatively simple situation with no extraneous uncertainty factors. True, he has to have his wits about him, and for this, intellectual brilliance is no substitute. The absent-minded professor will not shine in this kind of situation.

Pedestrians, no matter how confident, can rarely tell you how they estimate whether it is safe to cross a busy road against fast traffic or not. If you ask them, they will usually reply that they know from experience—no doubt from that elementary kind of experience which is almost subconscious. At best, they may mention an accident in which they have been involved or which they have witnessed, but they neither know how many yards in front of an approaching car they can cross safely, how to judge the distance of the car from its apparent size, nor under what conditions they would consider it more advisable to wait for the car to pass. Even experienced drivers cannot give you exact quantitative estimates of this kind. The licensing authorities do not demand this kind of knowledge—possibly with every justification, since too much knowledge and reflection in the face of immediate danger may well paralyse our responses.

Despite the increasing accident rate, the ratio of false to correct estimates of traffic situations is very small. In Paris, for instance, statistics show that there is one fatal road accident per day, i.e. the chance of a Parisian losing his life on a given day is one in five million. If we include non-fatal accidents, the ratio becomes 1:100,000 Ignoring collisions between cars, we find that the risk run by a Parisian pedestrian is roughly one in three hundred thousand. Now, assuming that every Parisian crosses no more than three streets every day, we find that he makes one wrong estimate in every million correct ones. Appearances notwithstanding, the average Parisian therefore behaves with a high degree of foresight, at least on the road.

Everyday Predictions

However, everyday prophecies are by no means restricted to the kind of short range predictions we have been discussing. Most people manage to organise their free time for days and even for weeks ahead, i.e. they can predict where they and other people will be at a given future date, and for what purpose. The fact that they can organise their leisure does not mean that they know nothing about the rest of their time—quite the contrary is the case. Their work, their family and other obligations, their habits and physiological needs—for instance sleep—enable them to predict that they will carry out certain activities at certain times in certain places, precisely because these obligations are taken for granted. Most people are not even aware that, in this way, they are in fact predicting the future as it affects an integral part of their lives. Commitments of this kind may be said to form the framework into which decisions about the use of free time have to be fitted. But, even the organisation of free time is usually connected with social commitments and must therefore be organised and predicted fairly accurately. Thus all sorts of everyday prediction have a high degree of probability and are subject to roughly the same number of uncertainty factors.

The fact that two people feel entitled to make an appointment to meet in the future does not gainsay the presence of many uncertainty factors, even if some of them are not usually taken into account. Needless to say, the appointment can only be kept if both are alive and fit at the time, if the meeting place still exists, and if transport is not paralysed. These factors—continued life and the absence of major catastrophes—are basic assumptions of all prediction about human behaviour. It is, of course, quite possible, that people may have a stroke or be run over on their way to an appointment. However, the shorter the interval between the original arrangement and the actual meeting, the smaller are the hazards involved, so much so that for all practical purposes, they can be neglected. This is no longer true of long range predictions.

Failure to keep an appointment, i.e. to predict correctly, is very often explained by the fact that something "happened" to one of the people concerned, a polite way of saying that he found something better to do with his time. Such questions of preference, which are often purely subjective, play a considerable role in everyday predictions and even more so in political and economic life.

All the same, it is common practice for busy people to plan their day, their hours, and even parts of their hours for weeks ahead. Politicians and directors of big companies have private secretaries for the express purpose of arranging their appointment books, while the directors themselves play the passive role of keeping the arranged meetings to the best of their ability. In this way, they turn themselves into the objects of organised prediction, and the organisers, the secretaries, pride themselves on their ability to say that their employer is booked up for lunch every day for the next six weeks.

But less important people, too, can usually predict their future for weeks and even for months ahead. Thus, they may begin to make preparations for their summer holidays in early winter. The more limited their financial means, the more they must plan, i.e. predict. Travelling has ceased to be an interruption of regular routine, and is nowadays planned down to the last detail, not least because the general holiday rush, and the consequent shortage of suitable accommodation, make it essential to book hotel rooms well in advance, and to plan an exact itinerary. In the case of holidays, individual foresight is usually aided by such organisations as travel bureaus which do most of their customers' planning for them; the customer need only state the date of his departure and return, and the bureau does the rest.

The uncertainty factors involved are considered so negligible that people who tell you that they will be in Madeira, in Iceland, or in Hawaii in six months' time, are not credited with possessing special prophetic gifts. Not so long ago anyone claiming that he would reach some distant place on a given day, would have been taken for a ridiculous braggart or, if successful, for a divine seer. From this alone, it must be obvious that the art of predicting the future, at least in certain fields and particularly those related to technology, has made tremendous advances. What was previously a matter for prophets has become a commonplace activity. Our certainty has become much greater, and the greater our certainty, the less our need for oracles.

Experience makes us prophetic

So far we have been discussing "activist" predictions, i.e. predictions of future activities. To provide for the future, people must act in the present. In some cases—e.g. when we arrange an appointment—prediction and planning are practically identical: the date is foresight and intention all at once. In other cases— e.g. on crossing a road—the prediction is a means towards an end. In either case, the prediction is purposive.

However, purposive predictions are not the only ones. If, on the night of 20th March, I remember that the sun will rise at six o'clock tomorrow—a prediction which every schoolboy can make nowadays though it took astronomers a very long time to establish this simple fact—my prediction cannot be called purposive by any stretch of the imagination. I do not intend getting up with the sun, neither my work nor my leisure is in any way affected by the equinox, and even if I realise with pleasure that the days will henceforth be longer than the nights, my wishes are in no way engaged. If I did not like the equinox, there would be nothing I could do about it. All I have really done is to relate two events: a future date and an astronomical phenomenon.

Scientists—no matter in which of the scientific disciplines they are trained—make this type of prediction all the time. Thus, when a scientist tells us what will happen under given conditions (i.e. when we drop a body in a vacuum, or if we heat iron beyond 780°C.) he is merely making generalisations from past observations. Formerly, scientific laws were always so phrased as to stress their causal character, and the discovery of cause and effect was considered to be the *ultima ratio* of all scientific work. Nowadays scientists have grown a little more reserved in that respect. For practical purposes, however, this change of heart need not concern us, and we may take it that, under given conditions, predictable changes will occur with maximum probability, if not with absolute certainty.

The most important of these predictable events have become common knowledge. Others are known to the specialists alone, and if need be we must consult them. The engineer will tell us under what conditions a given machine will work with optimum efficiency, and the doctor will tell us what diet to adopt if we are to recover quickly. In either case, theoretical perfection does not concern us so much as practical advice.

Scientific predictions, even if they are not part and parcel of every man's intellectual stock in trade, nevertheless play an important part in his life. They form a reservoir on which he can freely draw the moment his own elementary knowledge becomes inadequate. Without them, a great many of our activist and purposive predictions would be impossible or at least impracticable.

Man therefore lives in a world of predictions and the question whether human beings are capable of foretelling the future is purely rhetorical. All we can ask is what events human beings cannot predict at all or only with a small degree of probability, and what are the limits of man's foresight. This leads us to a second question: Is there any means of extending these limits?

Uncertainty Factors

To answer this question, we must first look at the negative aspect of the problem: completely unpredictable phenomena. They can all be classified as accidental, complex, or aleatory, uncertainty factors.

In the first group, i.e. the accidental uncertainty factors, we include all those events of which we commonly say that "they just happened". They are generally untoward events, and even if they may come as pleasant changes to some, they will nevertheless often cause inconvenience to others. In any case, they cause predictions to go wrong.

Many such unforseen factors do not, in fact, have to be absolutely unpredictable. Thus, in our previous discussion of activist every-day predictions, we have mentioned some implicit or explicit uncertainty factors (viz. premature death, natural catastrophies, etc.) which, even in what are apparently the most certain plans for the future, could well be taken into account, if only as a precautionary measure. Particularly natural catastrophies, though no less frequent than in the past, have become more predictable and hence less of a risk. True, scientific meteorology is still in its infancy but its progress is such, that some of the worst weather-phenomena can be anticipated to a far greater degree than was formerly possible.

In addition to accidents beyond human control, there are the accidents due to human carelessness. In this field, too, preventive techniques have been successfully applied, and no longer can entire cities be laid waste by a carelessly started fire. While increasing motor-traffic has driven up the accident rate, and while our own chances of being run over are unpredictable, at least the individual risk of material suffering from such accidents has been appreciably reduced by third-party-risk insurance. Statistical or collective predictions, i.e. the assessment of the total number and extent of future accidents, have therefore more than purely academic interest; they are a very important means of anticipating and mastering the future.

The second category of uncertainty factors is of quite a different type, even if it, too, may sometimes look like pure accident, and play havoc with an individual's plans. It consists of factors too complex to be predicted with ease or certainty, simplification, condensation, and rigid exclusion of extraneous considerations being essential conditions for making any kind of correct prediction. If someone were to try to obtain an overall view of all terrestrial phenomena, and delve into all their implications his predictive faculty would be effectively paralysed. Active every-day predictions on which we base our activities are generally over-simplified predictions which rigidly exclude all extraneous or unimportant factors, and which concentrate on the essential problem alone. It is for this very reason that they go wrong so often—the price we have to pay if we wish to predict anything at all.

There are, however, processes and events in which this simple method of thought must fail, not only because of the possibility of unexpected accidents or the neglect of extraneous considerations, but because of their very nature. Thus, political, economic and cultural trends quite obviously depend on so many different factors, that no completely satisfactory predictions can possibly be made on the basis of any given set of factors. Even if it were possible to consider *all* the factors, the result would be altogether nebulous and vague. No wonder, then, that man's world view has undergone such unpredictable changes. To take just one example: at the beginning of the 20th century, for instance, naturalists were sharing the literary field with symbolists and no one could have told you which school would eventually win the day.

Political predictions are even more difficult to make, because the factors involved are more complex still. In particular, international politics continue to be a cloak and dagger game, with secret services whose main task it is to confuse the opponent while trying to gauge his own intentions. Predictions about war and peace are therefore among the trickiest of all.

In business, too, which has apparently shed its love of secrecy, and where large companies have begun to publish their plans, future investment policy, budgets, and statistics about the most complicated operations, for years in advance, the uncertainty factors are still so great that few experts can claim to have given correct estimates of the course of a single business, let alone of price fluctuations, for a number of successive half-year periods.

Despite all these enormous difficulties, the art of prediction has made advances even in these complex fields. Instead of direct predictions, experts nowadays prefer to analyse the past and to isolate clear cyclical movements—war and peace, booms and slumps—and to use these cycles as the basis for taking precautions against future contingencies. Cycle theories were in vogue for a great many years, and though they seem less fashionable nowadays, they may well become *à la mode* once again, particularly since scientists, too, are constantly coming up against periodic phenomena.

The most important method of predicting the economic, and to a lesser extent the political, future, is, however, an activistic one. Men have begun to plan and to fashion the future accordingly. Whenever they succeed in doing so, they may be said to have prophesied correctly.

Of dice and atoms

The third category of uncertainty factors is called aleatory. *Alea* is the throw of a die, and dice did, in fact, play a paramount role in elucidating the problems we are about to discuss. It was with dice that Galileo, Pascal, and Fermat laid the foundation of the theory of probability 300 years ago. The die is the symbol of chance, since, theoretically, it favours no one and enables every player to stake an equal claim to fortune—zero, if the game is continued long enough. In practice, however, the dice fall without any recognisable pattern, so that one player can win while another loses, and the run of luck may continue until the loser stops playing for lack of patience or funds (see Plate I, p. 47).

Similar considerations intervene in a thousand everyday chance coincidences. Perhaps it is mere chance that one of two shopkeepers who start up business in the same street flourishes, while the other goes bankrupt, for the one who scores an initial (accidental) success can expand his business, increase his turnover, and therefore sell his goods more cheaply and attract an ever wider circle of customers, while the other's business stagnates. The longer he has to wait for a similar bit of good fortune, the more unequal his chance.

Probability theory is very reassuring since it tells us that inequality is a mere illusion. If only we wait long enough, we, too, shall have a run of luck. But even probability theory must admit that the longer the game continues, the smaller our chances of recouping our previous losses. Even if we were to play the same game of chance for a million successive times, staking the same amount on every throw, we should have to devote a whole year to this activity and risk three thousand times our original stake. Only few players are prepared for such losses. But though probability theory has been unable to teach us the art of winning, it has nevertheless taught us much that is useful. Above all, it has shown that those who play longest are the most successful. In this way, the arithmetical foundations of insurance were laid, and the risks not only of aleatory but also of accidental losses were considerably reduced. (We must clearly distinguish between accident and pure chance. Accidents have assignable causes, and only seem to be pure chance because we did not expect them. Pure chance, on the other hand, has no causes, and all we can say of it is that it exists.)

The question whether pure chance exists in nature as well, has been the subject of keen discussion between physicists and mathematicians during recent decades. While few of them would be prepared to state that chance is the kind of natural phenomenon which must be taken into account in the formulation

1. Mercenaries throwing dice. Woodcut by Anton von Woensam.

of all "natural laws"[1], most scientists would nevertheless make allowances for certain chance factors since, in view of recent scientific developments, it seems doubtful whether all natural processes are rigidly determined, i.e. follow strict and universally valid laws. These doubts are not due to the recognition of our ignorance, and do not entitle us to hope that greater knowledge will one day reveal the missing causal nexus, but are doubts of principle based on the mathematical recognition of the limits of human knowledge.

The main evidence for this approach is Heisenberg's Uncertainty Principle formulated in 1927, when Werner Heisenberg then 25 years old, was struck by the impossibility of measuring the position and the velocity of an atomic particle simultaneously. This is how he put it[2]:

"It was discovered that it was impossible to describe simultaneously both the position and the velocity of an atomic particle with any prescribed degree of accuracy. We can either measure the position very accurately—when the action of the instrument used for the observation obscures our knowledge of the velocity —or we can make accurate measurements of the velocity and forego knowledge of the position."

Heisenberg's uncertainty relations have been generally recognised, and have caused a veritable revolution in science and philosophy. While Heisenberg himself has always been very reserved about the general validity of his findings, many scientists believe that he has sounded the knell to determinism in science, and that probability has taken the place of all certainty.

Boiled Ice

We cannot possibly ignore this basic question if we are to make any serious attempts to predict the future. If we assume that the Heisenberg uncertainty relations are not restricted to atomic physics, but are rather an expression of a generally valid, and perhaps the only assured, natural law, then uncertainty rules

---

[1] Pierre Vendreyès: *Déterminisme et autonomie* (Paris 1956) p. 165 ff.
[2] W. Heisenberg: *The Physicist's Conception of Nature* (translated by A. J. Pomerans) London 1958. pp. 39 f.

supreme in all spheres of life. In that case, despite all the findings of modern physics, despite Einstein's Theory of Relativity, and despite nuclear research, we are back at the *ignoramus-ignorabimus* with which Du Bois-Reymond (1872) characterised our inability to grasp the nature of atoms.[1] If the Uncertainty Principle were, in fact, universally valid, we could make no predictions whatsoever, and our future would be as closed to us as the outcome of a game of chance. We could not use the same medical prescription twice running, for what was harmless yesterday may well be poisonous tomorrow. It would even be inadvisable to knock a nail into a wall, since there is no reason to suppose that it will not fly back at us like a rubber ball and gouge out our eyes.

Famous scientists have spent their valuable time calculating the probablity with which such absurdities may occur. The second law of thermodynamics states that heat can only travel from a body with a greater to one with lower heat energy. Now this law—which was known long before Heisenberg—is only valid within certain limits—heat can travel in the opposite sense as well. Thus J. H. Jeans calculated the probability of water, placed on a hot stove, freezing instead of boiling by transferring its heat to the stove.

The American physicist J. W. Gibbs (1839-1903) had shown a few decades earlier how to combine the theoretically possible with the practically impossible. According to kinetic theory, one cc. of air at normal temperature and pressure contains 27 million billions of molecules, all of which move in all directions with great velocity. Now it is impossible to predict the trajectory of any given particle, since collisions with the walls of the containing vessel and with other particles will alter its path in unpredictable ways. Nevertheless, we can state that the mean square velocity of all the particles taken together is proportional to the temperature.

This law, too, is only approximately correct. Ludwig Boltzmann has called the behaviour of the molecules chaotic: they move as if they were governed by pure chance. For this reason, Boltzmann is today considered one of the founders of indeterminism, i.e. of the rejection of strict causality in all

[1] F. A. Lange: *Geschichte des Materialismus* (Leipzig undated) Vol. II, p. 196 ff.

natural processes. In Boltzmann's day (1844–1906), such attitudes were frowned upon by all reputable scientists, who believed that in nature everything was orderly, and that all talk of chaos simply reflected an inability to assess the real facts. Chaos was nothing but a veil covering the face of order.

Josiah Willard Gibbs, a great innovator and discoverer, but at heart a conservative with a firm belief in the Newton's classical mechanics, found a way out of Boltzmann's dilemma by comparing kinetic theory with statistics. In neither case can we make any precise statements about the individual components, but in both cases we can say something about total processes with a fair degree of accuracy. By analogy with established statistical methods, Gibbs became the founder of statistical mechanics, the fore-runner of modern theoretical physics which is based exclusively on statistical laws, i.e. on probability statements.

The law of chance

From recent developments in physics it does not, however, follow that all predictions of the future will henceforth be of no value. Not even professional prophets need hang their heads in shame, for by studying the past they can still look confidently into the future. Statistical, like the old determinist, predictions make use of just that principle. No laws have ever been absolutely certain but, by and large, laws have always enabled us to look at tomorrow, particularly when we can see where and how they went wrong yesterday.

The layman who usually looks on modern physics with its atom bombs as most "realistic", often forgets that theoretical physics has become more abstract than ever it has been, and that it has withdrawn to the ivory tower of pure mathematics. Quite possibly physicists may one fine day revolt against the dictatorship of the mathematicians, and look for concepts which can more readily be brought into harmony with conceptual models.

Above all, determinism—if the term is understood to connote not only determinability but also pre-determinability—is an unavoidable working hypothesis. Indeterminists are only indeterminists when they calculate; the moment they carry out a laboratory experiment they have no real doubts that identical experiments will produce identical results under identical conditions. Even Heisenberg's uncertainty relations are deterministic, at least to the extent that they assume that the experiments by which they were established can be repeated.

Indeterminism must always be based on exceptions to a given rule, not on a rule that changes with time and that is founded on inadequate observations and false calculations. If 2 x 2 were found to make 5 tomorrow, we should still have a determinable system of numbers. Only if we can show that, for no apparent reason—or cause, though the causal nexus can never be rigidly established—2 x 2 may make either 4 or 5, could we speak of an indeterminist process. Fortunately, such processes are very rare indeed in everyday phenomena.

The problem of determinism vs. indeterminism in nature—as opposed to morals—is therefore, by and large, a linguistic problem. When the French mathematician Emile Borel, one of the foremost probability theorists, after paying tribute to the indeterminist fashion for many years, came to the end of his life —he died in 1956 at the age of 85—he realised that we can safely dismiss such theoretical possibilities as Jeans's water-freezing hypothesis as completely out of the question.[1] According to Borel, there is only a single law of chance, which, in simplified form, states that improbable phenomena do not occur. True, this, too, is no more than a hypothesis, but it is a wise hypothesis which helps to link thought with action, and calculation with observation.

Those who are sceptics on principle or by inclination—and modern indeterminism is nothing if it is not sceptical—are at liberty to express Borel's argument negatively: certainty is only the least degree of uncertainty, and the so-called natural laws are only valid for phenomena in which chance plays no preceptible role. For all practical (and logical) purposes, however, we might as well state positively that what is highly probable is as good as certain. Naturally this does not mean that we must choose between absolute certainty and uncertainty—between determinism and indeterminism—we must rather assess degrees of probability, even in strictly scientific predictions. This is

[1] Emile Borel: *Probabilité et certitude* (Paris 1956) pp. 5–6, and 118–125.

precisely the approach which we shall use to examine former and present methods of predictions in the following chapters.

The long and the short of it.

It would seem reasonable to suppose that one of the most decisive factors in assessing the degree of probability of a future event is the interval between the moment when we make a given prediction and the time at which it is supposed to come true. The greater the interval, the greater apparently the number of accidental, complex, and aleatory factors involved, i.e. the greater the chances of mishaps, complications and accidents. While this argument seems quite logical at first glance, it is, in fact, fallacious.

Time does not necessarily work against the prophet and, precisely in the case of very daring predictions, it may become his close ally. According to probability theory, the chance of losing (or winning) in a continuous game with equal stakes, decreases rather than increases with time. Similarly, it may be far less risky to make long rather than short-range predictions about a unique future event. In ancient times, when the court astrologer told the king that his impending marriage would result in male issue ere Jupiter had circled the sun (which takes twelve years) he was on much safer ground than had he promised a son and heir for the next year. Again, if we predict that it will be terribly cold next winter, we are on safer ground than if we predict cold weather for a particular day at the beginning of winter. The trick is to give time a chance of working in our favour.

Moreover, long-range predictions have the additional advantage that they may be forgotten, though most prophets will make sure that only their errors fall into oblivion. Here time may cover error with a benevolent cloak, and this alone is one of the reasons why professional prophets generally prefer to prophesy well into the future. Though modern man is curiously impatient, and often prefers inaccurate short-range predictions to even the most accurate long-range prophecies, there are certain fields in which the opposite is the case. The farmer requires long-range weather predictions, and we know the tremendous difficulties which meteorologists have to satisfy him even vaguely. In the economic field, the chances of correct prediction depend on special factors. While the chances of success of a given business can generally be predicted for a month ahead with as much probability as for next week, long-range general economic predictions are less certain than short-range predictions.

As a rule of thumb, we can say that long term predictions are easier to make whenever we deal with aggregates which may balance out, e.g. days of good and poor business. When we predict unique phenomena, on the other hand, the uncertainty increases with time. This rule too requires a restriction, for it is largely a question of what we mean by "unique". If a firm of builders contracts to finish a new building on a certain day, this apparently simple prediction referring to a unique event, is, in fact, a highly complex prediction, since the building operation involves innumerable separate factors: labour, deliveries, transport, etc., every one of which affects the others. A delay in any one set of factors, may throw the whole plan out of gear. It is for this reason that so many professional plans go wrong.

Basic forms of prediction

Even if the interval does not affect the probability of the predicted event crucially, it nevertheless has a considerable bearing on its character. In very short-range everyday predictions, we generally manage without a general picture, and consider facts in isolation. I wish for something, I realise what I must do to implement my wish, and I act accordingly. I expect no complications and no set-backs, and take it for granted that my action will proceed without any hitches.

This is not even changed in principle if my action involves someone else on whom I have no direct influence, as for instance in our example of crossing a road. If a car is approaching, I simply judge the distance and act accordingly. I never expect the driver to run me down deliberately, or to force me to change my mind.

In long-range predictions, however, other factors must be taken into account, and this can be done in four basic ways which we may represent visually by a zigzag line, a sloping straight line, a circle, and a balance.

Average-term predictions are generally based on the belief that every persistent action is followed by an opposite reaction after a crucial point has been reached, i.e. the total process can be represented by a zigzag line. This belief clearly has a physiological basis and is founded on self-observation. All of us know that our strength is not inexhaustible, and that all our exertions are followed by fatigue. Similarly, oppression of one person or group by another may sooner or later result in the kind of reaction we call rebellion or revolution.

The word "revolution" is also applied to cultural and technological trends, when a radical innovation or invention replaces more orthodox ideas or methods. However, only the rarest of cultural or technical revolutions can be shown to be direct reactions to the past. Thus Max Planck, the father of quantum mechanics, made a point of stating that no deliberate wish to discard the classical picture of Newtonian physics entered into his new formulation. On the contrary, his new approach was the direct result of his attempt to adhere to classical determinism.[1] Similarly, we should be wrong to look upon modern atomic theory as a reaction against older concepts, or on the atom bomb as a reaction to previous explosives. Very few correct predictions can be made about revolutions in the technical field, because the only great changes that can be foreseen with any degree of certainty are those which are in the nature of a definite reaction.

But even in the case of pure reactions, it is still very difficult to predict where and when a revolution will occur, and how intense it will be. Action and reaction are not necessarily equal and opposite, particularly in the political field where a long period of oppression is often followed by a fairly bloodless revolution, or where a violent revolt is often followed by a weak government. If this were not the case, we should never see the end of revolutions. However, the opposite course of events is just as common: great revolutions may start from small causes. The

[1] Max Planck: *Wege zur physikalischen Erkenntnis* (2nd ed., Leipzig 1934) p. 244.

Four Forms of Prediction

(————progress to date — — — prediction)

Prediction

2. The zigzag line. Action and Reaction (I). Assumption: Every action is followed by a reaction in the opposite sense, which need not be equal in intensity or duration.

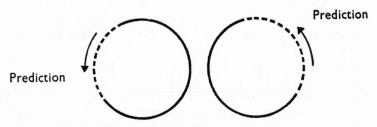

Prediction   **Prediction**

3. The circle. Recurrence of equal phenomena (II). Assumption: Historical, economic, and many other events are periodic repetitions of similar phenomena. Once the phase of a given cycle is known, the subsequent phases can be predicted.

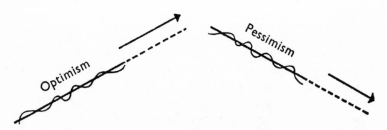

4. The straight line. Rise or fall (III). Assumption: All main trends have a basic direction, though the direction may be subject to minor fluctuations. Optimists assume continuous progress, while pessimists assume a continuous decline.

Prediction

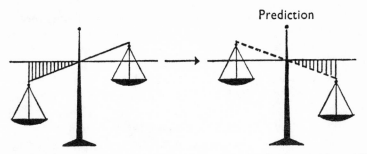

5. The balance. Tendency toward equilibrium (IV). Assumption: All fluctuations are so many deviations from a state of perfect equilibrium, which is always restored in the end. The principle (and symbol) of justice.

classical example is the French revolution of 1789, which, though its mental climate had been prepared well in advance, occurred at an unsuspected moment. One might almost be led into believing that political, like organic, life is full of enzymes, i.e. small doses of catalysts which can produce large effects. While some of these catalysts are well known to every government and to every revolutionary, others, and often those which cause the actual upheaval, have remained quite mysterious.

Line and circle

In long-range predictions about the life of future generations, the reactive method proves unprofitable to even those with the greatest prophetic gifts. The man in the street, when faced with predictions whose truth he will be unable to test in his lifetime, prefers to be told that life will continue along an even path, so that he can face the future optimistically. When all is said and done, action and reaction are no more than counterparts, and even if we take them for granted, we prefer to look on life as a straight rather than a zigzag line. The line may be interrupted here and there, but the main slope must not be allowed to be reversed. Thus even prophets who have never heard of Darwin will usually assure us that, in the long run, things will become better and better.

But while long-range optimism is very soothing, people generally prefer more tangible predictions. What they really like to hear is that, statistically and logically, by virtue of the progress of modern technology, the achievements of science, growing organisational and intellectual capacities, the living standard will rise annually by a fixed amount, and that what lean years there may be will be more than offset by the fat years.

Admittedly, pessimists have appeared from time to time who, using the same approach, have procalimed that the long-range line of development has a downward slope which may be interrupted temporarily by favourable trends. In the last century, the foremost of these pessimistic prophets was Thomas Robert Malthus, a Surrey curate. Malthus asserted that men would multiply so rapidly that they would outstrip their resources, with the result that human misery would become ever greater. The only solution was for the poorer classes to practise voluntary sexual abstinence. Another of the blackest long-range prophecies was the concept of entropy, derived from thermodynamics: inevitable heat losses will eventually force the universe to freeze up, causing all life on earth to become extinct. Still, even according to the most pessimistic estimates, this freeze-up would not occur for thousands of millions of years, so that there was no cause for immediate alarm.

Linear theories of developments, which lead either to maximum happiness or to maximum unhappiness, undoubtedly reflect the hopes and fears of many people, but are far too frequently disproved by the subsequent course of events, for anyone to worry overmuch about them. Straight lines exist only in geometry, and have no reality in nature herself. The world itself is round rather than straight, and looking at the horizon, the sun, or the motion of the planets, we begin to feel intuitively that the circle is more representative of life than the straight line.

It must have been thoughts like these which first persuaded ancient philosophers to consider all natural processes as circular, without beginning or end. Time moves uniformly. Having come full circle, the world is back at the same spot, and everything starts all over again. In science and economics, cycle theories are in particularly great vogue, even if they are being questioned by many experts. Thus doctors and biologists have discovered short cycles connected with the development of certain bacteria, and long cycles connected with the return of certain epidemics. All this is grist to the prophetic mill, for there are no more simple and credible predictions than those which are based on well-tested periodic phenomena. Thus the much-derided cycle theories derived from Asia and Ancient Greece have given rise to the theory of business cycles—a young but serious branch of economics.

The balance

The fourth type of prediction, which we have likened to a balance, springs from the belief that nature is always in equilibrium, or that equilibrium is invariably restored, at least in the long run. If only we know which way the balance is weighted, we can state with certainty that there will be a swing in the opposite direction.

The balance resembles the zigzag line, in that here, too, action is always followed by reaction, but where, in the former the movement is equal, in the latter it is not. This can be shown graphically: a normal line drawn through the fulcrum of the balance will produce two congruent triangles.

The American statistician R. W. Babson—one of the few men to foresee the 1929 crisis—used this principle to make correct Stock Exchange predictions. Babson, who was a pious and just man, did not so much object to speculation as to excess. He was firmly convinced that the inflated prices due to over-speculation were bound one day to drop as much below the—admittedly imaginary—normal line as they had previously risen above it. This is, in fact, what happened. The collapse of Wall Street in October 1929 which brought in its train the great slump, was therefore simply explained as the re-establishment of divinely pre-ordained equilibrium, transgressions against which are invariably punished.

In fact, this type of equilibrium is rarely represented as a horizontal line, since predictions based upon it are generally optimistic, and make allowance for natural growth. We are assumed to be living on a gentle slope, a fact which we must not neglect when estimating the economic development of a given country. In other words we must tip one side of the scales in advance to compensate for the natural rate of growth. In so doing, we must be very careful not to be deceived by sporadic accelerations of the rate, since excessive increases are unnatural, and will inevitably have to be paid for later on.

This idea of natural equilibrium plays a very large place in applied biology, in agronomics, and particularly in medicine. Most therapeutic steps have a compensatory aim: they are meant to offset excesses or shortages of a given substance, or to increase or decrease the rate of output of an organ. In this respect, medicine is in a particularly favourable position, since it knows what it means by "normal", i.e. not a statistical average but a general state of health. In economics, on the other hand, there is little agreement on what degree of unemployment, for instance, must be looked upon as normal, and within what limits it can safely be permitted to exist.

The main fields in which predictions of the balance type are usually made, are those involving man's sense of justice or his belief in a higher power which leaves no good deed unrewarded and no evil deed unpunished. While human justice may fail here and there, divine justice is infallible. It is on this belief that all religious prophecies are based, and particularly those of the Old Testament. Most biblical prophecies are conditional predictions, and in that respect resemble scientific prognoses. Future events are not immutably fixed in advance, as they are in ancient Greek myths, but are largely dependent on human behaviour. If only men remain steadfast, if only they observe the laws of God, they will be rewarded. But if they deviate from Jehovah's law, they and theirs will be stricken down as inevitably as night follows day. Men can do what they will, but they must pay for the consequences of their actions.

Only in particularly blatant cases does Jehovah punish a sinner or a people on the spot, for He generally prefers to allow them enough rope to hang themselves. Nor does He usually give immediate rewards, but prefers to wait for decades or even generations. But one day justice will be done, and men forget it at their peril. To remind them of it, is the prime task of the prophet.

The New Testament[1] adds the magnificent vision of the Day

[1] Revelation, 20.

of Judgement, a general day of reckoning for the dead and the living alike. St. John probably preached the resurrection not so much as an event in the far distant future, as a final warning before an impending world catastrophe. The fact that 2000 years have elapsed since his prophecy, has not done much to reduce general faith in its validity, for the idea of just retribution obviously appeals to man's belief in fair play (see Plate II).

Ignorance by choice

Although the modern scientist indulges in much more prophecy than even the most prolific old-time prophet, he is somewhat chary of admitting it. This is borne out by the fact that, although we speak of predicting and prediction, we have no suitable word for a "predicter". It almost seems as if we were ashamed of this occupation; the prophet no longer wants to be known in the land.

The reason seems obscure, for it is far less reprehensible to be thinking honestly about the future and to state one's conclusions, however vague, than to bury one's head in the sand and allow oneself to be taken unawares. The refusal to make predictions on principle, just because so many past predictions were false, is nothing but fatalism or deliberate escapism. In any case, it is dishonest, for all of us must constantly predict if we are not to go under. People who claim that they never predict are therefore very unobservant of their own behaviour. No builder, doctor, or merchant could go about his daily business without making predictions to outsiders. Poking fun at those who try to look ahead is, therefore, merely foolish.

However, we must be able to recognise the limits within which prognostication is possible. This applies, *a fortiori*, to professional prophets, whose clients are often unable to test their oracles' grounds of belief. Many expert predictions are taken on trust—all the more reason for conscientious prophets to be doubly circumspect, and to be fully conscious of what they are about. Unfortunately, they far too often are not. Even in science—for instance in the case of medical prognoses—personal experience and opinion still takes the place of objective standards and systematically verified methods far too frequently.

Intuition, Induction and Deduction

Since antiquity, it has been common practice to distinguish intuitive from empirical prophecies. These two categories have been given all sorts of names, i.e. intuitive vs. inductive; divinatory vs. empirical; subjective vs. objective; endogenous vs. exogenous, etc., but, basically, all the terms amount to one single distinction. In predictions of the first type, we assume that the prophet has received his knowledge by way of divine inspiration or by inner illumination of another kind—in any case he himself can rarely offer an alternative explanation. Predictions of the second type are thought to be more subject to rational examination, since the empirical facts or arguments on which they are based can, in turn, be verified by anyone who cares to do so.

However, they may also be based on empirical arguments that are not generally accepted, i.e. on astrological observations. And astrological prophecies must be considered prophecies based on objective facts (i.e. the motion of the planets) while, for instance, predictions based on dreams are, in principle, intuitive and subjective. The distinction between subjective and objective prophecies is therefore no criterion for judging the validity of their fundamental soundness.

The distinction is not a very revealing one from another point of view, as well. The greatest scientific discoveries and inventions have often been the result of intuitive flashes of genius. True, no complete outsider has ever discovered any important natural laws, and only a trained scientist like Newton could have seized upon such accident as the drop of an apple to formulate a general law of gravitation, but his interpretation was nevertheless a brilliant stroke of intuition. Great scientists will follow their intuitions by submitting them to the necessary tests, thereafter to construct a set of inductive propositions. Intuition and induction are therefore not necessarily contradictory, and both may be necessary to arrive at the correct prediction.

Many scientific discoveries have a purely deductive character, i.e. they are deductions from general laws. Here, general conclusions are applied to particular facts, and the verification of these facts simultaneously reinforces the validity of the general law.

One of the most sensational astronomical feats was the discovery of the planet Neptune by Challis and Galle in 1846, 23 years after Bessell had postulated the existence of a new planet from observations that the motion of Uranus was perturbed by an unknown factor, and shortly after Leverrier had calculated its probable path. Similar discoveries based on purely theoretical considerations and calculations, and subsequently verified by observation, have also been made in modern physics, where a number of elementary atomic particles, e.g. antiprotons, neutrons, and mesons were postulated first, and discovered afterwards.

The most astonishing discoveries of this kind, however, were made in chemistry. The classical example is Mendeleev's classification of the chemical elements based on their arrangement into vertical and horizontal rows according to their atomic weight. According to Mendeleev's own account this idea came to him in 1868 while he was writing a textbook of chemistry. He was looking for an easy classification for teaching, rather than for serious scientific, purposes. However, he was convinced from the start that any such classification must be based on atomic weights. Having entered the atomic weight and other characteristics of every element on separate cards, he was struck by the fact that the properties of the elements were related to their atomic weights. From certain gaps in his Periodic Table, chemists were quick to conclude that the empty spaces represented undiscovered elements, an assumption that was amply rewarded by their experimental discovery of the new elements Gallium, Germanium, and Scandium, which were found to fit neatly into the gaps. Here we had a combination of both types of scientific prediction: an intuitive idea, an inductive collection of available experimental data, and finally a deductive discovery.

In the biological sciences, too, there have been many deductive discoveries. A typical instance was Darwin's assertion that particularly large insects ought to exist in Madagascar, since the fertilisation of the giant flowers on that island could not be explained in any other way. Soon afterwards, giant butterflies were, in fact, discovered there. Things proved more difficult, with attempts to find incontrovertible proof for Darwin's general theory of evolution. For decades, the search went on for ape-men who could be considered our direct ancestors, but time after time zoologists and anthropologists insisted that the prehistoric creatures reconstructed out of fossil bones, let alone the existing anthropoid apes, could not possibly be looked upon as the authentic link between ape and man. All they would allow is that some of these creatures and man had a common ancestor that had so far eluded all searchers.

Thus Darwin's theory is difficult enough to apply to the past, let alone to the future. Even the geneticists' trick of working with rapidly propagating insects (e.g. the fruit fly) the better to observe genetic changes in a large number of successive generations, has proved rather unavailing. Many bold predictions were made, but only a few have stood the test. In the absence of deductive or inductive proofs, even the most plausible "natural law" becomes a matter of faith—which does not preclude it from persisting for a very long time and from exerting a considerable influence on lay opinion.

What is experience?

The main field for inductive predictions is the world of affairs where businessmen rely on their "experience". Now, "experience" in this sense simply means a faith in one's own judgment. "Once bitten, twice shy," sums it up.

If we look at "experience" from close quarters, we find that deduction plays a much larger part in it than experienced men normally believe. Not only is their own experience very limited, but most of what they consider their own experience is actually based on the experience of others. In fact, even the most down-to-earth businessman is guided by the work of academic economists, though not necessarily by their most up-to-date work. This guidance, however, is unacknowledged and even unconsciously used: the academic theories have become a matter of blind faith.

Perhaps this is precisely the reason why "experienced" men are far less experienced than they think they are. We generally look upon experience as a sieve that allows true and relevant facts to filter in, and which keeps false, confused and impracticable ideas out. In fact, all new experiences must first jump the formidable hurdle of our prejudices. For this very reason, we experience so little that is truly individual, and most of our inductions are no more than vague generalisations.

Nevertheless, individual "experience" continues to play an immense role in everyday predictions. The main advantage of experience is quick reaction to stimuli. True, it is often contended that the experienced man reflects on matters before he judges them, while the inexperienced man is far too ready to give an ill-considered answer and to act arbitrarily, injudiciously, and recklessly. The experienced craftsman generally makes much quicker and more decisive predictions than his inexperienced apprentice, and he can do so precisely because his experience enables him to exclude a host of possibilities which the conscientious beginner dare not ignore. Experience leads to confident decisions—the experienced man is not continually faced with a choice. In relation to a large number of problems he has already made it, once and for all.

The self-confidence of experienced men is expressed in their mistrust of, and contempt for, all systematic attempts to gain an intuitive over-all picture. They are therefore opponents of all statistics, and, at best, admit those facts and figures which agree with their own experience. Conversely, all statistics which gainsay their narrow viewpoints are dismissed as erroneous, misleading or unreliable.

Creative Foresight

The "man of experience" has another enemy whom he hates even more than the statistician, viz. the planner. Of course, there can be no serious planning that is not based on experience, but real planning worthy of its name must go beyond experience. It not only copies the past, it combines and constructs, and introduces a host of new factors. Planning, like other predictions is based on intuition, deduction, and induction, but what is so characteristic of planning alone is its forward look. Planning is more than mere prediction—it means shaping the future as one wants it to be.

On the small scale, this may be true of all activist predictions, but there is a difference of principle between my plan to hang up a picture on the wall and a large scale economic plan for the erection of a new industrial plant or an electric grid supplying an entire country. Large-scale planning does not merely work on given conditions, but tries to modify them. It makes radical changes in productive processes, throws labour forces and material into the most unlikely places, re-distributes, increases or diminshes the consumption of certain goods—in short, it creates a new world within its own chosen limits. The fact that large-scale planning, too, is subject to a hundred accidental and aleatory uncertainty factors does not alter this general principle. Wherever possible, the planners will make allowances for accident and chance, and set aside enough reserves to provide against unforeseen contingencies.

Thus, planning means meeting the future halfway, by reducing unpredictable factors to the unavoidable minimum. For this reason, the more powerful the organisation that initiates and implements the plan, the greater its chances of success. It used to be thought that small and isolated plans could be carried out more readily than large and comprehensive ones, but in reality the opposite has proved true. This is only to be expected, since the more limited the plan and the smaller the power of those behind it, the more it is at the mercy of opposition from outside and difficulties from within. Minor planning errors and unforeseen events are less easy to absorb in the general operation. Man can very well achieve things without planning, but as a rule he can achieve little or nothing under a partly planned and partly improvised system—a poor compromise between two opposing trends which generally makes the worst of both worlds. Planning and improvisation make poor bed-fellows.

Utopias

Visions of the future do not only come in the form of predictions of future reality. Many prophets have preferred to describe mythical situations in mythical lands; they did this not because their feet were not firmly planted on the ground, nor even because they delighted in fanciful literary creation. Frequently, the absence of freedom of thought, and fear of political consequences—in other words, pressure and anxiety—caused these prophets to avoid the slippery slope of reality and to hide their predictions under the cloak of literary or poetic allusion. They would, as it were, assure their readers that "all the characters in this book are fictitious, and any resemblance to actual persons, living or dead, is purely coincidental," and make a point of prefacing remarks with sham homage to the Establishment—the better to elude the Censor.

This type of writing is called utopian, after Thomas More's *Utopia* (1518). *Utopia* was, however, by no means the first utopian book, for the ancient Greeks held this kind of writing in high esteem. Plato's *Republic* was not strictly one of these, for though his model state might have been utopian, he did at least try to implement his ideas when he went to Syracuse, as the guest of its tyrant, Dionysius, with disastrous consequences to himself. Thomas More, on the other hand, even when he became Lord Chancellor under Henry VIII, made not the slightest attempt to bestow the blessings of Utopia on his compatriots: a six hour working day, houses with gardens for all, the abolition of excessive luxury, of fashion, of taverns, etc. When Henry VIII had him beheaded, it was not so much for his utopian ideas as for his reluctance to recognise the king as head of the Church of England, and his equal unwillingness to give way on the question of the royal divorce and re-marriage.

More's *Utopia*, taken literally, contains no prophecies apart from the one that no socialist model state can be set up on earth. Many of his literary successors took socialism far more seriously and wrote utopian novels about the happy life that would result when economic inequality was abolished. Although Karl Marx himself was violently opposed to this type of socialist day-dreaming, and contrasted utopian socialism with his own scientific socialism, i.e. his prediction that the capitalist system was bound to collapse and to lead to the removal of private property by virtue of its own inner contradictions, socialist Utopias remained a recurring literary fashion. One of the most successful was the American writer Edward Bellamy's *Looking Backwards* (Looking back at the year 2000) which appeared in 1888 and which sold more than a million copies in the United States alone. Bellamy's view of the future was a moderate kind of patriotic socialism based largely on state enterprise. His European counterpart, the Austrian writer Theodor Hertzka, scored a similar hit with his socialist Utopia *Freiland* (Freeland) which appeared in 1890.

When socialism had become reality in the Soviet Union, it became fashionable to direct utopian novels against the Soviet regime. The most important work of this kind is George Orwell's novel *1984* which appeared in 1949, just at the beginning of the Cold War. In it, Orwell describes a tyrannical state in Oceania which had gained control of America and most of the British Empire.

Other Utopias were concerned with imaginary scientific developments. The two outstanding representatives of this type of writing were a Frenchman and an Englishman, Jules Verne (1828–1905) and H. G. Wells (1866–1946), both of whom used the literary device of placing their imaginary inventions and technical innovations in a contemporary setting with fantastic consequences. Jules Verne's prophecies—trips to the bottom of the sea and to the moon and record voyages round the earth— have partly been fulfilled or even outstripped by current technical achievements. H. G. Well's less fantastic and more thoughtful novels have the added flavour of describing the present just as it is, and adding just one unusual fact which suffices to produce the strangest effects.

A hybrid born of the marriage between political and scientific Utopias is the kind of writing found in the very many books about future wars and the havoc they will cause. Their authors, aware of the devastating possibilities of whatever happen to be the most recent weapons, are generally pacifists, though it is an open question whether they manage to convey their pacifist ideas to their readers. Unfortunately fear of destruction has never yet dissuaded men from waging war; on the contrary it has usually incited them to anticipate their opponents by starting preventive campaigns.

What ought to be the most fertile field of utopian speculation, viz. the biology of the future, has been rather neglected, at least in literature. The most convincing writing on this theme is probably George Bernard Shaw's play *Back to Methuselah* (1921) in which he describes the prolongation of human life.

6. Jules Verne's conception of flying. He died in 1905, shortly before the aeroplane came into its own.

Poets and Dreamers

This short selection is no more than a bird's eye view of writings about the future. In English-speaking countries, science-fiction, i.e. the discussion of fictional scientific facts, discoveries, and inventions, has become a special branch of literature. The devotees in this field have tried to make good their own lack of creative genius by joining science-fiction organisations, at whose meetings they can discuss their professional problems to their heart's content. Thus hundreds of authors, publishers, broadcasters, film directors, and lovers of this kind of prophecy assembled at an International Science Fiction Congress held in London in 1957.

Nor does this exhaust the list, for there is hardly an important novel which does not contain some general reference to the future. If we add the painters who depict their view of the future, we shall see that there are such vast numbers of prophecies that their mere enumeration would fill an entire book. We shall thus ignore illustrations of biblical texts, variations on themes drawn from Greek mythology, Dante and the classics in order to reduce the field to manageable proportions. Moreover, we shall exclude pseudo-prophecies, i.e. those which are based on considerations of the kind discussed above: suggestions for reform and political attacks disguised as prophecies. Most utopian writing is thus eliminated from consideration.

The quality of the remaining prophecies is greatly inferior to the quantity. The belief that great writers are better judges of the future than all professional, amateur, and practical prophets taken together is altogether fallacious. What literary pundits have said about the future has generally been brilliantly put, but has rarely shed any new light on the future. By and large, literature and particularly the fine arts are more like the moon than the sun in this respect: they reflect, but are not themselves the original source of light. The truly inspiring and illuminating residue of literary and artistic prophecies was absorbed by religion. In this very way, it lost its purely imaginary character.

Religious prophecy claims to be absolutely true and un-assailable—much more so than even the best-founded natural law. Thomas Hobbes pointed out that miracles and pills must be swallowed whole rather than chewed, and this applies, *a fortiori*,

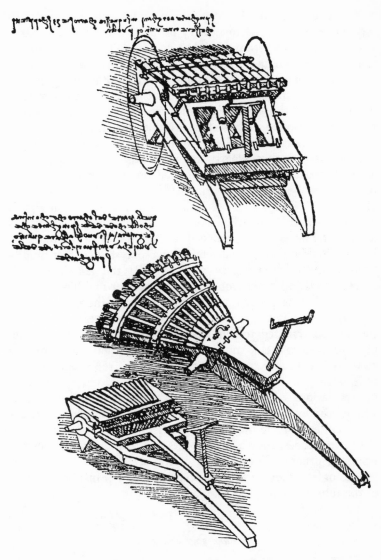

7. Leonardo da Vinci's idea of a field gun. The cart holds 33 barrels, 11 of which are fired simultaneously.

to revealed religion. You can take it or leave it, but you must never analyse it. True imaginary prophecy, on the other hand, does not claim to be anything but fiction, and even if an author hints between the lines that he really means what he is saying, as often as not he may change his mind the moment reality gains the upper hand of the situation and retreat into the realms of pure fantasy. While the writer need not accept responsibility for any of his prophecies, the humblest fairground prophet must.

This irresponsibility—here we mean moral rather than legal irresponsibility—has clearly damaged the cause of fantasy. Though great poets are often looked upon as great seers, the moment this belief is put to the test the result is most painful to all lovers of poetry. Even so eminent a poet as Heinrich Heine, whose predictive faculties must have been sharpened by his journalistic activities, produced a host of false predictions. Luckily for their prophetic reputations, only the correct predictions of poets are usually remembered; the false ones are allowed to fall into oblivion out of kindness or indifference.

In the field of prediction, literary prophets therefore occupy a peripheral if not a secondary place. Literature has not perceptibly contributed to our knowledge of the future—and the place of the fine arts is more modest still, as their role is mainly restricted to giving concrete and humanised representations of religious notions such as the Last Judgement, and to futuristic interpretations of technical developments. Leonardo da Vinci, who was an inventor of genius far in advance of his time, was the only painter to have made valid predictions.

In many cases, the vision of poets and painters resembles the vision of dreams. While such visions are of great interest to psychologists, they do little to widen the rest of mankind's view of the future.

Take your choice

If we wish to form a total picture of all the methods used in prediction and prophecy, our classification of predictions into intuitive and inductive ones will be found to be inadequate. Even the classification used by modern lexicographers, viz. inspired, speculative, and logical is far from adequate. Thus the calculations

I. On their voyage to Troy, the Greeks were becalmed for some time. It was then that Palamedes is said to have invented the game of dice as an effective way of combating boredom.

II. Dürer's view of the end of the world (From: *Heimlich Offenbarung Johannis*, Nuremberg 1498).

which led to the prediction and discovery of the planet Neptune have nothing in common with the mathematical methods used in economic research, or with the mortality tables of insurance companies, though all of them fall into the category of logical predictions. The speculations of astrology are completely different from the speculations on which Utopians build their state of the future. While our own classification (below) is admittedly less concise than the lexicographers', it is probably much closer to reality.

By setting up a classification of our own, we do not wish to assert that other classifications are impermissible. In the field of prediction, it is always inadvisable to make fine distinctions, since none of them ever agrees with reality. What we are concerned with is simply to demonstrate the wealth and complexity of the methods with which mankind attempts to form a picture of the future, for only in this way can we overcome the prejudice that true prediction and prophetic speculation are identical, and that the only way to the future is through charlatanism and black magic.

Human beings have always wanted to look ahead, and to a large extent are capable of doing so. Methods of prediction have changed over the ages; some have been discarded, others, no less confused, have been retained, but many new and valuable facts have come to be appreciated. Only by taking complete stock of all the available material, can we hope to choose correctly. This is the task I have set myself in the following chapters of this book.

Methods of Prediction

Classification	Basis	Characteristics	Applicability
Intuitive	Revelation	Belief in transcendental inspiration and absolute faith in the validity of the prediction.	Religious prophecy.
	Inspiration	Sudden realisation of hidden connections.	Many discoveries and inventions.

Classification	Basis	Characteristics	Applicability
Deductive	Verifiable laws	Deduction of particular predictions from a general principle.	Science, Sociology.
	Pseudo-laws	Predictions from illogical or antiquated principles.	Astrology, Fortune-telling, Palmistry, etc.
Inductive	Individual experience	Unsystematic deductions by false analogy.	Work, particularly crafts.
	Experiment	Generalisation of systematised individual investigations.	Science, Technology.
	Statistics	Conclusion from aggregates according to probability theory.	Meteorology, Medicine, Public Opinion Polls, Economic research, Insurance, Government.
Activist	Individual action	Predictions of the results of voluntary behaviour.	Everyday life.
	Planning	Long-range and complex objectives; creation of new conditions.	Industry, public finance, armaments.
Imaginary	Creative fiction	Utopias, Science fiction.	Literature, Art.
	Unconscious fiction	Visions, generally based on wish-fulfilment and past events.	Dream Visions, Hallucinations.

CHAPTER 1

Short History of the Art of Prophecy

*A*LL *WESTERN PEOPLES HAVE A DOUBLE LINE OF* ancestors: their own forefathers and the great Eastern civilisations. Both sets of ancestors have contributed to modern methods of prophecy. Thus only very few prophetic beliefs are original to a given people—most are mankind's common cultural heritage, i.e. they have been transmitted to us along the well-trodden paths of civilisation from the ancient East via Greece and Rome. This is particularly true of the most persistent and most common branch of prophecy, viz. astrology.

Prophecy is believed to have originated in Mesopotamia, the country between the rivers Euphrates and Tigris, more than 5000 years ago. It was in Babylon and in the other cultural centres of Mesopotamia, that brilliant men first systematised these arts, and raised them to the status of a science. Astrology in particular, i.e. the belief that the future can be read in the stars, is of Babylonian origin.

Babylon's claim to supremacy in this field has not always been recognised. Thus Newton asserted that astrology was of Egyptian origin, and only reached Mesopotamia very much later. According to Newton, astrology was first systematised by the Egyptian King Nicepsos of Sais

8. The Babylonian god Adad was the "Lord of the Oracle", but also the god of storms, thunder, and lightning.

51

(ca. 770 B.C.) or by his counsellor, the priest Petosiris, and carried to Babylon a generation later, when the Ethiopians invaded Egypt and many Egyptians escaped to that town.[1]

Mesopotamian beginnings

However, when men learned to read cuneiform writings and hieroglyphs, Babylonian priority in the field was established beyond dispute, and orientalists were able to antedate the real beginnings of astrology by many thousands of years. Astrology originated in Babylonia and Assyria, was handed on to Egypt and from there to Greece, Persia, India and the Far East. The Chinese, too, are indebted to the Babylonians, and the astrological prophecies discovered in China seem to be mere copies from the library of the Assyrian King Assurbanipal in Nineveh.[2]

Those of us who have driven through the Syrian desert at night or have visited the ruins of Babylon, will not find it difficult to

believe that Babylonia was and is the ideal country for star-gazing. Nowhere in the Northern hemisphere is the sky clearer or more beautiful, and not even the profusion of the Southern sky is nearly as enticing (see Plate III).

True, the oldest extant Babylonian prophecies were dream interpretations rather than astrological predictions. They are contained in the glorious Gilgamesh epic, which is believed to have been written in about 4000 B.C.[3] In this epic, Gilgamesh

9. Head of the giant Humbaba, formed of intestines (British Museum). Humbaba played a great role in Assyrian divination.

[1] William Tucker: *Principes d'astrologie scientifique* (Paris 1939), pp. 11–12.
[2] Paul Couderc: *L'Astrologie* (Paris 1951) p. 91.
[3] Alfred Guillaume: *Prophétie et Divination chez les Sémites* (Paris 1950) p. 12.

prepares himself for the final struggle against his enemy Enkidu, whose approach he has seen in a dream. His mother prophesies that their struggle will result in inseparable friendship, and this is what eventually happens. The real point of the story is, no doubt, to stress the value of peaceful co-existence between the Sumerians, the ancient rulers of the country, and the Semites from the desert who had taken up residence in Akkad (Plate V).

The Babylonians looked upon the legendary Sumerian King Enmenduranna or Enmeduranki, who was said to have lived before the Flood, as the real founder of the art of divination. He was regarded not only as a great law giver who codified the rules of prophecy, but as a leading prophet in his own right. Interpreters of signs were called the "sons of Enmeduranki". Detailed prophecies have been known since the First Dynasty of Ur (ca. 2500 B.C.) by which time the art of prophecy had become highly developed. These prophecies generally bear the name of the king under whom they were made, and it seems likely that the kings themselves acted as prophets, particularly since most of the prophecies deal with their own persons. Still, all kings had their sages to assist them—men of action need men of thought to support them. But though the gods themselves inspired the prophets, there was no real reliance on them. The future could only be probed objectively according to fixed rules.

Hepatoscopy

The most common method used was hepatoscopy, literally the inspection of the liver. The Babylonians used the liver—and in fact the liver of sheep—rather than the heart or other organs for divination, simply because they looked upon it as the seat of life. Evidently this large and highly vascular organ impressed them more than any other. Similar ideas are still held by primitive races in Borneo, Burma, Uganda, who also use the livers of pigs, goats, and chickens to divine favourable or unfavourable omens for the future.[1] The Babylonians were apparently not so much interested in the quantity of the hepatic blood as in its quality,

[1] G. Contenau: *La Divination chez les Assyriens et les Babyloniens* (Paris 1940) p. 237.

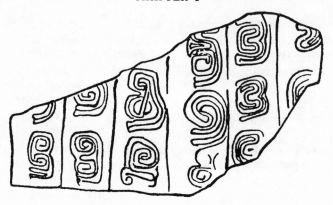

10. Diagrams of coiled sheep intestines on a Babylonian clay
tablet. Every turn had a special prophetic significance.

though experts on the history of hepatoscopy are still arguing
this point. For, though we know 700 Mesopotamian tablets containing hepatoscopic prophecies, none of them gives any clear
indication about the origins or the extraordinary importance
which was attributed to that method. Hepatoscopy continued to
be the fashion even when, in about 2000 B.C., medical opinion
had begun to look upon the heart, rather than the liver, as the
real seat of life. The liver remained the centre of vegetative
existence, though all passions, both in man and in animals, were
now said to come from the heart. It was only in about 500 B.C.,
that physicians first began to recognise the significance of the
brain and, particularly under the influence of the Greek physician
Hippocrates, to look upon it as the seat of mental activity. But
neither heart nor brain took the place of the liver in ancient
divination; at best secondary predictions were derived from
them. The liver retained its predominance until the late Roman
period, i.e. for a full three thousand years.

Perhaps it was for reasons of convenience that the liver
attained and preserved its position. The liver is not only easily
located, but it can be separated very easily from the rest of the
organs. And this was important, for the liver had to be removed
and consulted on the altar of the particular god who controlled
and predicted man's future. In Mesopotamia hepatoscopy was a
solemn act of state, for great matters were involved, and only
kings and nobles were entitled to use this form of divination.

From the shape, the number of lobes, the blood vessels, and the processes of the liver, experts could predict the dates and outcomes of future wars and revolutions. The *bârû*, i.e. the seer, would inspect the liver very carefully before he submitted a written report about its condition and his interpretation of it. Hepatoscopy was a highly respected art, though not without its dangers, for its prophets had often to pay dearly for their mistakes.

But the seers understood their business. Hepatoscopists—just like the dream interpreters and later the astrologers—made sure of couching their interpretations in the most ambiguous possible terms, and of stressing the impending difficulties—with the rider that the King and his councillors would be sure to avert the danger once they had been warned in good time. As a rule, the prophets were patriotic and enterprising men, who lent their masters courage. They were usually familiar with internal and external politics and above all with the King's temperament— for if they were not, their prophetic career was likely to be short-lived.

Like all prophetic methods, hepatoscopy gradually became mere routine. As early as Babylonian times, seers had clay models of sheep's livers on which pupils could be taught to practise the art systematically. The earliest finds of this kind probably date back to the First Babylonian Dynasty (ca. 2000 B.C.), but some others from Hattus, the ancient capital of the Hittite empire, from Magiddo, from Palestine, and above all from Tell Hariri on the Euphrates may well be older still.[1]

To Mesopotamia we also owe the art of reading the future from the intestines of animals. Great seers would claim that they could judge the position of an animal's intestines by the ani-

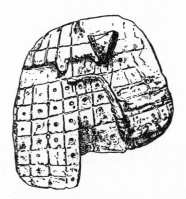

11. Clay model of a liver used by Babylonian diviners. (British Museum.)

[1] M. Rutten: *32 modèles de foies en argile inscrits, provenant de Tell-Hariri*. Revue d'Assyriologie XXXV (1938) pp. 36–70.

mal's appearance. What accounts we have on this subject sound utterly fantastic and do little to enhance our faith in the powers of observation of the "seers" concerned. Thus, one text tells us that the intestines of a sheep with small ears and with a black nose and feet, and also of a sheep with a thick neck and red eyes, have 14 turns, and those of a sheep with black ears, a black nose and black feet only 10 turns. Particularly large and squinting animals were said to have no intestinal turns at all.[1] The very fact that such claims, which could have been refuted on the spot by anyone prepared to cut open a sheep, could be put forward at the time, shows to what level professional prophets were prepared to stoop and to what kind of quackery Babylon had descended.

Even though solemn prophecies applied only to the great of the land, more humble men did not need to feel completely left out of things. There existed a host of prophetic maxims for domestic consumption, and though some were rather far-fetched, e.g. "if a snake coil up in a man's bed, his wife will roll up her eyes and sell her children for money," others were commonplaces or primitive medical predictions. Large quantities of ants were considered a bad omen, the flight of birds a good or a bad omen according to whether the bird flew straight ahead, or crossed one's path from left to right, and so on.

People were afraid of all kinds of abnormalities and even twins were often considered to be evil omens. Twin brothers were thought to forebode catastrophes, mixed twins indicated strife, and twin sisters were thought to spell the collapse of their parents' house.[2] In the rather Machiavellian tract *If a Town*, which tells by way of prophecies how a good city must be run, we can read that the city will perish if many twins are born to its citizens. In the self same tract we are also told that the city will perish if it has too many sages and seers, and that it will prosper if it has many doves and fools.[3]

All the Babylonian and Assyrian prophecies which we have

[1] B. Meissner: *Omina zur Erkenntnis der Eingeweide des Opfertiers.* Archiv für Orientforschung IX (1933–1934) pp. 118–122.
[2] Ch. Fossey: *Présages tirés des naissances.* Babylonia V, Paris (1912–1913) p. 11 ff.
[3] F. Nötscher: *Haus- und Stadt-Omina der Serie: Shummu âlu ina mêlê shakin.* Orientalia, Rome, Fascic. 31 (1928) p. 47.

discussed so far have something in common: their completely irrational and mystical procedure. With the exception of pseudo-prophecies which were, in fact, no more than moral prescriptions, all their predictions lacked any perceptible causal connection between the prophetic omen and the prophetic substance. Why should the outcome of the next war be reflected by the appearance of a sheep's liver? What possible influence could an abnormal dog have on the future welfare of Babylon? No doubt, not even the Babylonians believed that there was any logic in the whole business. The omens simply had to be believed because they had occasionally been proved right and because the priests claimed that they had been sent by the gods.

Chaldean astrology

It was a tremendous step ahead when prophets began to consult the stars and the planets. The stars moved so uniformly and with such magnificent regularity, that they, as well as the gods which moved them, were thought to have a direct effect on terrestrial affairs. This thought was daring in the extreme, for the sky was unlike anything on earth. Up there everything was lucid and regular, while on earth everything was confused and arbitrary, or, in any case, not directly determinable. Perhaps the sky might hold the key to all mysteries, particularly since everything in it moved in perfect circles. If only one observed the motions of a given star long enough and kept exact records, one could easily predict where it would be in a month's or even in a number of years' time, and by associating its position with observed terrestrial processes, one might then be able to predict the future much more logically and reliably than by any other prophetic method.

It seems unlikely that the Babylonian astrologists had much idea of the real size and mass of the stars or that they assessed their effects on the earth and its inhabitants accordingly, since even the Greeks, who had much greater astronomical knowledge, were extremely ill-informed on this subject. Thus when Cleanthes, a Stoic philosopher, maintained in about 300 B.C. that "the sun was larger than Peloponnesus", few people believed him. To the Babylonian astronomers, the stars were still small luminous spots large enough to allow the gods to rest there, but in no way comparable with the earth in size. But despite their smallness, a tremendous force emanated from them over immeasurably great distances, and it was this telekinetic effect which was said to give astrological prophecies the rational basis that other methods of prophecy lacked. Astrology was based, at least intellectually, on the assumption of causal connections— the omens read in the stars were not mere warnings from the gods, they were real causes of the terrestrial events which astrologers deduced from them.

Admittedly this claim, too, was a mere assumption, though even laymen could be shown its relevance to meteorological processes. In fact, the oldest astrological predictions had to do with the weather—rain, storm, drought, etc., and represented a special class of Babylonian astrology: *adad*, named after the ancient weather-god who ruled over storm, lightning and rain from the great heights in which he dwelt.

However, the moment particular weather phenomena were related to particular stars, the door was opened wide to fantasy, since it is only the sun that can have any measurable effect on our weather. Unfortunately, the Babylonians were moon rather than sun worshippers, and the Sumerian city of Ur on the Euphrates, half way between Babylon and the Persian Gulf, was the centre of their lunar cult. Here people paid homage to Sin, the lunar deity, whose son was Shamash, the Sun—a singularly strange belief, since it meant not only that the moon was the ancestor of the sun but, mythologically speaking, his superior in strength. The calendar was based on the moon, and all good things, particularly fertility and rain, were her direct attributes. The sun, on the other hand, filled the inhabitants of an arid country with great fear—not so much Shamash, the friendly sun of the dawn, as the blistering mid-day sun which brought drought and pestilence and was therefore in league with Nergal, the god of war (see Plate III).

But though the astrologers of the Ziqqûrat—the tapering tower which stood by the side of the Temple, as Italian bell-towers, the *campaniles*, stand by the side of great churches— usually observed the night sky, they also studied the motion of the sun, and its changes of colour and its eclipses. From this it

was only a step to the Babylonians' greatest astrological feat—
the discovery of the Zodiac, the imaginary belt, based on a projection of the apparent orbit of the purely ideal "sphere" of the
fixed stars in the course of a year. By dividing the Zodiac into
twelve "houses", they provided the framework for describing
the constellations of the stars, even though the latter were not
thought to be of great astrological importance. Astrological
predictions are, by and large, based on the motion of the planets,
and the invention of the Zodiac was, therefore, merely an astrological afterthought, possibly due to Greek influence. In any
case, the oldest Babylonian astrological tables make no reference
to a complete Zodiac belt.[1]

Apart from the sun and the moon, which were looked upon as
planets, the Babylonians also knew Jupiter, Mercury, Mars,
Saturn, and Venus, which they called *bibbu*—"wild goats"—in
contradistinction to the fixed stars which were thought to be
"tame". These five *bibbu*, small though they looked, were said to
have a tremendous influence on human fate. All were the seats of
different gods, and each had a characteristic effect on the earth.
Four of these gods were male and one was female—Ishtar
Astarte, the goddess of sexuality and fertility. Jupiter, the
brightest of them all, was the seat of the main Babylonian deity—
Marduk, the beneficent. Mercury was the seat of Nabu,
the son of Marduk who, though capricious, was generally
well disposed towards men. But Mars which spread the heat
of the sun, and Saturn, were the seats of Nergal and Ninurta,
two war gods, and Ishtar (the sun) was quarrelsome in the
extreme.

The military note thus introduced into astrology reflected the
wishes and needs of the astrologers' chief clientele—the ruling
princes. Quite naturally, kings were concerned not only with the
next harvest, but also with the outcome of their future campaigns
and with their enemies' plans. Astrology had proved itself in
meteorology, and had now to show its mettle in politics. And in
fact, astrologers proved that they were in no way inferior to the
hepatoscopists. "If the moon appeareth on the fifteenth day" an
astrological report of the time tells us, "Akkad will prosper and
Subartu fare ill; if the moon appeareth on the sixteenth day,
Akkad and Ammuru will fare ill and Subartu will prosper; if the

[1] G. Contenau: *La Divination*, p. 308.

moon appeareth on the seventeenth day Akkad and Ammuru will prosper, and Subartu fare ill."

Hundreds of such predictions are known, but only a handful could be called horoscopes in the modern sense, and these came from a later period, when the fame of Greek astrology had reached Mesopotamia. But despite their inability to predict man's individual future from the stars, it was the Babylonians who laid the foundations to astrological prophecy. We do not know when they began, or the names of the pioneers, for though the oldest known text dates back to 2000 B.C., we know that the Babylonians had begun to read the future from the stars 1000 years earlier. So widespread was their fame throughout the ancient world that the term Chaldean —the biblical word for Babylonian—became synonymous with astrologer.

From the mere fact that astrology continued to exist side by side with older branches of prophecy, we must conclude that no individual method fully satisfied the Babylonians' thirst for knowledge. True, astrologers were generally more circumspect in their predictions than their great rivals, the hepatoscopists, but they too blotted their copybook by trying to give more than was in their power.

The Lo-King

Babylonian astrology must have reached the Far East, possibly along the well-trodden smugglers' route which led through the whole of ancient Asia, for though the Chinese Zodiac uses a different set of stars and terms from the Babylonian, the two systems have so many similarities that they cannot have arisen independently. There is no doubt that the Chinese were the pupils and the Babylonians, who were better observers, shrewder mathematicians and clearer thinkers, the teachers.

Chinese astrology probably goes back to 3000 B.C., though the oldest Chinese astrological documents are much more recent. What alone seems to be quite certain, is that the Chinese have attached great significance to the heavenly signs since early antiquity. Thus Kung-tse (Confucius, 551–478 B.C.) asserted that predictions from the planets were not only possible, but

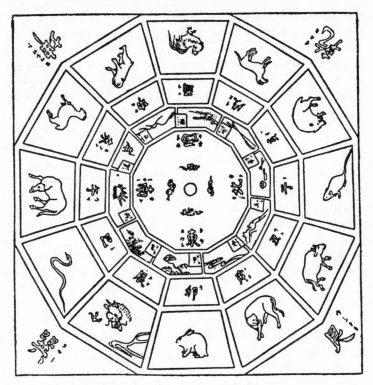

12. Ancient Chinese Zodiac-plate.

necessary: "Heaven sends down its good or evil symbols, and wise men act accordingly."[1] And this is precisely what they did. Chinese, like Babylonian astrology, was a solemn business and continued to be directed by a court astronomer until the 18th century. The state has priority even in heaven; the "permanent" constellations were related to the imperial offices, and the other professions had to content themselves with less glittering stars.[2] (Plate VIII).

What did the Chinese ask the stars? At first, just as in Babylon, they consulted them about the weather, and about

[1] Appendix to the *Book of Ji.*—J. J. M. de Groot: *Universismus* (Berlin 1918) p. 341.
[2] Ernst Zinner: *Sternglaube und Sternforschung* (Freiburg-Munich, 1953) p. 33.

eclipses of the moon and the sun, the better to assuage the wrath of the gods by sacrifices and castigations. Astronomy at that time was an honourable but a very risky profession. In one report, we are told that two court astronomers, Hi and Ho, were sentenced to death because they had failed to predict an eclipse of the sun.[1] In later times, however, eclipses came more and more to be blamed on the people rather than on the astrologers, and on one occasion—this was something altogether unheard of—an Emperor blamed himself for having caused an eclipse of the sun through his own errors of government.

In time, emperors, ministers, and generals became more and more demanding. Astronomers were expected to give them precise dates for waging victorious campaigns and for solemn ceremonies. Private life, too, fell under the sway of the stars. Astronomy became pure astrology. Still, the Chinese were not, by and large, suited to the profession of astrology. Unlike the Babylonians who were analysts and searched for precise answers to even the most complex questions, the Chinese were more given to synthesis, and tried to explain too much from too little. Every constellation has its protector, its beasts, its musical scale, its number, its own taste and its smell, for all nature was preordained harmony. This idea may be very poetic but it does not lend itself to concrete prophecy.

This need to put all one's eggs in one basket led to the invention of the Chinese magic disc, Lo King, a kind of universal horoscope. The disc was divided into six circles showing the star symbols and a host of "associated" facts. With the help of this instrument, which continued to be used in China until fairly recently, a man's future and after-life could be foretold with great ease. Marco Polo tells how the Chinese used this magic disc in the thirteenth century to establish a suitable date for cremating leading court officials. Whenever a great ruler died, the magic disc would be consulted as to the constellations and planets which governed the hour of his birth, and if these planets did not happen to be "in the ascendant" just then, the corpse was left unburied for weeks and sometimes for up to six months. It is easy to see how much this macabre type of astrology must have contributed to the spread of epidemics (Plate VIII).

[1] Rudolf Thiel: *Und es war Licht* (Hamburg 1956), p. 29.

Old Testament Prophets

The only people which resolutely and on principle refused to be influenced by Chaldean prophecy belonged to a small and young state founded after a hard struggle by a group of Semitic nomads in the fertile strip between the Mediterranean and the Syrian desert. They were a very headstrong people, preferring their new country to that of their ancestor Abraham, who according to their own tradition, had come from Mesopotamia. Though their myths and laws largely corresponded to those of the Babylonians, they had a characteristic religion which set them apart from all their neighbours; they had but one God who was particularly kindly disposed towards them, and spoke direct to their religious leaders and prophets. This God, Jehovah, revealed himself in three ways: in dreams, in visions, and in miraculous signs. Inspired dreams and visions often referred to the distant future rather than to specific dates, while signs and miracles were thought devoid of all prophetic character. They came direct from Jehovah as a token of his omnipotence or occasionally to lend greater authority to the words of one or other of his prophets—as in the story of Moses and the burning bush. All endogenous, subjective prophets must first overcome popular disbelief, since in the absence of established prophetic practices like hepatoscopy or astrology, it is difficult to distinguish true prophets from false.

The Old Testament illustrates this point most strikingly in the story of the dispute between Micaiah, the outsider, and the four hundred established prophets who advised King Ahab to wage war against the Syrians.[1] In the final analysis, it is prophetic fulfilment which proves the worth of a prophet, but fulfilment may be a long way off, and the true—but pessimistic—prophet may have to linger in gaol until events vindicate him, or sometimes die a martyr's death.

The decline of the Jewish prophetic movement was due not so much to a lack of inspiration, as to a lack of divine signs and miracles. Their struggle against superstition and magic, finally spelt the prophets' own doom. Those who cannot produce miracles from time to time are rarely believed by the people.

Although Jewish, like Babylonian, prophecy was a special

[1] 1 Kings 22.

vocation, and for centuries even a tightly organised "closed shop",[1] the prophets did little else than make political predictions of the kind commonly made by modern statesmen and their advisers. They were never given to making exact predictions associating certain social events with, say, an eclipse of the moon, as the Babylonians did, and usually preferred to speculate about general moral or religious questions. The Jewish prophets were moralists and politicians whose main task it was to keep their people's faith alive. For this very reason they frowned upon alien prophets whose sayings were generally bound up with native polytheistic beliefs.

True, astrology and even prophecy from the intestines of animals or from the flight of birds was not necessarily associated with polytheism, since Jehovah himself could conceivably reveal the future in a like manner, but in fact these methods of prophecy had become part and parcel of polytheism, and were the stock in trade of idolatrous prophets who were anathema to pious Jews. Moreover, the Jews bore a political grudge against Babylon, the capital of their largest and most powerful neighbour. Hence everything out of Babylon was sinful and evil. In fact, the first Jewish state, and with it the Old Testament prophetic movement, came to an end in Babylonian captivity (ca. 400 B.C.). The place of the Nâbi, the prophet, was usurped by the Rabbi, the sage, whose task it was to explain Jehovah's past revelations. New revelations were no longer believed, and all those who continued to prophesy were derided as common swindlers who deserved no better than death.[2]

But despite these severe measures against Chaldean prophecy,[3] and finally against prophecy as such, the prophetic movement was never completely eradicated amongst the Jews. The Old Testament is full of stories of how Jews from all walks of life continued to explore the future by forbidden means. The most striking account is the story of King Saul and the woman at Endor who consulted the spirits on his behalf. Now, no Jew was allowed to consult the spirits, and Saul, who knew this, had vainly consulted Jehovah first. But Jehovah had ignored him and failed to send him either dreams or signs, or to speak to him

[1] Alfred Guillaume: *Prophétie et Divination chez les Sémites*, p. 136.
[2] Zechariah 13, 3.
[3] Deuteronomy 18, 12.

III. Worship of the Babylonian Sun-god Shamash (*British Museum*).

IV. Prophecy from the intestines of an animal (Greek vase, 500 B.C.).

V. Gilgamesh (Babylonian seal). The Gilgamesh epic contains the oldest-known dream interpretation.

through the mouth of the prophet.[1] Jehovah's silence was, of course, a bad omen in itself, and the conclusion that God had abandoned Saul seemed unavoidable. But Saul would not see this, and since an important military decision had to be made by him, he abandoned the path of the Law and turned to magic instead. Secretly he stole to the woman at En-dor and forced her to conjure up the spirit of Samuel, his former adviser. And when the spirit of Samuel appeared—to the eyes of the woman and not to Saul—it was only to scold Saul for disquieting him. For this act of blasphemy, Saul was punished next day by defeat in the battle of Gilboa and by his death.

Conjuring up the dead, i.e. necromancy, was practised all over the East, and even found its way into Greek mythology as in the story of Circe's inciting Ulysses to disturb the shadows of the dead.[2] The dead alone can look clearly into the future, and can often be consulted about it. This notion, too, is probably of Mesopotamian origin, for the Babylonians had special priests who were experts in necromancy and made it possible for the living to keep in touch with their dead relatives and friends. Even so, necromancy, this darkest of all magical arts, played no major part in ancient prophecy, for the ancients respected the peace of the dead, and assured their comfort by ritual and solemn burial ceremonies, and by putting nourishment into their graves. If the dead became restless and roamed about, or came unsummoned, they generally frightened men and gave them bad dreams. True, this was prediction as well—but usually of evil things to come—and no one in his right mind would go out of his way to elicit exclusively terrifying forebodings about the future.

Egyptian mystifiers

Babylonian prophecy, no matter how many magical elements it contained, always preserved a core of sobriety. Since prophecy was not given to all, those who knew their job were expected to practise it openly and with the minimum of mumbo jumbo. Prophecy was first given its esoteric aura by the Egyptians, who

[1] 1 Samuel 28, 6 ff.
[2] Odyssey X, 517–534.

turned it into a mysterious art. While they introduced far-reaching metaphysical and philosophical factors into it, they also robbed it of much of its previous lucidity.

This change was seen in the external features of the practice of their art, as well. The Egyptian diviners preferred to work in complete darkness, ostensibly because inner illumination shines forth more brightly under such conditions, but really because people are far more credulous in the dark than they are in the light of day, and much more prone to be taken in by sleights of hand. The Egyptian temples held "living" statues of the gods whose jaws could be moved by mechanical means like those of puppets, and by which the audience was deceived into believing that the gods were addressing them.

Apart from such childish deceptions, there was little that the Egyptians added to prophetic methods. Their special claim to fame was that they were masters at interpreting dreams, and nightmares in particular. Dreams, like dead spirits, had the power of plaguing the living, and the Egyptians would often consult both simultaneously by sleeping on graves.

Those dreams and dream interpretations, however, which we know from inscriptions and papyri are not distinguished by excessive imagination or originality, no doubt because the dreams in question were generally those of the reigning Pharaoh, and in his case the prophets had, of course, to be doubly circumspect. Sometimes the gods would give the dreamer direct hints, as in the case of King Thothmes IV, who is said, as a youth, to have fallen asleep in the shadow of the Sphinx. In his dream he saw a god who promised him the throne on condition that he re-establish the god's temple and raise the great Sphinx out of the sand.[1]

The most famous Pharaonic dream is reported not by Egyptian sources but in the Bible. It is the story of Joseph's interpretation of Pharaoh's two dreams, which none of the official magicians could read: the dream of the seven fat and the seven lean cows, and the seven good and the seven thin ears of corn.[2] Joseph's interpretation that the dream foretold seven years of plenty and seven years of famine and his advice to lay

[1] G. Contenau: *La Divination chez les Assyriens et les Babyloniens*, p. 168.
[2] Genesis 41, 1–36.

up stores of corn, strike us as far too realistic to have been typically Egyptian. What Joseph did in fact do was to make the first recorded economic prediction of all time. It was more than mere prophecy for it involved scientific foresight and planning.

In the days of the later Pharaohs, divination came increasingly to be performed in the temples of the sun god Amon-Râ, one of whose shrines, particularly favoured by Ethiopians, was in Natopa, and another in the Lybian desert, a twelve days' journey from Memphis, the capital. The Lybian shrine, despite its geographical isolation, became a place of pilgrimage, and its oracles were heralded with great pomp. Eighty priests, accompanied by a women's choir carried a "holy ship" with a statue of the god through the streets of the temple district in festive procession and, if it was a question of selecting a high dignitary, stopped before the "right" man at the behest of the god.

This is how Alexander the Great had himself proclaimed the son of Amon-Râ, that is to say as Pharaoh. No doubt he encountered little opposition from the priests who had already acclaimed him as their future ruler. The priests of Amon-Râ also had to deal with other problems, for instance with public prosecutions. In this case, too, the god would give his verdict by "speaking" to them in sign language, probably by means of mechanically operated arms.[1]

The Egyptian centre of purely astrological prediction was Heliopolis, close to Memphis and the modern city of Cairo. Unlike the Babylonians, the Egyptian took no interest in the rational part of astrology, i.e. meteorology, probably because the Nile, as it periodically flooded their country or else dried up to bring drought in its wake, told them all they needed to know about this subject. The idea of periodic phenomena entered into many of their other beliefs as well, for they held that the dead returned to human form every 3000 years, after an interval spent as beasts. Still, such long periods could hardly have played an important role in everyday prophecy.

The astrological prediction of the fate of individuals only began in earnest when the Greek city of Alexandria became the intellectual centre of Egypt. It was Egypt that provided the soil for the *Tetrabiblos*, Ptolemy's long treatise, which has remained

[1] J. H. Breasted: *Ancient Records of Egypt* (Chicago 1906–1907) Vol. IV, p. 328.

the bible of astrologers to this day. Ptolemy (ca A.D. 150) was also a great scientific astronomer, whose *Almagest* and *Syntax* remained the foundations of astronomy until Copernicus overthrew the Ptolemaic cosmic picture 1500 years later. In astrology on the other hand, Ptolemy was not a great innovator, for what he mainly did was to record and to systematise current beliefs about the influence of the stars on the earth and on man.

The Greeks

Greek love for astrology was a relatively late development, and was the last stage on a thousand years' road of prophecy. Many historians have tried to explain the Greeks' preoccupation with prophetic matters by their belief in the Fates, but this explanation does not stand up to closer scrutiny. The Greeks were far too logical a people to have combined fatalistic faith with a need for prophecy: fatalists can afford to wait. But then the Greeks were never real fatalists, and though philosophers and poets exhorted them to look at the future with equanimity, they never learnt to accept what was in store for them with Stoic peace of mind. Even when the oracle had revealed the future, they would try to temper it by prayers, sacrifices, good deeds, and even by deception. Thus the fight against fate is a typical Greek attitude, and gave rise to their tragedies and great dramas on the stage and in real life.

If we speak of Greek fatalism, we must first of all define the term, for to the Greeks the term "fate" meant two distinct things. On the one hand, it was the moral belief that transgressions were punished by the gods, not only on the perpetrators but also on their children and children's children, and even on a whole nation. Thus individual crimes could involve innocent bystanders, and each man bore a grave responsibility for his fellow men, and particularly for his descendants. True, not even in ancient Greece was it a crime to be a murderer's son, but it was recognised that sin can set off a chain reaction, since the Furies, the goddesses of vengeance, would involve the sinner's children in new crimes, thus justifying the punishment meted out to them.

These moral involvements emerge most strikingly in the

tragedies of Aeschylus and Sophocles. Although they were generally based on ancient myths—for instance the fate of Orestes or of Oedipus—it was no accident that they were written in the fifth century B.C., i.e. at the time of the Persian wars and the consolidation of Athenian democracy: the story of the fate of the mythical kings of Mycenae and Thebes was a simile about the banished Athenian nobles who ceaselessly conspired with the enemies of Athens, thus adding to their own onus of guilt.

On the other hand, Greek fatalism involed a belief in *moira*, the kind of inexplicable fate which often seems mere blind accident. *Moira* is essentially amoral and beyond human logic. The Greeks, like all people who think about the world, realised that not everything can be explained by logic, and Homer even placed *moira* above the gods, including Zeus himself. The symbol of *moira* was the lottery, for in the lottery of fate there are black and white lots, and not even Zeus Moiragetes, the ruler of fate, can do better than draw lots, if he is to be fair, and distribute man's share of luck and misfortune without fear or favour.

The more democratic Athens became, the greater grew the importance of *moira*, for once one assumes that all citizens are equal, it is exceedingly difficult to bestow offices of state on anybody. Thus not only the jury, but also all ministers, members of the senate, and (since 457 B.C.) the *Archontes* were chosen by lot.

Cleromancy, i.e. divination by lot, also played a very important role in Greek prophecy. Cleromancy was, in fact, an old established Greek custom, the throw of dice, bones, or coloured pebbles having for long played the part of arbiter in arguments and difficult decisions. Lithology—divination by throwing stones —was later replaced in popular esteem by the drawing of beans on which names or alternative choices were written beforehand. This method was also used for selecting candidates for public office.

But in the case of far-reaching decisions, the throwing of lots was usually left to professional prophets who, since they were inspired by the gods, were thought to be specially fitted to this task. Apparently, the priests did not take kindly to this role, for not only did they deem such primitive methods unworthy of the true prophet, but they also considered them too "objective".

They much preferred to rely on the far vaguer pronouncements of the temple priestesses. Still, the people insisted, and in the end the prophets had to comply.[1] Wherever there were oracles—in Dodona, in Delphi, or in Olympia—the lot was consulted, and the Delphic Pythia, in particular, would keep a store of beans in her tripod.

The Delphic Oracle

The Pythia had always been a "medium" whose trance-like inarticulate sounds were understood by no-one but the priests. Now she was expected to play the part of a mere lottery supervisor, whose main function it was to draw lots, albeit in a trance.[2] (Plates IX and X).

Although there is no conclusive evidence that the Pythia entered a state of trance before pronouncing any oracle whatsoever, ancient records, from Heraclitus to Plutarch, attach great significance to her states of ecstasy. According to popular belief, this state of divine intoxication was quite naturally enhanced by the very geographical position of the shrine at Delphi—originally the altar of Gaia, the Mother of the Earth. It lay on the slopes of Parnassus, above a hole in the ground from which sulphur fumes sent forth an everlasting evil smell, later said to have emanated from the rotting corpse of the dragon Typhon. This may be borne out by the term "Pythia", for, in Greek, "pythein" means "to decay". (On the other hand Pytho, Delphi's original name, may have been derived from "pynthanomai"—"to ask".) The Pythia sat on her tripod in a subterranean chamber, the Adyton, through which a holy fountain, the Cassotis, was said to flow. Excavations have shown that, at least in later times, the Cassotis was, in fact, a man-made canal.[3] Clearly, things were so arranged in Delphi that the Pythia and her petitioners were surrounded with impressive mysteries.

At first, oracles were pronounced no more than once a year, on the seventh day of Bysios (February-March), Apollo's

[1] G. Contenau: *La Divination*, Chapter III.
[2] Pierre Amandry: *La mantique apollinienne à Delphes*. (Thesis, Sorbonne 1950).
[3] Marie Delcourt: *L'Oracle de Delphes* (Paris 1955) p. 43.

birthday, but, as the stream of petitioners grew bigger, oracles came to be given on the seventh day of every month. In the interval, the Pythia probably made less solemn prophecies by lot, but not even this increase in activity could satisfy the quest of the ever growing stream of visitors. Two Pythias and at the height of the season even three Pythias, had to be used to satisfy the demands of princes or their ambassadors alone. In urgent cases, special sessions were held. Oracles were very expensive, and though satisfied customers would shower impressive presents on the Pythia, presents alone proved inadequate to cover the costs. For this reason, a fixed minimum tariff was introduced, and those who required an urgent oracle had to pay a special priority fee, the "promanteia".

So as not to turn the oracle into an exclusive privilege of the rich, a mass oracle was held once every year, not in the darkness of the Adyton, but in broad daylight. The Pythia would sit down unceremoniously on the temple steps to answer the people's questions. The priests, who normally commented on her pronouncements, did not participate in this mass oracle, and so the Pythia's answers lost most of their value, as the commentaries were an integral part of all real oracles and, in difficult cases, probably the most important part. Homer wrote that true prophets inspire the priests to pronounce oracles.[1] This may strike us as the direct opposite of what happened at Delphi, though even in Delphi the priest-interpreters were called prophets. In any case, even in Homer's time there was a clear division: the prophet or prophetess revealed the will of the god, and others attached to the temple made it known.

In Delphi, and probably elsewhere in Greece also, the priests' job was not merely to communicate the oracle literally or to put it into verse—the oracles recorded on stone tablets are, in any case, all in prose—but to interpret it very skilfully and shrewdly. The priests were not expected to have "second sight" like, for instance, the Pythia who told the ambassadors of King Croesus that their master was this very hour preparing a soup of mutton and turtle in Sardes, his capital,[2] but they had to be well-informed and were often called upon to answer the most complicated political questions. For rulers and town officials, at

[1] Iliad, XVI, 235.
[2] Herodotus: History I, 47.

least, Delphi was not merely a mystical source of prophecy, but a hive of political activity, for they knew that its priests were in touch with all the world. Thus, from the very way foreigners formulated their questions, the priests could often deduce their real intentions.

Delphic priests were generally of noble descent, and their office was frequently handed down from generation to generation. By and large they were conservative in outlook, and thus closer to Sparta than to liberal Athens. Nor were they opposed to imperialist exploits, and their great political skill was, no doubt, a decisive factor in colonising Southern Italy. Though they were called defeatists and even traitors for having tried to dissuade Greece from waging what eventually turned out to be a successful war against the Persians, theirs had nevertheless been the well-considered advice of elder statesmen.

Prophetesses

While the priests were highly educated people, the Pythia herself was an illiterate woman of the people. She was therefore not expected to be particularly intelligent but had to be morally beyond reproach. For many centuries the Pythias were young virgins, but after a particularly attractive Pythia was abducted, the office was increasingly entrusted to elderly women. But no matter whether young or old, the Pythia had to be celibate, for carnal knowledge of men might make her too worldly and could decrease her divine powers of inspiration.

It is most odd that, in Greece, where women normally lived such retired lives, it was they who were chosen for the high office of official prophet. Women were otherwise not allowed to enter the Adyton, and had to put their questions to the Pythia through male intermediaries. This strange contradiction is no Greek peculiarity, for amongst Israelites, too, where women were almost completely excluded from the religious life, prophetesses were held in high regard. The most famous of them, Deborah, was even made a judge. In Egypt, priest-prophetesses were among the highest state dignitaries, and in Babylonia and other countries of the Near East, prophetesses were a common phenomenon. According to an Arab legend, man's prophetic gift was handed to him by Zaripha—a prophetess. Clearly, the ancients believed that women were more receptive to inspiration —on condition that they renounced their sexuality.

The fame of Delphi lasted for over a thousand years,[1] but began to decline after Euripides had launched his great attack on it. From the fourth century B.C. onwards, the critics grew more and more vociferous. In late Roman times, a fresh, if abortive, attempt was made to burnish Delphi's fading renown: Plutarch (A.D. 49 to 120) was appointed High Priest of Delphi. In the end, however, all Plutarch could do was to bewail the decline of the Oracle in elegant phrases. The gods had simply ceased to reveal themselves. Even the Pythia would occasionally refuse her services, and, on one occasion, the people were forced to pour cold water over a prophetic goat so that it would speak to the reluctant Pythia.[2] But all was in vain, the oracle had lost its power, and the people knew it.

Not that they had become less credulous or less superstitious; it was merely that their credulity had assumed different forms. Despite bitter opposition from the most important Greek astronomers—Eudoxus and later Carneades, the founder of the New Athenian Academy—the Greeks, persuaded by Pythagorean number myths, had become converted to astrology. Astrology had a patron saint in Aristotle, behind whose authority it was to shelter for 2000 years both in the Christian and the Arab world. While Plato had still held fast to the old forms of prediction and had even stressed the importance of the Delphic Oracle in his model state of the future, his pupil Aristotle asserted that the earth was governed by the motions of a superior world.

Thus the door was opened wide to astrology. The Alexandrian wars brought Babylonian and Greek astrologers into closer contact, and on the island of Cos, the seat of the famous medical school which produced the great Hippocrates, the Babylonian priest Berosus founded an institute for the study of oriental astronomy and astrology.[3] Chaldean astrologers began

[1] H. W. Parke: *A History of the Delphic Oracle* (Oxford, 1939).

[2] Plutarch: On the decline of the Oracles, 51.

[3] P. Schnabel: *Berossos und die babylonisch-hellenistische Literatur* (Leipzig 1923).

to come to Athens in growing number and were revered as if they were the harbingers of a new message of salvation. Really adventurous Greeks would go to Mesopotamia in order to be in more direct touch with the true sources of wisdom. Since the Greeks were better mathematicians than the Chaldeans they soon outstripped their masters. It was in Mesopotamia that Hipparchus made a major contribution towards turning astronomy into an exact science by cataloguing the stars into six classes according to their brightness and "size". Hipparchus was a master of astrology, as well, and it was from him that Ptolemy and later astrologers derived much of their wisdom.

The Romans

The Romans owe far less to the Greeks in the sphere of prophetic wisdom than in most other fields. Their methods of prediction came either direct from the Orient, or else across Etruscan by-paths. Rome never had an oracle of Delphic importance, and the legendary Sibyl of Cumae in Etruria was probably of Asian origin. It was the Sibyl of Cumae who was said to have pronounced the traditional collections of oracles kept in the Temple of Jupiter in Rome, which were consulted before any great decision was made. Of Etruscan origin also was the prophetic method used in Roman temples, viz. prophecy from the intestines of sacrificial animals (*hostiae consultatoriae*).

The priests, who determined which animals were fit to be used for this exalted purpose and who consulted the entrails, were called *Haruspices*—inspectors of sacrifices or of entrails—according to whether we derive the word haruspex from *harviga* or from *hira*. In principle, the method was very similar to that used in ancient Babylon, except that new medical knowledge was increasingly introduced into the predictions. Apart from the liver, which was the *chef d'oeuvre* of the Roman Haruspices as well, they also "consulted" five other organs—the so-called *exta*—about the future: the spleen, the kidneys, the lungs and —since Pliny's contribution in 274 B.C.—the heart. In later times astrological ideas, too, were introduced into entrail-prediction. Thus, an Etruscan bronze liver discovered in Pia-

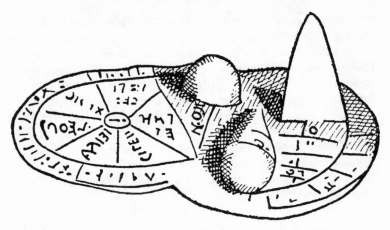

13. Bronze Liver from Piacenza. Etruscan model for hepatoscopic predictions (300–200 B.C.).

cenza (Italy) in 1877, and dating back to the second or third century B.C., resembled the astrological implements of the time. In addition, every part of the liver was governed by a special god and by different elements (water, fire, earth, and air).[1]

The Haruspices were an organised body of soothsayers and were highly respected specialists, even though they were never as influential in Rome as their counterparts in Babylon. Since most of them came from Etruria they were called Etruscans, and Etruscans were considered to be good Romans, unlike Chaldean astrologers and Oriental soothsayers who, despite their acknowledged superiority, were persecuted as foreigners from time to time. Thus in 139 B.C., under Cornelius Hispalus, all Chaldeans were driven from Rome. Subsequently, the emperors Augustus, Domitian, and Hadrian passed edicts against them but other men of rank like the Gracchi, Sulla, and Julius Caesar were believers in astrology, and the emperors Tiberius, Nero, Otho, and Vespasian appointed Chaldean court astrologers. Under the Emperor Alexander Severus (A.D. 223–235), who was of Phoenician origin, astrology became an official Roman science, with a special school and with state subsidies.

Still, the greatest Roman contribution to the art of prophecy,

[1] G. Koerte: *Die Bronzeleber von Piacenza.* Transact. Germ. Arch. Inst. (Roman section) Vol. XX (1905) pp. 348–379.

was a negative one: Cicero and Pliny the Elder were the first to muster arguments which are used against astrology to this day. They pointed out that the planets were too far from the earth to have perceptible influence on human beings; that astrologers were often robbed and even murdered without having had any foreknowledge of such attacks; that twins born under the same star would have to have identical fates, which was far from being the case; that of those born at the same hour some become rich while others become beggars. It was Pliny, also, who first remarked how odd it was that the stars were supposed to exert their influence at the moment of birth rather than at the moment of conception.

The end of the world

Christianity put an end to all the prophetic methods which savoured of heathen rites, of oracles, or of Haruspices. The Druids, too, were forbidden to prophesy from the rustling of the leaves. Everything that smacked of magic—black or white—was eradicated. But astrology managed to survive even this holocaust, and St. Augustine, who had consulted astrologers in his own youth, was forced to exclaim in despair: "No art at all is involved in soothsaying, and only accident makes some of its predictions come true."[1] Though the Church fulminated against astrological superstitions and insisted that there was no need to defer marriage or the building of new houses until the new moon, she never pronounced a formal condemnation of astrology. The reason why astrology, nevertheless, fell into decline for centuries, was not so much because of Church opposition, as because of the decline of the mathematical knowledge needed for understanding such astrological works as Ptolemy's *Tetrabiblos*. Astrology had fallen into the hands of the commonest swindlers.

More serious astrologers took refuge in the courts of the East. For a time, Persia became the home of this Greek science, and helped it to spread across the entire Arab world. Some astrology also reached the South directly from Mesopotamia, but on its journey it had accumulated so much dust and rubbish that the results of the astrological "renaissance" in ninth century

[1] St. Augustine, *Confessions*, Book VII, Chapter 6.

14. Ancient Arab Zodiac.

Arab learning were, in many respects, vastly inferior to those of the much older Greek astrology. While Ptolemy had realised that the fixed stars, too, must affect terrestrial events if there was anything to astrology at all, the Arabs fell back on the primitive Babylonian idea that the planets alone governed man's fate. Cosmogenetic predictions, too, became more primitive. Thus Albumazar or Abu-Maaschar (A.D. 805–885) "calculated" that the Creation had occurred "when the seven planets were in conjunction in the first degree of Aries" and announced further that the end of the world would coincide with a similar conjunction "in the last degree of Pisces."

These prophecies, because of the time involved, are of course wild and fancy-free, but the Arabs insisted on great accuracy in short-range predictions. Albategnius, or Al-Battan (A.D. 850–929), a brilliant mathematician, was the first to introduce "houses" into astrology, thus making it possible to consult charts from which every man's future could be read off precisely once his birthday was known. Horoscopes, i.e. predictions based on the hour, or, short of that, on the day of birth, had been cast for a thousand years before, the first detailed horoscopes having been composed in Greece, in about 250 B.C. But the Greek system had been laborious and unreliable. From now on, there was a system that everyone could master and test for himself. The Arab system of houses, with many innovations and different innuendos —for astrologers are notoriously given to vacillation—subsequently became the basis of Western astrological predictions.

At first, the West had pre-occupations of its own. Hell had been painted so hot, that miserable sinners everywhere feared the Day of Judgement like the plague. The Day of Judgement was expected at any moment, and only numerology could reveal the exact date. Numbers, and beginnings of centuries and of millenia were either lucky or unlucky, and played an hitherto unsuspected role in man's fate.

As the year A.D. 1000 approached, this faith turned into collective anxiety, for some passages in Revelation seemed to indicate that the end of the world would come on that date. There were other dark omens, as well: in 992, Good Friday fell on Lady Day, a most disastrous coincidence. Many numerologists were convinced that the world would end in the year 995.[1] Fortunately that year passed by uneventfully, but the fear remained. An eclipse of the sun, an extraordinarily severe winter, pestilence, an eruption of Vesuvius, Magyar, Norman and Saracen invasions were further portents of inevitable disaster.

True, similar misfortunes had happened in earlier times, as well, but now the number 1000 oppressed Europe like a nightmare. A wave of fatalism seized the people: the great cataclysm was about to engulf the world and mankind was powerless to do anything about it. All that could be done was to offer fervent prayers, though it seemed unlikely that even prayers could avail as the dreaded moment approached. Whole towns repaired to church as one man, or assembled round crucifixes under the open sky, there to await God's judgement on corporately bended knees. When nothing happened, fear was quickly forgotten, but neither belief nor superstition suffered any damage—a strange human phenomenon that was to be repeated time after time.

Barely two hundred years later, false prophecies caused a new

[1] Paul Villiaud: *La Fin du Monde* (Paris 1952) p. 94 f.

15. The end of the world as seen by Scheuchzer in his *Physica Sacra* (1734).

panic. The new prophecies were not based on Revelation, but on the stars, for meanwhile astrology, nurtured by Arabs in Spain, had regained lost ground in Europe. Through the secret letters of an astrologer who signed himself John of Toledo, the world learned in 1179 that a terrible catastrophe would occur in 1186 when all the planets would unite under the sign of the Scales. This conjunction under a "stormy" sign made it inevitable that a terrible storm followed by an earthquake would occur in September of the fatal year.

The letters of John of Toledo made a great impression on Europe and Asia. In Germany, people began to dig shelters, in Persia and Mesopotamia they repaired their cellars, in Constantinople the Byzantine Emperor caused the windows of his palace to be walled up, in England the Archbishop of Canterbury proclaimed a national fast of atonement. And, in fact, the astronomical part of the prediction did take place. John of Toledo

16. The 17th century combined great technical process with crude superstition. Erfurt prophecy about a bad harvest (1627) based on "celestial signs".

was clearly an astronomer or at least a scholar well-versed in the astronomical tables of Ammonius. But the astrological consequences failed to materialise: the Emperor of Byzantium could once again open his windows—there was neither storm nor rain. Later it was given out that John of Toledo's prophecy had been purely symbolic, for he had really been referring to the Hunnish invasion.[1] The ways of astrologers often pass human understanding, and this is by no means the most striking example of their versatility.

This failure of a world-shaking astrological prophecy to materialise left no lasting disillusionment in its wake, largely because the astronomical part of the prediction had been fulfilled. The fact that a planetary conjunction could be forecast so accurately seven years before the event, redounded so much to the astrologers' credit that they were acclaimed by European courts, by the Pope, and even by the universities. In Italy, in particular, chairs of astrology were endowed, and only when astrologers forgot themselves so far as to make prophecies involving Church dogma, were some of them prosecuted. In 1327, Cocco d'Ascoti was burned at the stake for just that offence.

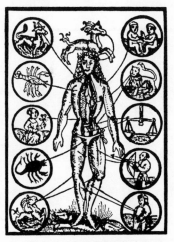

Despite such setbacks, the end of the Middle Ages became a period of triumph for astrology, which was then looked upon as the most useful of all sciences, and as the fountain-head of alchemy. The Greeks had long before associated the planets with certain metals and precious stones, and astrologers were increasingly turning their hands to the art of making gold out of base metals. Astrology also played a paramount role in medicine, and any doctor who failed to consult the stars before a serious operation was open to charges of wilful neglect.

17. "Phlebotomic" figure. Every part of the body is related to a sign of the Zodiac. The stars show when a patient must be operated on or have his blood let.

[1] Paul Couderc: *L'Astrologie* (Paris 1951) p. 97.

"Astronomical" clocks showing "phlebotomic figures" had become the latest craze. From the figures' dissected body even laymen could tell which stars governed which human organs.

Nostradamus

The Renaissance, one of the most superstitious epochs in world history, raised astrology to still greater heights in Europe. It took Rome so much by storm that Pope Julius II called upon an astrologer to predict the most propitious day for his coronation. His successor Leo X, a highly educated and otherwise sceptical gentleman greatly concerned with his failing health, was surrounded by astrologers who cast the most unequivocal horoscopes about the duration of his reign. Unfortunately the stars failed to reveal that Luther's theses were more than idle monkish chatter. Paul III, the first Pope of the Counter-Reformation, also had no scruples about using astrologers in determining what hour was propitious for holding his Consistory.[1]

18. In the 16th century, chemistry was an important means of prophecy. Chemical still from *Destillierkunst* (The art of distillation) by Brunswig (1547).

The Vatican's high regard for astrology was one of the reasons why Luther was so opposed to it. All the same, though the notion that the stars governed man's fate ran counter to his belief in free will, he never called for the complete suppression of astrologers. His friend Melanchthon, who was otherwise so critical of all superstitions, even looked upon astrology as a very serious science. It would therefore be wrong to suggest that, at the time of the Reformation, the Catholic Church was for, and the Protestant Church against, astrol-

[1] Zinner: *Sternglaube und Sternforschung*, p. 104.

ogy. Differences of opinion on this subject cut right across theological divisions.

It was under the reign of Paul III that the writings of Nicolaus Copernicus were given the Papal *imprimatur*. These writings were later to deliver so crushing a blow to astrology, that it would never again fully recover. His first work, the *De revolutionibus orbium cœlestium*—On the Revolutions of the Heavenly Spheres—seemed to have little bearing on astrology as such and was therefore ignored by all but a few experts when it first appeared in 1543. Only some decades later did the devastating astrological consequences of Copernicus' revolutionary doctrine come to be fully appreciated.

Astrology had previously been based on the fact that the planets move about the earth, and Copernicus had shown that they do not. Fortunately, true believers in astrology are extremely conservative and rarely allow themselves to be influenced by mere facts. To this day, they continue to base their predictions on the tables set up by Regiomontanus eighty years before the Copernican revolution. But astronomers began to grow rather wary of astrology. Thus Tycho Brahe, who had been reared on astrological notions and who began by being extremely sceptical of the Copernican system, turned his back on astrology towards the end of his life, and—according to Kepler—dismissed all casters of horoscopes as ignorant and corruptible charlatans.[1] But what were the serious and critical astronomers to do when their patrons demanded predictions rather than scientific knowledge? Kepler who, like Tycho Brahe, was expected to cast horoscopes for his noble employers, consoled himself with the fact that astrology, though a "mad daughter", came to the aid of her poor and aged mother, astronomy, and helped to support her.

Such was the tragic plight of real astronomers, and it took ages before a clear distinction between astrology and astronomy was finally drawn. Still, astrology was on the wane, and even astrologers began to worry about their colossal blunders.

For instance, Geronimo Cardano (1501–1576), equally famed as a physicist, a mathematician, a physician, and an astrologer, was known to have foretold that King Edward VI of England

[1] Johann Kepler: *Vorrede zu den Rudolphinischen Tafeln des Tycho Brahe* (1627).

19. Geronimo Cardano, the great 16th century
physician and mathematician, was a poor
astrologer.

(Figure opposite), would fall ill at the age of 55 years, 3
months and 17 days. When the King failed to oblige by dying at
the age of sixteen, Cardano was forced to admit that, in the case
of men with a constitutional weakness—a clear sign that they
had not been adequately marked by the stars—astrologers
would have to cast the horoscopes of all their associates as well.
When his "environmental" theory was generally ridiculed,
Cardano is said to have taken his own life at the age of 75, to
prove the validity of the horoscope he had cast for himself.[1] His
younger compatriot, Giambattista della Porta (1535–1615),
who founded the first European seat of scientific learning—the
"Academy of the Mysteries of Naples"—had already learnt the
bitter lesson of defeat. According to him, the stars merely

[1] Alexandre Arnoux: *Le Seigneur de l'Heure* (Paris 1955).

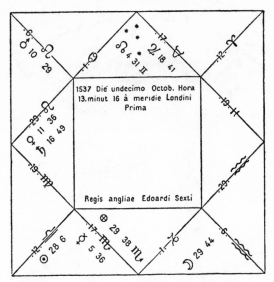

20. Horoscope cast by Cardano for Edward VI of England. The horoscope proved to be completely wrong.

caused men to have certain predispositions—*astra inclinant, non necessitant*. This proposition which is found in della Porta's *Cœlestis Physiognomiae* continues to serve astrologers as a convenient excuse to this day.

Times were clearly changing, and the greatest prophet of the 16th century, the French physician Nostradamus (Michel de Nostre-Dame, 1503–1566) is remembered for his political[1] rather than for his astrological predictions. These were typical intuitive prophecies, in the style of the ancient oracles. His mystical quatrains have been used to predict the entire future history of France, and some of his prophecies were subsequently related to explain the rise of Napoleon, and even of Mussolini, Hitler and Roosevelt.[2]

To his contemporaries, Nostradamus was above all a necromancer, and in this field he truly excelled. Having correctly predicted the death of Henri II of France during a tournament, four years in advance, Henri's widow, Catherine de Medici,

[1] Nostradamus: *Centuries* (Lyons 1555).
[2] Nostradamus: *Centuries* II, 41.

21. Nostradamus, the most famous of all 16th century prophets. His political predictions are still in great vogue.

who had a strong mystical streak, summoned Nostradamus, and for 45 nights the two of them conducted spiritualist seances. Nostradamus managed to conjure up the angel Anael who showed Catherine the future of her children in a mirror. Her three sons, later to become kings of France, appeared first and paraded across the mirror, once for every year of their reign. Since none of them was destined to reign for long, the parade took up little time, but when Catherine's son-in-law, the King of Navarre, who later succeeded to the French throne as Henri IV of France, appeared in the mirror, he took 23 turns in it. Catherine was so frightened at this revelation that she desisted from pressing Nostradamus for any further glimpses of the future. Both Nostradamus and the angel Anael obliged and the mirror reverted to its former, more prosaic, role of ordinary looking glass.[1]

Pascal's Wager

Though the 16th century was a particularly superstitious epoch, rational thought managed to make great strides in it. For the first time in history, men had begun to plumb the future by statistical methods and to act accordingly. While the life of the individual was recognised to depend on too many unpredictable factors for even the wisest of prophets to come to any reliable conclusions, the collective fate of hundreds or thousands of men was so regular that general predictions about it seemed quite possible.

Questions about the average life expectancy of man, the total number of spinsters or orphans in a town of a given size or the number of shipwrecks began to be asked, and the mere fact that they were asked was an entirely new and very courageous step, for it meant asking questions about the future without the aid of magicians and astrologers. It appeared that, if the death-rate had been fairly constant for some years, the same number of people would probably die in the next year, as well. True, one did not know which particular family was going to be affected, but, if only enough people clubbed together, they could at least make good some of the worst financial repercussions of an individual breadwinner's death. It was from such considerations that Insurance Societies were originally set up.

The first of these societies was established in Italy, though the idea was initially suggested by English merchants. It was in England, too, that Sir William Petty laid the foundations of statistical science in the second half of the 17th century. Statistics was a way of catching a glimpse of the future by methods that had been used before, but never deliberately or systematically.

The mathematical tools and the intellectual framework of this new art of prediction were provided by France. Blaise Pascal (1623–1662) and Pierre de Fermat (1601–1665) were the acknowledged masters of a calculus by which probabilities could be compounded from mathematical formulae. While

[1] Jean Moura and Paul Louvet: *La vie de Nostradamus* (Paris 1930).

"scientific" astrologers and magicians had always tried to predict future details with complete accuracy and had therefore committed the most colossal blunders, the new school based its predictions on the fact that between total certainty and total uncertainty there lay a vast range of possibilities, the probability of each of which could be calculated with mathematical precision (Plates XI-XIII).

Probability calculations, far from being mere games with numbers, are a most useful science—even though they originated on the gaming tables. It all started when a fellow gambler, the Chevalier de Méré, asked Pascal how the stakes could be fairly redistributed among players when a game of dice was suddenly interrupted, i.e. how a given player's future chances of success in the game could be taken into account in the redistribution. Blaise Pascal, then thirty years old but already distinguished not only because of his mathematical papers but also because of his invention of the calculating machine and of the hydraulic press, tackled the problem with great zest, for he realised that its solution might have tremendous repercussions far beyond the gaming table. But since he was primarily dealing with a gambling question, he called his probability theory *aleae geometriae*—the geometry of the die.

Unaware that Galileo[1] had studied the chances of winning in games of dice some 12 years, and Cardano some 100 years, earlier, Pascal thought that he had founded an entirely new branch of science. And in fact, though he was not the first to have appreciated the problem and to have attempted its solution, probability theory is commonly agreed to have begun with the letter to Père Mersenne (1654), in which Pascal developed the ideas.

A few months later, Pascal withdrew from worldly life to devote himself entirely to religious studies. Still, his thoughts returned time and again to the concept of probability, so much so that he attempted to solve the most intricate religious problems by probability theory—and this despite his faith in miracles! In Pascal, rationalism competed strongly with an inner trend towards mysticism. Thus, when he was asked whether it was worth while working for eternal salvation, his reply[2] was

[1] Galileo: *Sopra la significazione del giuoco dei dadi* (1642).
[2] Pascal: *Pensées*, Chapter 7 (published posthumously in 1670).

that we must take a gamble for or against God. If we wager on God, our chances of success are greater than the risks we run, since, however small our chances of attaining eternal bliss, the reward is out of all proportion to the stakes. Thus no reasonable man would refuse to contract such a wager.[1]

Pascal's wager with God strikes us as a piece of medieval scholasticism which never questions the premisses on which it is based. Two hundred years later, another French scholar, Ernest Renan, objected that no business man in his right senses would stake even a hundred francs to gain a million, if the chances were as small as those of attaining life hereafter. Be that as it may, probability, which had been quite alien to ancient and medieval methods of prophecy, was now on everyone's lips. "Chance" began to obsess all men; and the weighing up of future gains and losses with all the tricks of mathematics, became not only a favourite social game, but occupied the greatest minds of the time. Thus the Swiss mathematician Jacob Bernouilli[2] set to perfecting the mathematical method, and made it possible for probability theory to play the very large part it does in modern astronomical, medical, technical, economic, and other scientific predictions.

Hypnosis

Naturally, the professional prophets were not slow in appropriating the new techniques, and they began to calculate the most absurd phenomena with mathematical precision. The stars might lie, but numbers could never deceive. A new age of numerology had dawned, and was directing its main efforts at gambling predictions, and gambling, since the advent of state lotteries, had taken sway of ever-increasing multitudes. It was generally known that, if only a man lived long enough and never missed a single draw, he was bound one day to hit the jackpot, and to make more than good all the losses he had incurred. Still, this was rather a lengthy method of attaining

[1] Léon Jantat: *Le pari de Pascal* in La Revue philosophique, Paris, March-April 1940; and Marcel Boll: *L'exploitation du hasard* (3rd ed., Paris 1955) p. 111 ff.
[2] Jacob Bernouilli: *Ars conjectandi* (Basle 1713).

riches, when the time of waiting could be cut short by prophetic selections of the winning lottery ticket. The ancient belief in lucky and unlucky numbers together with many other "recipes" was revived with enthusiasm.

Towards the end of the 18th century, the great magician Cagliostro set up number charts in which lucky numbers were associated with certain dreams. At that time, the French state lottery was using ninety numbers, and Cagliostro advised, for instance, that if you dreamt of asparagus you were bound to win with number 5. Dreams of priests, bathing, lions, and rain were favourably associated with the numbers 7, 31, 76 and 89 respectively, and so on[1].

Dreams and all somnolent states were re-introduced into prophecy, the moment the German physician Anton Mesmer discovered, or rather rediscovered, hypnosis, for hypnosis had probably been known even in antiquity. The fact that, by means of hypnosis, others could be made to do one's bidding, was seized upon by many "prophets" to suggest visions to hypnotised subjects, and women in particular, in the full knowledge that the clientele would rather listen to them than to the "magnetiser" himself.

The master of this art was Mesmer's pupil, the Marquis de Puységur, whose claim to immortality is based on the fact that he was the discoverer of "artificial somnambulism" (1784). It had long been known that some people could walk in their sleep with unusual footsureness, and no one had given a better description of their feats than Shakespeare himself in Act V of Macbeth, where the doctor observes that Lady Macbeth's antics are "beyond my practice".

Since Shakespeare's day, doctors had apparently perfected their "practice", for somnambulistic hallucinations and even prophecies could be artificially induced. The method was similar to that used in "incubation", the artificial creation of dreams practised in Greek temples—particularly in Epidaurus —but it had the advantage that the hypnotist, unlike the "incubator", kept the medium under his control.

One of the Marquis de Puységur's prophetic mediums was a young girl from the Black Forest, who predicted all the horrors

[1] Marcel Boll: *L'Occultisme devant la Science* (3rd ed., Paris 1951), p. 29 f.

of the French Revolution well in advance. Baroness Henriette Louise d'Oberkirch, a friend of the German poets Goethe and Wieland, recorded in her *Memoirs* how, during a somnambulistic session in Strasbourg, the Black Forest girl with the help of the Marquis de Puységur, managed to scare the daylight out of an old soldier.[1] (In fact, the girl did no more than confirm and elaborate the well-known prophecies of Cazotte, but her "somnambulistic revelations" obviously had a very much greater effect than the philosopher Cazotte ever managed to produce by himself.)

Clairvoyance and hypnotic prophecies remained the fashion until well into the 19th century. Though the universities and academies condemned all spiritualistic phenomena as sheer black magic, mystics like Kierkegaard and even such critical minds as Schopenhauer continued to believe in them. As always, spiritualism took three forms: communion with the dead, i.e. the temporary resurrection of the past; telepathy, i.e. bridging distances; and divination, i.e. bridging time. Particularly competent mediums were masters of all three branches of the art, while others, less skilled, specialised in two or even only one branch.

The decline of divination

However, from the middle of the 19th century onwards, the third branch of spiritualism, i.e. divination, which was previously the most highly esteemed, fell into a decline. Prophets and prophetesses became rarer, and above all they lost social status. It was a bad sign, indeed, that the despised Gypsies were increasingly taking over the function of fortune-telling. While prophets had once been respected men and women, their craft had fallen into the hands of ragged old women and tramps, whose customers had to keep an eye on their valuables while consulting them. Moreover, the methods of prophecy reverted to what had always been considered the lowest forms: palmistry, crystal-gazing, fortune-telling from cards or from tea-leaves. The new practitioners—women almost without exception— drew the vast majority of their clientele from the lower middle

[1] *Mémoires de la Baronne d'Oberkirch* (London 1852) Vol. III.

classes, and what few customers from the higher strata of society they attracted, stole to them in dead secret, and pretended to even their closest friends that the whole business was far beneath them.

The situation resembled that of the late Greek period, when Plutarch had complained of the decline of the oracle, and that of the late Renaissance when astrology had fallen on evil days. Pseudo-sciences were no longer needed to predict the future, for there were too many new discoveries in all the real sciences to leave much room for idle speculation (Plate XIV). True, Darwin's theory of evolution and Herbert Spencer's applications of that theory to sociology told the individual little about his own particular future, or that of his children. But nevertheless they cast a collective horoscope for humanity as a whole, and a very favourable one, too. Despite all dangers and setbacks, every-thing was getting better, the world was becoming more and more perfect, so that even the individual was bound to profit in the long run. The idea of progress had vanquished the profes-sional pessimists, and when the year 1881 approached, no one rushed into the cellars or fell down on his knees, despite the fact that, 500 years earlier, Mother Shipton had proclaimed that the end of the world would come at that date.[1] People had begun to laugh at the superstition of earlier ages.

At the turn of the century in 1900, it looked very much as if *Finis* could be written to all the magical, mystical, and imag-inary prophetic methods that had obsessed even the most intelligent minds for 5000 years. A new age, in which all things, past, present and future, would be based on the voice of reason alone seemed to have dawned. The French encyclopedia *Nouveau Larousse Illustré* had this to say about astrology in 1898: "It has hardly any adherents other than swindlers who play on public credulity, and even these are fast disappearing." The author of this mistaken belief was, however, careful to add: "From time to time a resurgence of mysticism or of diletantism may well produce a revival of astrology, of all kinds of magic, and of spiritualism."

Our recent past and even the present, fully confirm Larousse's observations.

[1] W. H. Harrison: *Mother Shipton Investigated* (London 1881).

CHAPTER 2

The Language of the Stars

*T*WENTIETH CENTURY ATTEMPTS TO PROBE INTO THE
future are of two kinds. There are, first of all, the many
scientific, and particularly economic, methods of prediction in
specialised fields, which will be discussed in subsequent chapters.
Side by side with these there exist completely childish techniques of prophecy, the like of which have not been known for the
past 250 years. Even where they appeal to reason, these methods
are an irrational mixture of crude superstition and traditional
misconceptions that take us back thousands of years. No
attempt whatsoever has been made to add anything new, and
the most characteristic attributes of this kind of prophecy is its
atavism, its uncritical reversion to outworn conceptions of the
past.

Its second attribute is commercialisation. This, too, is not
really anything new, for prophecy has always been a kind of
business. Prophetic services are needed by a great many people,
and these services must be paid for by those who use them. But
lately the "profession" has become a large-scale industry practised in the most unlikely quarters and particularly in newspapers and magazines.

There are many plausible reasons for this strange phenomenon. To some extent, it may be a simple reaction to the
rationalism of the 19th century. While the revolution which has
been changing the Newtonian world picture ever since 1900 has
made some people more sceptical, it has simply made others
more credulous. Scientific laws which our textbooks have taught
us to look upon as eternal truths have collapsed like ninepins, and
new ones still lack the authority that their predecessors enjoyed.
Scientists have grown a little more circumspect and no longer
dare to proclaim general laws with the facility of their 19th
century predecessors. Because of these developments, laymen
have begun to feel that it is impossible to distinguish truth from
hypothesis. Now, laymen have always been sticklers for

certainty, and where truth is uncertain, they will accept anything that is presented as being simple and sure.

Things are made more difficult for them still by the fact that science has become increasingly mathematical, and couches its findings in terms which laymen cannot possibly hope to understand, however vaguely. Admittedly, even the 19th century laws of thermodynamics were quite beyond them, but these laws could, at least, be presented in popular form. Those days are past, and the gap had to be filled by something else, perhaps only temporarily, for ignorance is merely a matter of habit. If only we read or hear a formula mentioned often enough, we begin to think that we really understand it. Modern children will tell you about the splitting of atoms as though they had observed the process personally.

Prophetic utterances were given a great impetus by the two World Wars. True, there had been no shortage of large-scale wars even in the 18th and 19th centuries but previous military campaigns had always been confined to limited theatres, decisive battles had usually lasted for no more than one or two days, and —above all—between the wars, there were periods of relative peace. People did not have that permanent fear of the next cataclysm which is so characteristic of the Cold War, during which governments have managed to keep mankind on tenterhooks from moment to moment. This constant fear of war, which had no parallel in earlier times—except perhaps the general dread of the Huns—is fertile soil, indeed, for the business of prophecy. Frightened people cling to the least semblance of reassurance, and prefer even the worst prediction to eternal uncertainty.

Symbolism triumphant

Mass anxiety leads to a flight into mysticism and the shadowy no-man's-land between this world and the beyond, in which man consorts, and sometimes becomes fused, with ghosts, gods and demons. A purely religious form of mysticism, which is divorced from man's mundane curiosity, appeals to only the few, since human beings are generally neither capable nor willing to exclude their rational faculties completely; what most men can do is to blunt these faculties: reason becomes overshadowed by faith and by gullibility, becomes degraded into unreason, and frequently expresses itself in terrible absurdities and childishness.

By invoking their mystical insights, the victims of mysticism fall into apparent reveries which, when all is said and done, are no more than idle dreams. Nevertheless, such mystically tinged reveries are held in high regard even by educated people, particularly when the "visions" are studded with mythological allusions, with ancient legends, and—better still—with elements of Red Indian or Negro folklore. The very word "myth" is enough to turn even the most tarnished alloy into the pure gold not of poetry or legend, but of down-to-earth reality since, as a modern psychologist has put it, "myth lives within us, because it is an archetypal property of us all, a lasting inheritance from time immemorial." Those who object to this kind of phrasemongering are considered to be grossly out of step with the times.

The bridge between the mystical world and the world of reality is said to be the symbol. Man does not have to construct this bridge, it is projected into him from another world, and, with some knowledge of signs, he can learn to understand its eternal *sign-ificance*.[1] A good symbol is therefore a sign that helps us to understand past and future, and the true prophet will look upon the symbol as his essential tool. By using symbolic language he not only makes himself understood most easily, but he is most readily believed.

This symbol madness is the scourge of the 20th century. Its germs have entered the body politic and not only come from the profound mystical depths, but also from very pedestrian and terrestrial sources, not least from all those advertisements which scream at us day and night. Thus the up-to-date prophet cannot afford to ignore the symbolic significance of dreams about detergents (the modern equivalent of dreams about angelic purity), or of dreams about "Halt" signals which nowadays warn many a dreamer to tread the strait and narrow path.

By and large, however, professional prophets prefer to deal in more time-hallowed symbols, and continue to instruct their

[1] Werner Kemper: *Der Traum und seine Be-Deutung* (Hamburg 1935).

clients in the use of high-sounding, if esoteric, professional terms borrowed from antiquity. They know full well that their illiterate clientele loves nothing better than to be blinded with science. In the words of Cardinal Caraffa—*populus vult decipi— decipiatur!*

Lion into Crab

This is one of the main reasons why astrology, after its setbacks in previous centuries, has once again become the fashion. Modern astrology, as we have seen, is based on notions first propounded by the Alexandrian scholar Claudius Ptolemy in his *Tetrabiblos*, some 1800 years ago. But perhaps to say even that, is to be too generous to "modern" astrology, for we might be implying that contemporary star-gazers, though astronomically backward themselves, are nevertheless the intellectual heirs of a great master of the past. In fact, if Ptolemy could see them, he would turn in his grave.

Astrologers still see the sky as it looked to observers in the Eastern Mediterranean 2000 years ago. At that time, the vernal equinox stood in Ram (Aries), one of twelve sectors of the apparent orbit of the sun. The subsequent sectors (from west to east) were called the Bull (Taurus); the Twins (Gemini); the Crab (Cancer); the Lion (Leo); the Virgin (Virgo); and (in autumn and winter): the Scales (Libra); the Scorpion (Scorpio); the Archer (Sagittarius); the Sea-Goat (Capricornus); the Waterman (Aquarius); and the Fishes (Pisces). Unfortunately for astrologers, the ecliptic (the sun's apparent orbit through the stars) is not uniformly inclined to the celestial equator, and hence undergoes fluctuations from a minimum of 22° 54′ to a maximum of 25° 21′ and back again over a period of 26,000 years. At present the ecliptic is tilted at an angle of 23° 27′ and in the course of a century this angle changes at the rate of 50″. Since it is at present decreasing, the minimum inclination will occur in 6600. Thereafter it will increase to reach a maximum of 25° 21′ in 19,600, and so on.

Small though these fluctuations appear to be, they nevertheless work great changes in the appearance of the celestial vault. Since Ptolemy's day—or more precisely since Hipparchus

22. Zodiac from the *Lucidarius* (Augsburg, 1479). The universe was still geo-centric: sun, moon, and planets revolve about the earth.

(150 B.C.) on whose observation Ptolemy's system was based —the Zodiac has shifted by an entire "House", i.e. by a full twelfth of the sun's orbit. Thus, while Hipparchus observed the sun entering Aries in March, we have to wait one month longer for this event to occur. All the other signs of the Zodiac have been shifted correspondingly.

Astrologers have taken no notice of these changes, and their predictions are therefore based on the stellar picture which existed 2000 years ago, and not on the real position of the stars today. For them, a man born between 22nd March and 20th April is born under Aries and not under Pisces, and so on. Since the particular "House" in which a man is born is said to stamp him for life, this slight discrepancy ought to worry astrologers far more than it does. Thus, all Pisceans born during past centuries should have been Arians, while astrologers have continued to predict their future as though they were "Fishes".

True, it would not be too difficult to correct this historical
error—which, needless to say, does not mean that astrological
predictions would become more relevant—by modifying the
traditional picture. Some astrologers have, in fact, done so, but
their colleagues and the vast mass of astromancers have chosen to
ignore them. They realise that in so fragile a structure as
astrology, the slightest tremor may cause the whole thing to
collapse like a house of cards.

Other astrologers have tried to find a way out of the impasse
by asserting that the signs of the Zodiac have after-effects
which are not influenced by mere astronomical shifts. This
explanation reminds one of the theory which was fashionable
with doctors and biologists in the 17th century: the doctrine of
telegony according to which all the children of one mother but
of different fathers resembled the father of the first child, since
on first pregnancy the womb was so modified as to affect all
future progeny.

Nowadays telegony is a mere historical curiosity while the
doctrine of stellar after-effects, which is even more preposterous,
continues in full sway. While telegony was at least theoretically
possible, the stellar hypothesis is not even that, since the astrological Zodiac of Hipparchus was not, of course, the first. The
precession of the equinoxes had by then been occurring for
millions of years, and there is no means of saying which particular position must be called the "original" one. Thus every
new-born child can be said to have been born under all kinds of
signs, and a horoscope based on any one sign must, therefore, be
dismissed as utterly worthless—even within the framework of
astrology.

Nor does this exhaust the (tremendous) list of astronomical
objections to astrology.[1] Another objection is that, since the
different stars and planets are all at different distances from the
earth, their alleged effects on mankind cannot possibly be equal.
Astrologers, on the other hand, continue to look upon the
Zodiac as a circle that is at all times equi-distant from the House
of an individual's birth. Mathematical considerations do not
seem to worry them at all.

[1] Paul Couderc: *L'Astrologie* (Paris 1951) p. 52 ff.

23. Mercury and his children. From an English astrological calendar of 1503.

Good constellations and bad

Clearly, therefore, modern astrology has no point of contact with astronomical science, and, if such contact ever existed, it was definitely lost as growing astronomical knowledge was increasingly forced to refute every one of the astrologers' absurd premisses. Not that astrologers are perturbed: they have withdrawn into a symbolic ivory tower where, as we must admit, they live in great comfort. Astrology, far from bothering about real stars, simply operates with signs, words, and symbols which, though derived from ancient astrology, have no real relevance to any known processes.

The astrologer's is an extremely primitive faith which is nowadays completely devoid of the philosophical content and poetic beauty once associated with it. Socially speaking, astrology has become a parlour game with seven pieces (sun, moon, and the five planets of antiquity) on twelve fields (the "Houses" of the Zodiac). Some astrologers have raised the

number of pieces to nine by including the planets Uranus and
Neptune, and others, more "progressive" still, to as many as
ten by including the planet Pluto (discovered in 1930), as well.
But even these great innovators will admit the predominance of
the first seven pieces. Every house of the Zodiac is governed by a
planet and, according to the classical rules, Mercury, Mars, and
Venus act as "rulers" twice a year.

Every planet—and the sun is considered one, as well—has
certain characteristics which, in the main, correspond with the
characteristics of the Greek and Roman gods after whom they
have been named. Astrologers have always been optimists and
"good" stars are therefore in the clear majority. Thus Sun,
Moon, Jupiter, and Venus are considered to be generally favourable to men and only Saturn and Mars to be unfavourable.
Mercury, like its Babylonian predecessor Nâbu—the Royal Star
—is a rather unreliable fellow: while he means men no real
harm, he causes ugly and nervous people to be born when he is
"in the ascendant".

The signs of the Zodiac, too, have characteristics corresponding to their names. This becomes clearest in those named
after animals, and in the effects these signs have on men. Thus
men born under Aries are said to be much more temperamental
than those born under Taurus, who far from being fighting
bulls, are, in fact, tame domestic oxen; the protegees of Taurus
are diligent, careful, reflective, patient, and even a little
slow.

In addition to the twelve classical constellations which, by the
way, play a rather insignificant role in the appearance of the sky,
some astrologers also include a number of stars in their prophecies; Sirius, Vega and Antares are considered particularly
effective in horoscopes. Still, even by considering no more than
the seven planets and the twelve signs of the Zodiac, a considerable number of prophetic combinations can be produced. Here,
too, luck is generally with mankind. Thus houses I and X (Aries
and Capricornus) are most propitious; houses IV and VII
(Cancer and Libra) are only very slightly less favourable; and
houses II, V and XI (Taurus, Leo, and Aquarius) are fairly satisfactory. House VIII (Scorpio) is a little disappointing and only
the other houses are downright bad, particularly houses VI and
XII (Virgo and Pisces).

24. Saturn, the evil star, bringing mankind troubles, imprisonment, illness, and death. (From *Meister des Hausbuches*).

Still, these general characteristics are not enough for casting horoscopes, and astrologers, being most anxious to please their customers, therefore add careful calculations of the position of the planets inside a given house. If two planets are in a direct radial line or separated by an angle of at most 10°, astrologers speak of "conjunctions". Conjunctions of the sun and the moon are favourable, and so are sextiles (angles of 60°), and trigons (120°). On the other hand, right angles and above all "oppositions" (180°) are unfavourable. These additional considerations by no means exhaust the rules of the game. Houses could be sub-divided into decans (10 days), and there were other tricks of the trade, too numerous to mention. The more complicated the tools, the more accurate apparently the look into the future, and the greater, certainly, the mystification of the customers.

Birth or Conception?

Try as they will, however, astrologers can do little to meet any serious criticism. Even if we ignore their astronomical ignorance and consider them as merely playing a game with symbols, we still have the right to demand a minimum of logic from them. But what we get is the precise opposite. The over-confident astrologer thinks nothing of over-riding what little knowledge we have of hereditary processes, and ignores all the findings of modern genetics. True, when a good customer makes a point of asking for it, the obliging astrologer may provide him with his parents' or forefathers' horoscopes, but such horoscopes have no more than historical value and can have no influence on the present client, whose future is solely determined by celestial events at the moment of his own birth, and not by such trifles as genes and chromosomes.

If that assumption were correct, everyone born at the same hour would have to have an identical future, for not only do the stars determine his luck, they also provide him with a fixed ability of making use of his opportunities. Now, ever since an exact record has been kept of birth dates, and even of the hours and minutes of birth, the asininity of this contention must have become obvious to even the most naive of astromancers.

Children born in the same hour and in the same locality very soon develop distinct characteristics and begin to live quite different lives, and even twins who, astrologically speaking, are born simultaneously, rarely follow identical paths.

Nevertheless, astrologers are absolutely opposed to obstetric interventions, which, they claim, may affect the child's entire future life by delaying or precipitating the "natural" hour of its birth, thus causing it to be born under a wrong star. These dangers were stressed by the master-astrologer Ptolemy in the Third Book of his *Tetrabiblos*, where we can read that: "when the fruit is fully matured, nature begins to move it, and in such a way that the child is born under the heavenly sign which corresponds with the first constellation at the time of conception".

Actually, modern astrologers ignore the time of conception altogether, though one would have thought that the stars would determine an individual's future at that moment rather than at birth. Biologists will tell you that, maternal accidents apart, little can change in an embryo's potentialities after conception. Even such factors as intra-uterine infections and maternal tuberculosis are today considered to be smaller than they were previously thought to be. In any case, biologically speaking, there can be no doubt that life begins with conception and not with birth. It would therefore be more logical to cast all horoscopes accordingly.

At this point, however, astrological science breaks down, and for the simple reason that the hour of conception cannot be accurately determined except in such rare events as rape or isolated acts of copulation. Neither by chemical investigations nor from the appearance and weight of a baby can the date of conception be deduced with certainty, and slight errors might, of course, make a great difference to the stars. Thus a child might mistakenly be said to have been conceived under jovial Jupiter instead of saturnine Saturn. While some astrologers have acknowledged the existence of this problem, when they explain away false predictions with the glib excuse that the birth horoscope was vitiated by the unfavourable hour of conception, most experts prefer to keep silent on this equivocal subject, or to deny its relevance, altogether. Needless to say, this viewpoint greatly simplifies their prophetic practice.

Political astrology

Though astrology is creaking in all its foundations, astrologers never cease from patching up its façade with the latest gloss. No political event escapes their keen glance. Thus, in the summer of 1956, when Nasser's nationalisation of the Suez Canal caused an international crisis, a well-known astrological journal was quick to predict the impending collapse of the British Empire. Britain would continue to wage isolated colonial wars in order to stave off the inevitable, but her case was utterly hopeless. Moreover, the Crown was in serious peril as well.

One of the main arguments on which this gloomy prophecy was based, was the Queen's own horoscope. This is how the

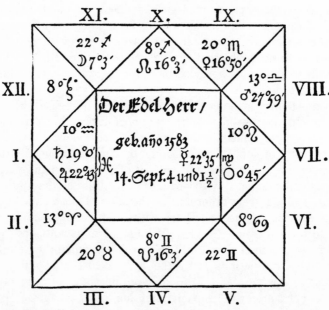

25. Kepler's horoscope of Wallenstein (1608). Kepler failed to predict Wallenstein's assassination.

astrologist Carl Heinrich Huter read it: "Anyone looking at the horoscope of Queen Elizabeth II will be deeply stirred by the ominous position of Saturn at the beginning of the tenth field, for all rulers and politicians with Saturn in this position have either been overthrown or have abdicated of their own free will. There is not a single known exception in the whole of world history."[1]

According to the same source, the horoscope of Anthony Eden, then Prime Minister of Britain, was not much more favourable either. In Eden's horoscope—as in the Queen's—Mars appeared in the first house, which clearly pointed to an increase in world tension. Moreover: "The conjunction of Moon and Saturn under the sign of Scorpio is remarkable, for Eden's Saturn, 25 degrees in Scorpio, is almost identical with Queen Elizabeth's Saturn which is 24 degrees in Scorpio."

On the basis of these perturbing cosmic signs, our perceptive astrologer came to the further conclusion that "after the abdication of the British Queen and of her Prime Minister there will occur world-shaking events, and changes in the economic, political and social structure". *Inter alia*, all over the world, the United States included, the oil magnates would be eliminated, and their fortunes nationalised. In this and other ways international peace would be assured without the world falling victim to Bolshevism.

In the same edition of the paper, the author is unfortunately forced to take a less optimistic view of the more distant future. "Immediately after the final collapse of England, America—whose planet is Uranus, the symbol of the Aquarist age of the next 2000 years to come—will rule supreme, but 100 years later supremacy will pass first to the Slavs, and in a further 150 years to the Mongols whose advancing yellow armies will flood across Russia and Western Europe. Before that time, a large proportion of the European population will have emigrated to North and South America, with the consequent disappearance of national states. Thereafter two gigantic continents, two ways of life, will confront each other culturally, economically, and militarily: America vs. Asia-Europe-Africa. Such is the future of the world."[2]

[1] C. H. Huter: *Babylons Untergang* in "Das neue Zeitalter," (Stuttgart, Year 8, No. 36, 31 August 1956).
[2] C. H. Huter: *Das Horoskop Englands* in "Das Neue Zeitalter," 31 August 1956.

This small sample from the repertoire of a leading astrologer makes it clear that horoscopes go much further than the mere cure of love-sicknesses, and that they often fly off at a tangent into distant times and worlds. The further the times, the less binding, of course, are the predictions, and no one can say with certainty that the Mongols will not in fact rule Europe in 2200. Still, not all astrologers are equally circumspect, and French astrologers, in particular, must be noted for their great bravery in making short-term predictions.

At the beginning of 1950, for instance, the official journal of the French Order of Astrologers announced that the stars had made it clear that the Fourth Republic could not survive for more than a total of three years and nine months from its inception, i.e. it would give way to a stronger system not later than the 13th July 1950. When July 1950 passed uneventfully, astrologers were not discouraged. True to Voltaire's dictum that "no astrologer should claim the exclusive privilege of being wrong all the time", they realised that, if only they continued to consult the stars often enough, they might come up with a real winner. Thus, when after the 1956 French elections the Socialist Prime Minister Guy Mollet fell out with the leader of the Radical Party, Mendès-France, the astrologer A. Martineau[1] explained that this was only to be expected from the fact that the two politicians were both born under Capricorn, which often led to close friendship but equally often to enmity. Moreover the election date had been very close to their respective birthdays and had fallen on a Monday—a very unhappy day for Capricornians. Less astrologically but more politically informed observers could have explained the facts more simply, if not more elegantly.

As a rule, however, astrologers rarely dabble in politics. Although they have been known to plug a particular party line on occasion, political astrology is far less harmful than some other branches of "applied astrology", unless of course maniacs like Hitler really start to believe in it.

Moreover, most of the "correct" horoscopes of leading politicians which astrologers often boast about, were in fact drawn up after the event or at best at a time when the character of the personality in question was already fully formed. But even then,

[1] *Astres* (Paris) March 1956.

errors have to be explained away, as in the posthumous astrological report on the Emperor Franz-Joseph of Austria: "In the Emperor's horoscope there occurs an important concentration of lights and of three planets in the fourth celestial quadrant. Sun, Moon, and Saturn in Leo point to a ruler of fame. The ascending planet in Libra reflects the monarch's work for world peace and internal harmony—a labour which was notoriously unsuccessful. This is explained by the position of Mars in his horoscope."[1]

On the other hand, those rare cases in which a famous man or a famous woman completely fulfils the "promise of the stars" are heralded as great triumphs of astrology, and no one bothers to ask questions about the real reasons that made these "triumphs" possible. An example is the case of the Duchess of Windsor, the wife of the ex-King Edward VIII who says in her memoirs[2] that when she was still known as Bessie Wallis Warfield, a New York astrologer told her that she would marry three times, and attain great power when she was 40-50 years old. Her power would be connected with a man.

Now it is not too difficult to predict that a vivacious American woman of her temperament and social standing would contract three marriages, since two divorces, under these conditions, are statistically more probable than a single marriage. As for her power, if by power we understand political influence, this is precisely what she lost when her marriage caused her third husband to abdicate. True she has achieved a far greater position than she could have expected in her youth, but this is not what the astrologer could have meant. Thus even this "true" prediction, which is often adduced as evidence in favour of astrology, was anything but prophetic.

Collective Horoscopes

Obviously the stars move with the times, and affect the latest achievements of science. In ancient Rome, whenever technical

[1] P. L. Winter: *Leitfaden der Astrologie* in *Mächte des Schicksals* (Vienna 1953) p. 432 f.
[2] The Duchess of Windsor: *The Heart has its Reasons* (N.Y. 1956).

innovations—for instance, canals—were introduced, they were entrusted to a new god or goddess. While astrologers do not emulate this noble example—though the modern star catalogue with its scores of millions of stars would clearly enable them to do so—they prefer to burden their old trusties with new tasks.

Thus a modern textbook of astrology tells us that House III, in Gemini under Mercury, is particularly favourable to radio installations—no wonder when we realise that Mercury has forever been the patron saint of traffic and communications. Diplomatic matters, the theatre, and education come under House V (in Leo under the Sun), while Church matters, parliamentary matters, the Navy, and scientific discoveries fall under House IX (in Sagittarius under Jupiter), etc.

Such generalities, however, do little to satisfy the quest of those who seek information about personal or love affairs. These people nowadays turn for their information to the popular press, which is often hard put to it to fill an entire issue with social scandal and cooking recipes, and welcomes any opportunity of pleasing its readers in simple ways. Thus many papers publish daily horoscopes that are apparently compiled with the other news. In fact, they might just as well publish horoscopes for a year ahead, for as we know, the stars are eternal. But people who believe in the stars, generally prefer their bits of wisdom in small doses, and like to have their fortunes told from day to day, even when it is a question of contracting such long-term obligations as marriage. It seems logical that people who believe in the stars would consult an astrologer for years in advance, but this type of prophecy seems to have fallen into disuse. Mass media have changed astrology from the kind of prophetic message it used to be into a mere set of mechanical directions for immediate implementation. Only on special occasions, such as New Year's Day, do some astrologers still make more far-reaching predictions.

The Planets of Chance

Though astrology has lost much of its dramatic quality and has, as it were, cut off its grey prophet's beard, it has become highly specialised. There is, for instance a special branch of astrology which deals exclusively with the race-course, and which has much in common with other tipsters' methods, except that it introduces special variables—the stars.

Oddly enough, astrologers prefer to read the horoscopes of the jockeys rather than of the horses. After all, the stars which have so much influence on our fate, ought to have an equally great influence on other creatures also. Moreover, horse horoscopes should not be too difficult to read since the hour and day of birth of all race-horses is carefully recorded in the stud book, and their chance of winning should therefore be eminently predictable from the stars

Be that as it may, horse horoscopes are not in popular demand, possibly because they would complicate the work of astrologers by introducing an unnecessary complication.

As it is, if astrologers bother to cast even the jockey's horoscope, it is only as an afterthought, for it is the gambler's and not the jockey's lucky day which really counts. Similarly careful people who, needless to say, make a point of *buying* lottery tickets only on lucky days, will make doubly sure of success by only participating in lotteries that are also *drawn* on lucky days.

Still all these considerations are merely secondary, what matters most is the gambler's own luck. Only in one field do modern astrologers rely on more "objective" data: in the stock exchange, which was apparently born under a star of its own, though, of course, stocks and shares must still be bought and sold on the client's lucky days. The successful speculator will therefore do well to synchronise his own horoscope with that of the stock exchange. Once that is done, the rest is child's play and heavy losses can easily be avoided. Fortunately, this branch of astrology has few adherents, since their combined psychological pressure might otherwise play havoc with the markets. Stock exchange astrology is a very difficult science, understood by only a handful of experts, who usually base their special prophecies on Jupiter and Venus. Thus we can read in a Parisian Astrological Monthly[1] that "since Jupiter is trine to Venus, the third, fifth, eighth, tenth, thirteenth, nineteenth and twenty-fourth days of March will see a rise in the market, but the market will be dull on the second, sixth, seventh, twelfth, and

[1] *Astres* 56 (Paris, March 1956)

thirty-first days of that month". For more detailed information still, the readers are referred to the special Stock Exchange Bulletin published by the same editor. Strangely enough, few of the experts seem to have been able to amass any vast fortunes for themselves with the help of Jupiter and Venus, but the very existence of a "Special Stock Exchange Bulletin" indicates that others are not deterred by this odd circumstance.

Other astrological specialities are more dangerous, and particularly those which dabble in medicine. Unlike their mediaeval predecessors, modern astrologers do not maintain that they can produce miraculous cures, but they do claim to know from the stars on what days cures are particularly effective or ineffective. Moreover, astrological herbalists publish monthly bulletins of particularly favourable medicinal plants and of the lucky days on which they should be used. The planets themselves are alleged to produce certain diseases and to cure others. Thus Uranus under the sign of Cancer causes colic; Mercury under the sign of Aries causes facial neuralgia, Venus under the sign of the Aquarist causes varicose veins, etc. Even benign Jupiter can cause many complaints according to the house in which it rises. "If this were not the case," a critical astrologer pointed out, "one twelfth of all mankind would be free from all physical ills".[1]

This notion that health and disease are governed by the stars, induces many patients to delay medical treatment, and to use dangerous medicaments until the stars become more favourable to them. It can moreover turn believers into rank hypochondriacs who spend their lives running around with a Saturn-complex. Astrological medicine, far from being a harmless game, must be considered a particularly stupid and dangerous form of quackery.

The balance sheet

Although astrology is based on a coherent framework, astrologers, like scientists, are often at loggerheads with one another. For this reason, we may read the most divergent ex-

[1] *La Médecine astrologique*. Astrologie-Psychoanalyse (Paris) January 1956, p. 153.

planations about the effects of the stars during one and the same period (see p. 112).

Contradictory astrological predictions are printed daily by the million, and are certainly read by millions of people. Who are the suppliers of this prophetic industry? At first, they were pure amateurs who tried to gain an extra living in this way, but as demand for their services grew, they turned professional. Nowadays, astrology has become a large-scale industry, and big agencies do nothing but supply the press with horoscopes for the day, the week, or the month.

Unlike special astrological journals, most daily papers do not employ a special sub-editor or specialised staff to run their astrological department. They find it much simpler to print the ready-made horoscopes supplied by the agencies instead. These they publish with a lack of concern that they would find distasteful in any other column.

Most editors hold that the whole business is sheer nonsense, for which they cannot accept any responsibility—moral or otherwise. But whether they like it or not, they are to blame that astrology is so widespread today.

Investigations in America and Europe have thrown greater light on this subject. The first great wave of collective horoscopes in newspapers and journals started in English-speaking countries after the First World War, at about the same time that crossword puzzles became fashionable. Like crossword puzzles, astrological predictions were at first considered a mere game, until countless letters from readers proved that they were being taken very seriously. From then on, there was no going back. After the Second World War, astrology became more popular still. A questionnaire prepared in 1943 showed that in the United States alone five million people act according to astrological advice, and pay 200 million dollars annually for the privilege.[1]

At present, more than two thousand U.S. dailies and weeklies run a regular astrological column, and there are a further twenty magazines which deal exclusively or mainly with astrological questions. The most popular of these magazines has a circulation of more than half a million copies. The radio, too, used to run an astrological programme, until the U.S. authori-

[1] Paul Couderc: *L'Astrologie*, p. 106

Predictions for *Aries* published in Paris during the same week.

Name of Journal	Portents	Business	Home	Love	Health
Elle	Lucky number: 3; Colour: bright red; Lucky Days: Monday, Friday.	Rather confused, especially for those in creative professions. They will waste much time on useless tasks, and be unable to do their jobs.	Relations between friends and male relatives will be cordial, but women will quarrel among themselves. Questions of self-regard will lead to arguments.	Your charm and vivacity of spirit will help you towards superficial success in the sentimental sphere, but you will tire of your own gaiety.	You will suffer from headaches, probably due to eye strain. You may need spectacles, but refuse to wear them for reasons of vanity.
Jours de France	Lucky number 48; Lucky symbols: red and violet bouquets, pink pearls, marmalade cats.	Much energy and daring will enable you to begin something new, or perhaps to tackle a commercial task. Unforeseen factors will play an important part but require considerable reflection.	Approach your relatives and give them proof of your affection. Be careful not to break with them. Luck though small children. Prepare a pretty room for them.	Chance will bring you into contact with nervous people whom you must try not to contradict, or with adventurous spirits who will give you harmful advice.	Rest during digestion. Avoid bathing or violent exercise. Do not expose yourself to risks.
Images du Monde	Lucky number: 3; Lucky colour: auburn	Money, Work: good.	3rd decan: be constantly on your guard, particularly when travelling or when making important decisions. 1st decan will prove a good week, which will even favour unforeseen profit.	Average	Average
Noir et Blanc	Lucky numbers: 10, 55; Lucky day: Thursday	Organise!	—	Weakness will not displease	Renewed stomach upsets.

ties clamped down on this form of popular edification. Nowadays enterprising radio-astrologers are reduced to using Mexican transmitters. All in all, the number of astrologers in the United States alone is said to amount to 30,000.

High though this number may appear to us, America runs a poor second to rationalist France—at least in this respect. Officially, divination of all sorts has been prohibited in France for more than 100 years. The penal code[1] stipulates maximum fines for professional diviners and dream interpreters (*persons qui font métier de diviner, de pronostiquer ou d'expliquer les songes*) and imprisonment for up to five days for fortune tellers. All instruments, props, and costumes are subject to consfication. The law of 4 October 1945, increased the term of imprisonment to eight days in the case of habitual offenders. All these laws notwithstanding, France is riddled with thousands of professional prophets.

According to a report of the Paris Prefect of Police, 3460 astrological and palmist establishments were registered in Paris alone, in 1935.[2] The most famous pre-war astrologer in Paris used to receive 1400 letters a day, and wrote 5000 replies with the help of a staff of 50. One of his colleagues, who was involved in a case of fraud in 1939, had a net annual income of 400,000 francs, which by modern standards is roughly equivalent to £7000 (free of tax). According to a report by the French National Institute of Statistics, 100,000 Parisians regularly consult 6000 astrologers, clairvoyants, and other fortune-tellers. In the whole of France the total number of professional fortune tellers is given by the same source as 34,000, with a total income of 34,000 million francs (roughly 30 million pounds in 1955.)[3] Apart from the many astrological columns in newspapers and journals, France can boast a host of astrological publications, the largest of which has a circulation of more than 100,000 copies.

In view of these figures and those for some other countries, we can make the conservative estimate that the annual world income of fortune-tellers is at least 300 million pounds, of which by far the largest part is earned by astrologers. This sum seems

[1] *Code pénal*, Art 479 ff—Law of 28 April 1832.
[2] *Révue internationale de Sociologie*, Sept.–Dec. 1939.
[3] *Science et Vie* (Paris), Sept. 1955, p. 72.

tremendous, but then human beings spend much vaster sums on much more harmful pastimes. However, the question remains: Do the astrologers really give their customers any return for their investment?

Is astrology scientific?

For centuries, serious scientists who have looked at this question objectively, have invariably and unequivocally come to a negative conclusion. There is no evidence whatsoever that the stars affect man's fate to any perceptible or verifiable extent— neither their past, their present nor their future. Even were astrology to be brought fully up-to-date, and cleared of all its erroneous ideas, the stars would still leave man severely alone.

Thus, in 1949, the German Astronomical Society, one of the most respected in the world, dismissed astrology as a mixture of superstition, quackery and big business, adding that even those astrological circles which have rejected the stupidities of fair-ground astrology, and which consider themselves purely scientific associations, have never provided evidence of their scientific methods and results.

An American commission, under the chairmanship of the astronomer Bart J. Box of Harvard University, after having declared its readiness to test all cases submitted to them by astrologers, concluded that not a single one of the influences attributed to the stars by so-called serious astrologers could be demonstrated. Similar conclusions were reached by a Belgian committee, set up in 1949 by the Rector of Ghent University (*Comité Belge pour l'investigation scientifique des phénomènes réputés paranormaux*), which consisted of thirty reputable scientists belonging to various fields.

Finally, according to the evidence of the American Society for Psychological Research (1940), "there is no evidence that astrology has any value whatever in revealing the past, the present or the future fate of any human being, and there is not the slightest reason for believing that social events can be predicted by astrology". Similar pronouncements have also been published by UNESCO and by many teachers, writers, and scientists.

True, no amount of expert derision is real evidence against the claims of astrologers. Still, the onus of proof is on the proponents rather than on their critics, and astrologers are notoriously (if understandably) loath to support their contentions with even the merest shreds of evidence.

The only argument which astrologers can muster is the fact that, despite all their alleged contradictions and failures, millions of people, and by no means the least educated people either, continue to believe in their messages. In other words, astrology must fulfil a deep human need. Now, the attraction of astrology for people who are not normally inclined to mysticism and magic is easily explained by the fact that astrology is a system, and, moreover, a very simple system, that any layman can understand. Like all systems, even the most strictly scientific, astrology is based on axioms, i.e. on basic assumptions that cannot be proved theoretically. Essentially, the axioms of astrology are (1) that everything in nature, and consequently in human life, follows a regular course, and (2) that the stars have a decisive influence on terrestrial processes.

The first of these axioms, which philosophers call determinism, is no speciality of astrology. Even if modern science has discarded rigid 19th century determinsim, determinism nevertheless continues as a cardinal principle of science, for without it no laws could be established. But in fact, astrology is not really deterministic, for it does not exclude human volition. The stars, even though they might cause us trouble, particularly in love affairs, are at heart very decent, and prefer to leave us a great deal of scope. They limit man's free will but do not utterly reject it or negate it on principle.

After all, astrologers take it for granted that men are always faced with alternatives, for why otherwise would they consult the stars? Astrologers can tell them what is most propitious for them, but the final choice is their own and they can, if they so desire, defy the stars by eating the wrong things in the wrong "houses", by starting love-affairs under the wrong planet, or even by buying lottery tickets with an unlucky number on an unlucky day. They are completely free to do all this, but, of course, they must not blame the stars for the consequences. In other words, astrologers advise their clients to live according to the stars, which, to them, is tantamount to living according to nature. "Live by the stars and you will prosper on earth", is the sum total of all astrological wisdom.

Astrological Morals

Because of this direct personal influence, astrological rules of behaviour must have an individual touch. Thus even when producing collective horoscopes for the daily press and address-ing a large anonymous circle of readers, astrologers nevertheless try to give their message a personal note, or else—to avoid astrological conflicts between, say, the members of a family born under different stars—they simply counsel general peace, harmony, and hard work. Astrological morals are life-positive—men are not born to suffer but must try to do everything possible to counteract what weaknesses certain constellations have endowed them with. They are meant not only to live but to live well. The stars abhor laziness, and all astrological injunctions have a clear activist character. Men must be ambitious, and constantly on the alert.

True, astrologers do not expect their clients to attain riches and fortune by work alone. They may sometimes use ruses or gamble with lucky numbers. In temperate regions, astrologers usually use a temperate language, but in the tropics, where men are often phlegmatic, they have to be shaken out of themselves. Admonitions become commands. In a large Brazilian newspaper, for instance, Sagittarians are ordered, rather than advised, to "stake on number six, your lucky number" during the week of May 20th–26th, 1956, while those born under Virgo and Libra are told summarily: "Do not gamble!"[1]

While all the people in question are not likely to fall over themselves to heed this advice, there is no doubt that astrological counsel, given as it is nowadays on a mass scale, does a great deal to encourage a somewhat robust form of egotism. Frequently the advice is coupled with a call to self-enjoyment, and a life of easy pleasure. We need, therefore, not be surprised

[1] O. Jomal (Rio de Janeiro) 20 May 1956.

that moralists of different persuasion have denounced the stars and their high-spirits as perverters of true morals.

But it is precisely this popular call to selfishness and ease which has contributed more than anything else to the success of astrology. Undoubtedly, the astrological columns of journals and newspapers are read and believed by many, precisely because of this kind of plain speaking. Astrologers are quite blunt about things that are usually concealed and rarely discussed with even one's closest friends: desire, private passion, greed, anxiety, secret hope, and deep longing. Shorn of all astrological claptrap, their utterances are only too human and very well adapted to their readers' mentality. Astrology is not literature; it deals with life as it is lived, or at least as people would like to live it, and even if only the smallest part of a particular prediction comes true, it affects them far more profoundly than the most profound philosophical remark or the most moving drama. It is for this reason that people look at what the stars have to say, at first, perhaps, sceptically, but then with growing conviction. One true prediction, and all the false ones are conveniently forgotten.

And astrology, unlike so many other forms of divination, is not an occult science based on supernatural forces. Astrology is "a science" which rejects miracles and inexplicable phenomena, on principle. It states its axioms openly, and gives written evidence of the way in which it arrives at its conclusions. Every client is at liberty to carry his horoscope home with him, there to read which stars and constellations are responsible for his fortune or misfortune.

All this may sound very absurd, particularly when we go into details, but there can be no doubt that information gained in this way appears to be more reliable than that obtained by such occult practices as necromancy or fortune-telling. Anyone who cares to do so, can study astrology for himself—no special gift is needed.

It is this tendency towards egotism and pseudo-rationalism which must be considered among the main reasons why modern astrology has not turned into a religion. Even in America, where it is notoriously easy to form new sects, belief in the stars lacks any religious character, although it undoubtedly contains elements that belong to religious faith rather than science.

Moreover, astrology, with its belief in the unity of different stellar influences, is by no means irreconcilable with monotheism and needs no religious premisses of its own. If this had not been the case, astrology would have perished in the Middle Ages, at least in Christian countries.

Apart from lacking a common religion, astrologers lack cohesion in other respects also. While there are astrological societies, their membership is very small indeed, compared with the vast number of unorganised believers. Those interested in astrology are generally individualists who have little contact with one another. Thus there has never been an astrological mass movement which could, for instance, have affected the outcome of elections or other public events. That is probably why astrologers have generally been left alone by the authorities. They represent an amorphous, unorganised mass, albeit an enormously large one.

It will never be known how many people really believe in the power of the stars, for even if there were an official census, far to many people would be ashamed to own up. After all, which one of us could swear with certainty that his nearest neighbour has never had his horoscope read? Even so, the estimates compiled in the U.S.A. and France lead one to suspect that at least three per cent of the total population, and probably five per cent of all adults, believe firmly that their future is written in the stars. A frightening number, if we agree that astrology is a form of mental disorder! In addition, there is an even greater number of people who, though not completely convinced of the truth of astrology, nevertheless flirt with it and occasionally act on its advice, particularly if it suits their own book. For this very reason, one must take this international affliction far more seriously than one commonly does, and see to it that its exploiters are not given their head nearly as much as they are.

CHAPTER 3

The World of Dreams

COMPARED WITH ASTROLOGY, DREAM INTERPRETATION plays a very secondary role in modern divination. It has lost much of its previous importance, mainly because its adepts have been unable to keep pace with the commercialisation and vulgarisation of astrology. Moreover, it is not nearly as easy to practise, for while the stars can reveal their general message in the morning paper, not even the greatest prophetic genius can hope to explain all the millions of different dreams readers may have had the night before and the many millions more they may have forgotten. While the ability to remember dreams varies from individual to individual, Kant's opinion[1] that there can be no sleep without dreams is still shared by many modern psychologists.

In any case, the number of people, and particularly of women, who remember their dreams and attribute a measure of prophetic significance to them is large enough to support a special profession, especially in rural areas, where the belief in prophetic dreams is very much more deeply rooted than the belief in astrology. Still, even the most simple-minded country yokel would be too ashamed to consult the "experts" about his dreams, and usually prefers to leave that task to his womenfolk.

Popular Dream Books

Lacking a rigid doctrine and an authoritative text book like Ptolemy's *Tetrabiblos*, dream interpreters are far more elastic in their interpretations than star gazers; their "Egyptian Dream Books", "Babylonian-Assyrian Dream Books" or "Persian-Arabic Dream Books" are meant to impress rather than act as rules of thumb. In fact, modern dream books are based

[1] Immanuel Kant: *Anthropologie in pragmatischer Hinsicht* Part, I, 37.

119

on regional folklore rather than on ancient or oriental sources. Dream books enjoy a vast circle of readers, and every year hundreds of thousands of new copies are printed, even though they add little that is not found in the older books. While the publishers—most dream books are anonymous—try to keep their products "up to date" (in some of the most recent editions there are references to the atom bomb), by far the largest number of entries remain unchanged from generation to generation. After all, the authors do not have to revise their work according to the calendar or to the sky, since all attempts to correlate dream interpretations with astrology have, apparently, fallen on deaf ears. Countryfolk like their prophecies to be simple and straightforward, so much so that almost all popular dream books have become mere catalogues of simple symbols, characterising entire dreams in which they appear. The sex, the age, or the circumstances of the dreamer are rarely taken into account, and most symbols are said to refer to all mankind. Moreover, while dream symbols are generally far more gloomy than astrological "signs", the dreamers are rarely told what evasive action to take. Dream books simply describe a situation, and leave it to the reader to deal with it as best he can.

Dream symbols are rather complicated—and this, after all, is the main justification for publishing them—and often anticipate psycho-analytic findings. For that very reason we shall mainly concentrate on dream interpretations from the home of psycho-analysis—Austria. While many Austrian symbols have a simple commonsense connotation—e.g. dreams of spring point to a happy future, and storms point to anger or upsets—others are anything but straightforward. For instance, a racecourse indicates loss of fortune, and a coronet is a sign of vanity. Even more frequently, the original sense of the word is completely reversed, turning happy events into painful ones and vice versa, and producing what psycho-analysts might call dream displacements. Thus according to the *Altbekanntes Wiener Schusterbuben Traumbuch* (Traditional Viennese Cobblers' Dream Book) marriage means severe illness, pain means a happy event, a hangman means great honours, and stabbing indicates good fortune. Similarly, in the *Vollständiges Zigeunerinnen-Traumbuch* (Complete Gypsy Dream Book), oranges on a tree mean an unhappy love affair, a fur coat means a gloomy future, birth means an unhappy loss, an ambulance means ingratitude.

More striking still is the strong sexual element in primitive dream books. When Freud and his pupils first began to analyse dreams, they must have been struck by the apparent sexual motivation of most traditional dream symbols, for though popular dream books studiously avoid obscene and particularly phallic symbols, they teem with quite unequivocal sexual allusions. Conversely, sexual dreams pure and simple are frequently given a non-sexual meaning. Here is a small selection from the Austrian dream books we have mentioned:

Erotic interpretations of non-sexual symbols		*Interpretation of sexual symbols*	
Unharnessing horses	= many love affairs	Kissing women	= profit
Fans	= unrequited love	Marriage	= arguments
Digging graves	= good marriage	Bachelordom	= joy
Spinning yarn	= successful love	Whore	= luck in lotteries
Dancing fairies	= sexual temptations	Keeping company with whores	= profit
Thimble	= virgin marriage	Marrying a whore	= luck in all enterprises
Squirrel	= Young marriage	Wearing female garments	= worry, misfortune
Buttonhole	= Impending marriage	Being kept out by men at night	= many children
Cat	= lasciviousness	Bearing boys	= much joy
Being painted	= successful love	Bearing girls	= illegitimate child
White mouse	= happy marriage	Pregnancy	= hope of some kind

Erotic interpretations of non-sexual symbols		Interpretation of sexual symbols	
Nunnery	= secret love	Promiscuity	= good health
Nun	= to fall out of love	Seduction	= bad luck
Peach	= reunited love	Intercourse	= sorrow, embarrassment
Knocking	= inconstancy in love	Seeing bride or bridegroom	= childless marriage
Man beats woman	= faithful love	Being a bride	= misfortune
Full moon	= blessed marriage	Bride dying	= long marriage
Easter eggs	= luck in love	Man with bosom	= promiscuity
Rubble heap	= marriage	Adultery	= fire
Finding stockings	= luck in love	Jealousy	= faithful marriage partner.

Freud and prophetic dreams

In the summer of 1900, Sigmund Freud, then Professor of Neurology at the University of Vienna, gave a series of lectures on a singularly unacademic topic: dream interpretation. Though his colleagues frowned at his bizarre notions, they felt it was better to pass over his activities in silence, than to cause a public scandal. And, in fact, what happened proved them right. The students showed not the slightest interest in Freud's eccentric behaviour, and no more than three of them attended his first lecture.[1] Freud's book on the subject, published in the same year was equally unsuccessful. This work, which was later to cause such a stir in academic circles, sold no more than 123 copies during the first six months of its existence, and it was not until eight years later that the 600 copies of this edition were sold out.

[1] Alfred Winterstein: *Über die Traumlehre Freuds*. Centenary address to the Viennese Society of Psychiatry and Neurology, 14th May 1956.

Perhaps Freud would have found a readier audience had he told his students and readers how to realise mankind's age-old ambition to tell the future from dreams. As it was, he told them quite unequivocally that dreams could tell them nothing whatever about real things to come. Prophetic dreams were of purely historical interest, for they were mere examples of archaic forms of primitive belief. His *Interpretation of Dreams* ended with this devastating attack on dream diviners: "And what of the value of dreams in regard to our knowledge of the future? That, of course, is quite out of the question. One would like to substitute the words: 'in regard to our knowledge of the past'. For in every sense a dream has its origin in the past. The ancient belief that dreams reveal the future is not indeed entirely devoid of truth. By representing a wish as fulfilled, the dream certainly leads us into the future; but this future, which the dreamer accepts as his present, has been shaped in the likeness of the past by the indestructible wish."[1]

Freud retained this basic attitude in all subsequent editions of the book, even though he became a little more conciliatory:

"Much as modest and unprejudiced scientists must welcome the attempt to include even despised 'occult' phenomena in the sphere of scientific investigations, they will nevertheless remain convinced that this study will fail to force two conclusions upon them: belief in existence after death, and knowledge of an incalculable future."[2]

Freud took an even .more uncompromising stand in his *Additional Remarks on the Interpretation of Dreams:*[3] "There can be no doubt that prophetic dreams can be said to exist in the sense that they deal with projections into the future; what is doubtful, however, is whether this structure corresponds, to any remarkable extent, with actual future events. I confess that, in this case, my principle of impartiality has deserted me. The fact that any mental effort other than shrewd calculation should be able to foresee future events in detail, is on the one hand far too

[1] The Basic Writings of Sigmund Freud (N.Y. 1938), p. 549, translated from *Die Traumdeutung* (1st. ed. 1900) by A. A. Brill.
[2] Sigmund Freud: *Die Traumdeutung* (7th ed., Vienna 1922).
[3] Sigmund Freud: *Ergänzungen und Zusatzartikel zur Traumdeutung,* Collected Works, Vol. III, p. 180 f.

opposed to scientific expectations and attitudes, and, on the other hand, corresponds far too closely with ancient and well-known human wishes, for critics not to reject it as an unjustified presumption. It is my belief, therefore, that if we set the unreliability, credulity, and incredibility of most reports side by side with the possibilities of affectively induced memory falsifications and the inevitability of occasional coincidences, we may expect the spectre of true prophetic dreams to dissolve into nothingness. I personally have never experienced anything that could cause me to form a less biased opinion."

The dream censor

We have quoted Freud's opinions at such length, because they have become the basis of most psychological dream investigations during the past fifty years. Not only psycho-analysts but other schools of psychology as well, have accepted the dicta of the undisputed master, and have resolutely set their face against any possibility of predicting the future from dreams. Nevertheless, psychologists are agreed that dreams may give them a fair indication of how the dreamer *imagines* the future, what his secret wishes and hopes are, and how, if it were left to him alone, he would try to fashion his life.

People might object that if this is all that dream-interpretation is good for, we might as well drop it right here and now, since most men do not need dreams to tell them what they long for. The psycho-analyst's reply would then be, that most men are, in fact, quite unaware of their unconscious wishes. From earliest childhood men are loaded with so many complexes, bitter disappointments, and spiritual injuries, that they bear the scars for life. It is these scars which frequently repress their wishes into subconsciousness, and only during sleep can they overcome their inner resistances, and realise their hidden wishes in dream images.

Admittedly, men cannot rid themselves of *all* their inhibitions even in sleep, so that their dreams often represent displaced rather than direct wishes, which the analyst then has to interpret correctly. Undisguised dreams normally occur in children or in

infantile adults alone;[1] the adult who has outgrown the psychic
life of the child is never quite free. Even his dreams are subject
to supervision by an inner monitor. Freud's dream censor has
psychological properties, quite distinct from those of the censor
who dictates our deliberate decisions. The dream censor
appears to be a bit lax when it comes to manifestly sexual
dreams.[2] This is probably due to the fact that we generally sleep
and dream in bed, and beds are notoriously immoral places.
Apart from this slight moral lapse, however, the dream censor
is no less strict and intolerant than the Lord Chamberlain. He
disfigures and displaces our wishes by changing them into their
direct opposites and plagues us with nightmares when our
wishes become too over-riding.

What we dream, therefore, is often as unconnected with
our real wishes, as, say, a Picasso painting is with a real nude:
the eyes have travelled to unaccustomed places, the nose looks
out of joint, arms and legs are too short or too long or else a
tangle of lines. Those who look at the canvas in the hope of
finding a photographic copy of a real woman will be sorely
disappointed, and only after those who understand the artist
have talked to them at great length, may they get a glimmering
of what he was really trying to tell them and why, of all things,
he called his painting "Portrait of a Woman".

In dreams, things are more complicated still, since dreams
rarely portray a single situation. As a rule, a dream is an entire
drama in which the dreamer sometimes takes the stage himself,
but in which more often he is a mere observer of the objects of
his positive and negative wishes dressed up in the strangest
disguises. Every dreamer is a poet who works with an almost
inexhaustible store of fantasy that rarely stops short where the
professional dramatist would. Laws of space and time, and of
cause and effect are completely discarded, processes are speeded
up even more quickly than they would be in American films, and
passions are masked beyond recognition. Freud mentions a
dream in which an old gentleman suffering from arterio-
sclerosis is surprised by a strange visitor during an act of

---

[1] Sigmund Freud: *Über den Traum* (1901), Collected Works, Vol. III,
p. 240.
[2] Sigmund Freud: *Ergänzungen und Zusatzartikel zur Traumdeutung*,
Collected Works, Vol. III, p. 176.

intimacy. The old gentleman's only reaction is to roar with
laughter, even though—at least according to Freud—the
stranger was death, and the laughter the old gentleman's way
of covering up his fear of approaching impotence.

Prophetic and creative dreams

If the mechanisms of dreams are so different from those of
conscious thought processes, what point is there in relating the
two and in deducing mutual effects? Is not the dream world a
world of its own from which it would be quite illegitimate to
draw conclusions about the dreamer's real attitude to the
future? Most modern psychologists reject so radical a separation
of the two spheres and prefer to look upon dreams as subsidiary
manifestations of consciousness. Some consider dreams as mere
reflexes of conscious thoughts, and in the 19th century it was
even held that dreams were the sludge of waking life, in which the
experiences of the preceding day were rehashed in disorganised
ways. Thus the leading philosopher amongst Freud's contemporaries, Henri Bergson, said that dreams contain all the
elements of mental life except one very important component:
concentration. In sleep we are completely detached, and allow
our thoughts to rush about foolishly and aimlessly.

Unlike all these theories which turned the dream into a mere
satellite of the waking state, psycho-analysis saw it as an
important manifestation of life. According to Freud, every
dream is significant, in that it expresses the dreamer's hidden
wishes or aims. For this reason dreams have to be interpreted by
the special psycho-analytical techniques, developed by Freud and
his pupils.

These techniques are questioned as much today as they were
fifty years ago. Critics point out that psycho-analysis works
with crude sexual symbols and they object particularly to the
mechanical list of such symbols, the first of which was published
by Freud's pupil Wilhelm Stekel in 1911.[1] Actually, there has
never been a complete psycho-analytical dream book with the
help of which one could decipher more complicated dreams, and

[1] Wilhelm Stekel: *Die Sprache des Traumes* (Wiesbaden 1911).

such a book is, in fact, unlikely to be published since the language of dreams is a highly individual picture language, and since there is hardly a single dream which, even according to psychoanalysis does not admit of more than one interpretation.[1] Leading dream interpreters, therefore, rightly rely on intuition and their own long experience rather than on fixed rules.[2]

In any case, however good the interpretations, they can tell us little about the future. For even if the dreamer were told his real motives by the analyst, it is an open question whether he will be able to do anything about them.

In some cases, on the other hand, the dreamer needs no interpreter to tell him how to act on his dreams. Childhood and later memories may rise up so vividly, that the effect is carried over into waking life, with a consequent change in behaviour that may have lasting effects on the dreamer's future.

Next to "prospective" dreams, i.e. dreams which reveal latent possibilities that may or may not be put into practice,[3] people also have far more painful premonitory dreams. We know that many people are extraordinarily sensitive in dreams to physical pain, so much so that the pressure of the edge of the bed, which they would normally ignore, can be felt as a paralysing pain. Now similar pains may also be "dreamt" at the inception of a disease, the symptoms of which are still too slight to have any effects in the waking state. Strictly speaking, such dreams are therefore prophetic in character, for though the disease has started, the patient is unaware of it. French psychologists call such dreams *rêves prémonitoires*[4] and some doctors attach some diagnostic significance to them. However, we must not exaggerate the importance of this phenomenon, for there are many perfectly healthy people who suffer similar pains in their dreams. Even in this respect, therefore, the dream is a very uncertain prophet.

Finally, we must mention a third and more pleasant kind of "prophetic" dream. It is a known fact that dreams can occasion-

[1] Peter W. Hofstätter: *Einführung in die Tiefenpsychologie* (Vienna 1948), p. 151.
[2] H. Schultz-Hencke: *Lehrbuch der Traumanalyse* (Stuttgart 1949).
[3] C. G. Jung: *Allgemeine Gesichtspunkte zur Psychologie des Traumes*. Psych. Trans. (Zürich 1948), II, p. 143.
[4] Jean Lhermitte: *Les Rêves* (Paris 1955), p. 54 ff.

ally release creative and particularly artistic or poetic faculties. Even important technical inventions and scientific discoveries are alleged to have been discovered in that way. Thus Gauss is said to have discovered his laws of induction in a dream, Kekule to have dreamt of the benzole ring, Paul Ehrlich of his side-chain theory, and Niels Bohr of his atomic model. On closer investigation, however, all these stories turn out to be so many old wives' tales.[1] What really happened is that the scientists concerned were day-dreaming rather than dreaming when they had their flashes of intuition. On the other hand, there is a good deal of evidence that poetic, artistic, or religious ideas have, in fact, been born in real dreams, subsequently to be developed by their dreamers.

Still, there is nothing particularly prophetic about such dreams. In no respect, whatsoever, have dreams been shown to be the real workshops of the future, even though they may occasionally provide man with hints of, or, in rare cases lend wings to, his creative faculties. If we compare the role of dreams even in that respect with the role of consciousness, we shall see how insignificant it really is.

Telepathy and Clairvoyance

This is true even if we extend our remarks to include such parapsychological phenomena as telepathic dreams, although Freud, who repeatedly stressed his disbelief in the existence of supernaturally inspired prophetic dreams, was nevertheless unwilling to dismiss them without further ado. While he considered telepathic dreams to be outisde his chosen field of analysis, he still felt impelled to grant that they might, in fact, occur.

Freud himself seems to have received one such "telepathic" message, when during the first World War he dreamt that one of his sons had been killed in action. Contrary to his usual practice, he did not analyse the dream, even though it looked very much like a displaced wish—i.e. that his son would come home alive. Fortunately, the message proved false for his son

[1] Werner Kemper: *Der Traum und seine Be-Deutung* (Hamburg 1955), p. 120–122.

VI. The *Kudurru* which gave rise to the the signs of the Babylonian
Zodiac.

VII. Astrological plate from Uruk in Mesopotamia (100 B.C.).

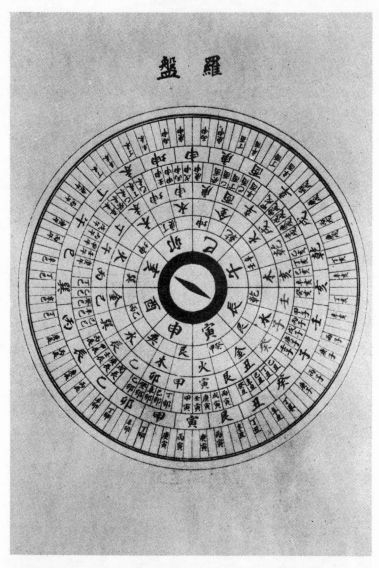

VIII.   The Chinese Magic Disc, Lo King, which was commonly used
for divination.

came home from the war unscathed.[1] Freud concluded that, at least so far as he himself was concerned, telepathic dreams were no guide whatsoever to the future or to present events of which he had no conscious knowledge.

In any case, he drew a sharp distinction between psycho-analytic and telepathic phenomena for, as he argued during the lecture to the Viennese Psycho-analytic Society in which he related his "telepathic" dream about his son, telepathic processes even if they did occur, were not dreams but merely "telepathic experiences in sleep". Telepathic messages, which are caused by external stimuli lack the true characteristics of the dream, viz. condensation, distortion, dramatisation, and, above all, wish fulfilment, all of which are internal stimuli. This is true even when some so-called telepathic dreams reflect the dreamer's wishes, for it is not immaterial whether castles in the air are reached telepathically or by one's own volition.

Modern Freudians do not object quite so strongly to the incursion of telepathy into their chosen field. Telepathic phenomena and dreams are said to be mutually compatible since "experience shows that somnolence, with its obliteration of time and space creates particularly favourable conditions for tele-pathic contacts".[2] Still, the question remains whether telepathic "messages" are mere fantasies, or whether they can provide real answers about the future.

Psycho-analysts usually avoid giving unequivocal answers to this crucial question, and prefer to state that telepathy falls out-side their field—they are concerned with man's psyche and not with his revealed future. Psycho-analysis is introspective and retrospective rather than prospective and not interested in predicting the future.

But then, even critical adherents of telepathy do not claim that prophecy or clairvoyance is a criterion of true telepathy. Telepathy, in the strict and original sense of its first proponent, the English psychologist F. W. H. Myers, is nothing but the transference of thoughts, feelings, pictorial concepts, and sensations from one person to another, without any perceptible inter-vention of either the senses or of artificial means. It is a kind of

[1] Sigmund Freud: *Traum und Telepathie* (1922), Collected Works III, p. 278.
[2] Kemper, op. cit., p. 127.

remote communication both in the waking state and in dreams, for which physiology cannot offer an adequate explanation, and for whose frequent occurrence there is a great deal of reliable evidence. Some persons are particularly telepathic, others less so, and most people not at all.

Clairvoyance, on the other hand, is the ability of perceiving remote objects and people or events in a state of trance or hypnosis, again without the intervention of the senses. Clairvoyants are alleged to have the gift of precognition, even though this gift is gainsaid by all the known laws of physics and biology. People with this gift are said to be able not only to practise pre-cognition but also retro-cognition, i.e. to look into the past, and thus to be particularly useful in solving difficult criminal cases. For this purpose they were consulted so frequently by the police that the Prussian government had to pass a special law against this practice in 1929. When similar laws were passed in other countries as well, clairvoyants had to revert to their more traditional role of "recognising" the future.

This fine distinction between telepathy and clairvoyance can hardly be maintained in practice since, by and large, most telepathists are also clairvoyants and, since, moreover, in most of the relevant experiments during past decades, it was rarely possible to distinguish between the two.[1] Psychology has long ago lumped them together with all other abnormal manifestations of mental life as "parapsychological", a term coined in 1889 by the German philosopher Max Dessoir.[2] In France, psychologists refer to the same phenomena as *"métapsychique"* a term first introduced by the physiologist Charles Richet, and in the United States it is fashionable to speak of E.S.P.—extrasensory perception—a term invented by the psychologist J. B. Rhine. All these terms may have slightly different shades of meaning, but in a field so shrouded in mystery, fine distinctions are not nearly as important as the facts.

As for these, they were remarkable by their absence. Until fairly recently, believers and sceptics alike looked upon telepathy and clairvoyance as the exception rather than the rule. For this

[1] S. G. Soal and F. Bateman: *Modern Experiments in Telepathy* (London) 1954), p. 8 f.
[2] Sphinx, Year VII (1889), p. 42.

very reason, it seemed impossible to come to any general conclusions on the subject. Those given to religious speculations would speak of miracles, and the others could only invoke our lack of natural knowledge.

Some spoke of secret rays, others of biological phenomena. After all, many animals can see in the dark, and birds have a very much better sense of direction than men. Parapsychological phenomena could easily be signs, not of superhuman qualities, but of a kind of atavism, which took some men back to their early stages of evolution. In any case, it was generally agreed that clairvoyance, prophetic dreams, and telepathic phenomena were altogether exceptional.

The English Dreamer

Then came an Englishman who averred the exact opposite: that all human beings have the ability of looking into the future to some extent, and that, given patience and practice, all of us could learn to make correct predictions. He was J. W. Dunne, one of England's first pilots and aircraft constructors and, though perhaps given to fantasy, a man well-versed in physics and particularly in mathematics. His ideas had taken 30 years to mature, and even the prosaic title of the book in which he first published his ideas—*An Experiment with Time*—showed that he was a serious thinker and not a mere sensationalist.

In any case, the book which appeared in London in 1927, was an immediate success not least because Dunne had very skilfully combined the description of his own prophetic dreams with a most complicated theory of knowledge. Most readers undoubtedly bought the book simply to learn about the intimate experiences of a famous aviator, but there is no doubt that he managed to arouse great public interest in his philosophical ideas as well.

England is not only the classic country of ghosts—ghosts not only haunted Shakespeare's imagination but that of a modern Provost of Eton, as well—it is also the first country in which a serious attempt was made to turn parapsychology into a real science. In 1882, the Society for Psychical Research was founded in London with the object of carrying out an impartial investigation of telepathic and allied phenomena. Four years later, three English psychologists[1] published a work, which, for decades to come, was to be considered the repository of all parapsychological knowledge, both at home and abroad.[2] The book was remarkable more for its methodology than for its case histories. While the few Continental scientists who had tackled the subject had all concentrated on exposing doubtful methods and telepathic swindles, the English writers attempted to correlate parapsychology with theoretical physics and mathematics, and particularly with the new ideas about the fourth dimension.

Thus Dunne found the field well prepared when he began to sow his seeds, and this despite the fact that his own dreams were singularly pedestrian. They were truly English dreams, steeped in Victorian prudery—psycho-analysts would, in fact, have been bored stiff by all his nocturnal Empire-building. Dunne's first dream occurred in 1889 when he was staying at an hotel in Sussex. He dreamed that he was having an argument with one of the waiters as to what was the correct time. Dunne asserted that it was half past four in the afternoon and the waiter maintained it was half past four at night. Dunne woke up, looked at his watch and found that it *had* stopped at half past four. He concluded that it must have stopped at half past four the previous afternoon and that he had subconsciously remembered this and then dreamed about it. He wound the watch without altering the hands as he did not know the exact time. On coming downstairs next morning he made for the nearest clock in order to set his watch right, only to find to his utter amazement that it had lost no more than a few minutes—the time between the dream and his winding his watch. In other words it must have stopped during his dream, and not, as he had assumed, during the previous afternoon.

Dunne's next reported dream occurred in Sorrento, and was once again a dream about a watch. Thereafter, his dreams become a little more exciting. In Alassio, on the Italian Riviera,

[1] E. Gurney, F. W. A. Myers, and F. Podmore: *Phantasm of the Living* (London 1886).
[2] Max Dessoir: *Vom Jenseits der Seele* (4th ed., Stuttgart 1920), p. 114.

where he was spending a holiday after being invalided out of the Army during the Boer War, he dreamed that he was in Fashoda, a place near Khartoum. In this dream he found himself talking to comrades from South Africa who had apparently crossed the whole of Africa on foot. On opening his *Daily Telegraph* next morning, Dunne read that the Cape to Cairo Daily Telegraph Expedition had just arrived in Khartoum. Dunne had known nothing about this expedition, though he must often have heard the term "Cape to Cairo" while he was in South Africa, where it expressed British colonial aspirations.

More thrilling still is Dunne's dream during the following year when he had rejoined his unit in South Africa. This time, he saw an island threatened by a volcanic eruption. He warned the French authorities who controlled the island to mobilise all vessels in order to save the four thousand unsuspecting inhabitants. When Dunne received the next batch of papers from London, the headlines proclaimed: VOLCANO DISASTER IN MARTINIQUE. PROBABLE LOSS OF OVER 40,000 LIVES. On another occasion, while holidaying on the borders of the Achensee in Austria, he dreamed of a horse that had apparently gone mad. Next day he actually came across a horse behaving just as it had in the dream, and in the same surroundings.

How the prophesy in your sleep

So Dunne's dreams ran on through decades, through small and large events, through factory fires and railway disasters, all of which were confirmed by subsequent events, at least to some extent. True, all his reports were published after the event, but since nobody doubted Dunne's credibility, his exceptional clairvoyant talents were generally admitted. He himself disagreed that there was anything exceptional about him for, he said, what he did, everyone else could learn to do also. All that was needed was paying close attention to what happened before and after every dream, and this was easily learnt.

Dunne's recipe for getting the best out of dreams was in fact very simple, since it involved neither deep analysis, nor such awkward procedures as were used in ancient Greece, viz. falling asleep in special attitudes and in special places. Dreams are prophetic, and all we need do is to record them immediately upon waking, for, otherwise, they are quickly forgotten. In the absence of dream memories, it is also useful to jot down the first waking thoughts, for these are frequently influenced by the preceding dream.

Experimenting with a small circle of relatives and friends—men and women—Dunne put his method to the test and proved it—at least, to his own satisfaction. Thus his cousin, Miss C., who though she dreamed very little, had a truly prophetic dream within eight days of being instructed in Dunne's method. In this dream she saw a suspicious German woman (this was during the final stages of the First World War). Two days later, Miss C. came across a foreign lady dressed precisely like the suspicious figure in the dream. Not all the dreams investigated by Dunne referred exclusively to the future—some were clearly inspired by recent events, and in others past and future images were blended together. This was true also of some of Dunne's own dreams.

In order to determine whether precognition was possible in the waking state also, Dunne devised a new method: he would observe what odds and ends of images would remain in the mind after he had read a book and look for a chain of associations between these images and future events. Thus, he found that, for instance, the word *narwhal* occurred in two books opened at random. However, on riper reflection, he concluded that this method was not as trustworthy a precognitive medium as the dream.

His method of having and remembering precognitive dreams, too, proved not as effective as he would have had his readers believe, for in 1932, when the London Society for Psychical Research carried out three series of tests based on Dunne's recipe,[1] the results were extremely poor. The first series of tests with members of the society as experimental subjects proved a total failure, and the second series carried out with students from Oxford was inconclusive, since most of the original 22 volunteers backed out or failed to produce the minimum of fourteen dreams demanded by Dunne. Of the 71 dreams supplied by the remaining students, four might conceivably have been called

[1] Alfred Winterstein: *Telepathie und Hellsehen im Lichte der modernen Forschung und wissenschaftlichen Kritik* (Vienna 1948), p. 135 ff.

precognitive, but only with some latitude, and of these three were produced by one and the same person.

More striking still was the failure of the third series of tests, to which Dunne himself presented himself as experimental subject, for of the 17 dreams which he produced, only one was even half-way precognitive. In this dream, he saw an American relative breaking his leg. Three days later he received a letter from the British Consulate in Los Angeles to the effect that this relative was destitute and about to be repatriated. That same evening he also read a detective story in which someone broke a leg under similar conditions to those of the dream. This double "coincidence" encouraged him, modest though he was, to list his dream as clearly precognitive. The fact that his own dream was, nevertheless, not nearly as precognitive as those of the Oxford student, was due to his age, for young people were characteristically more precognitive than their elders.[1]

What remained of Dunne's fame as a dreamer of true dreams after these unsuccessful experiments, was quickly forgotten after his death in 1949. Not that he was convicted of deliberate deception, but it becomes clear that he had modestly hidden the true character of his dreams from his fellow men. From the posthumous notes published by his widow,[2] it emerged that Dunne was no mere dreamer, but a theosophical visionary—a new Swedenborg, in fact. Like the Swedish visionary who not only "saw" the great fire of Stockholm from a distance, but also angels in the act of undressing, so Dunne, too, repeatedly dreamt of an angel which appeared to show him the path to true knowledge. On one occasion, he even saw God the Father disguised as a common working man, and he frequently heard mysterious voices. Thus, in his original watch dream, what had happened was that an angelic choir had implored him to wake up and to look at his watch.

Now, such visions and auditory hallucinations need not necessarily detract from the precognitive value of dreams, but they are, nevertheless, parapsychological phenomena of a special kind, and usually indicate pathological states. Dunne was apparently quite aware of this fact, and therefore concealed it

[1] H. W. Dunne: *An Experiment with Time.* Appendix to 3rd ed. (London 1942), pp. 215–251.

[2] H. W. Dunne: *Intrusions?* (London 1955).

from the public during his lifetime. He wanted to be thought
an ordinary, if attentive, dreamer and saw his mission in convincing mankind that all human beings were as capable of
dreaming up the future as he himself was. They might have been
far more sceptical had he shown himself in his true prophetic
mantle.

E. S. P.

During the last decade, the question whether precognition is a
special gift or not has been the subject of detailed investigation
particularly in the United States, where a new branch of psychology is devoting its efforts exclusively to the study of so-called
psi-processes, i.e. processes apparently contradicted by generally
held scientific principles. Among psi-processes, E.S.P. (extra-
sensory-perception) phenomena such as telepathy and clairvoyance play a leading part.

E.S.P. research is largely the work of J. B. Rhine of Duke
University in North Carolina, though his ideas are no longer
restricted to Duke University alone. E.S.P. research prides itself
on working with sufficient material to exclude mere chance
results as far as possible, and on having introduced adequate
controls which act as safeguards against experimental error and
deliberate deception. Mass tests of this kind tend to involve a
high degree of organisation and skill and must be prepared by
experts. Thus the methods of the 1927 B.B.C. enquiry involving
some 25,000 listeners, had to be rejected out of hand as being
open to interference by professional clairvoyants and other
interested parties. Modern E.S.P. research prefers to restrict its
test to a small number of experimental subjects, who are given
a large number of strictly controlled tests.

E.S.P. research being a young discipline, it has not yet ventured to experiment with such difficult and complex phenomena
as prophetic dreams. Intead, its activities are restricted to
investigating precognition in very simple processes. Here, the
favourite method is to ask the subject to guess which cards will
turn up next in a so-called Zener pack which consists of cards
with one of five symbols: circle, plus sign, rectangle, star, and
wavy lines (see Fig. 26). The subject is asked to predict a

sequence of 5, or sometimes of 25, cards, while the experimenter, in a control room from which he cannot communicate with the subject, checks the actual results. An English electrical engineer who was also a great Psi specialist, G. N. M. Tyrell[1] substituted a system of illuminated boxes for the Zener cards, and claimed that his box was more effective still in excluding external factors.

26. Zener-cards used in parapsychological research.

But no matter which method is used, the principle remains the same. In a pack of twenty-five Zener cards containing 5 x 5 symbols the chances are one to five that a given card, e.g. a circle, will lie on top of, say, a star. Probability considerations alone show that, though in the short run this ratio may not be maintained, it is certain to be the limit if only the game is continued long enough.

But does the human mind, in fact, react precisely like an automatic selector? This question cannot be answered in the affirmative *a priori*, for it might be argued that, because of various personal factors, people have a greater or smaller faculty for guessing correctly, i.e. of being more (or less) clairvoyant than, say, a calculating machine.

Now, hundreds of thousands of experiments particularly in England and America have shown that while most human beings lack any special predictive gift, there are some (including school children) who are particularly precognitive. A mass experiment carried out by Rhine and Gibson with 27,500 tests on adults and 12,500 tests on children indicated that the latter are generally more precognitive than the former. It also emerged

[1] G. N. M. Tyrell: *Apparitions* (London 1953). S. G. Soal and F. Bateman op. cit., pp. 82–87.

fairly clearly that great intelligence and a good education are negative rather than positive precognitive influences. Thus primitive Canadian Indian children were far more clairvoyant than particularly intelligent London college students.[1] A very interesting series of tests was carried out by Gertrude Schmeidler of New York City College (1943–1948), who divided her experimental subjects into sheep and goats,[2] the sheep being those who were optimistic or neutral about the results, and the goats those who were sceptical about E.S.P. The sheep produced considerably better results (1·3:5) than the goats (0·98:5), and this despite the fact that the number of subjects had been kept so large that even a number of proficient clairvoyants among the sheep could hardly have affected the outcome. Hence, it could be argued that goodwill and faith alone, are sufficient to turn every human being into a clairvoyant.

Nevertheless, leading psi-experts are not fully convinced of the existence of this faculty, even in exceptional cases. Thus, two of the most experienced English experimenters[3] assert that "at present, there is insufficient confirmation by experiment that non-inferential precognition really exists, though there is a certain amount of evidence which suggests that it is a possibility". In other words, after three decades of the most diligent experimental work, the experts are no further than they were when they began.

But even if E.S.P. results had been far more convincing than they are, they could tell us little about the phenomena they were originally meant to explain. The experiments are far too simply devised and take place under quite different psychological conditions from those of prophetic visions. The idea of basing the experiments on the very simplest factors was, of course, an excellent one, if only to establish unobjectionable techniques. However, in order to be of practical significance, the method must also be applicable to the more complicated phenomena involved in so-called everyday clairvoyance. So far, this has been found impossible to do, and the value of E.S.P. experiment is

[1] A. A. Foster: *E.S.P. tests with American Indian Children.* J. of Paraps. Vol. VII (June 1943), pp. 94–103.

[2] G. R. Schmeidler: *Separating the Sheep from the Goats.* J. Am. Sy. for Psy. Res. (1945), Vol. 49, pp. 47–50.

[3] Soal—Bateman, op. cit., p. 174.

consequently very limited. The fact that human beings cannot predict a series of cards correctly is no proof that they cannot predict personal events correctly.

There is in fact a great deal of evidence that if human beings have the faculty of precognition at all, it is usually associated with complex processes. Intuitive predictions, no matter whether they are true or false, have always a dream-like quality, and this means that they are anything but simple. If we wish to solve the problem of precognition experimentally, we must, above all, raise it from the card and number level of the fair ground, and return to the more inspired level of the world of dreams.

Is time reversible?

It is here that we face the greatest obstacle: our logical reluctance to accept the possibility of non-inferential prediction, i.e. the possibility of arguing the future from non-existent facts. All theories, which assume that the future can be seen intuitively, start from the belief that there is a special faculty or a mechanism which enables people to do so. The purely prophetic theories assume that this faculty is given man directly by a higher, omniscient, and eternal power—God—for whom past, present, and future are one, and who may grant a favoured few an occasional glimpse into the future. Those who are not satisfied with this explanation try to reduce or to eradicate the difference between past and future by arguing that the distinction exists in man's consciousness alone, and that, for instance, in dreams the line of demarcation breaks down enabling man to see time in its full extent—past, present, and future. This dream-like faculty, which runs counter to the classical notion of three-dimensional perception, involves the construction of a new concept of time.

For this construction, time must somehow be turned into space. No longer is time the Aristotelian concept for measuring movements or the Kantian basis of perception; it has become an independent fourth dimension.

The term "fourth dimension" made its debut in the middle of the 18th century in the French Encyclopedia, and has haunted man ever since. It became tangible—too tangible—only towards the end of the 19th century, when Newtonian physics was being assailed from all sides. The first broadside was fired by the English mathematician C. W. Hinton in his: "What is the Fourth Dimension?" which appeared in 1887. Spiritualists who read the book were deeply disappointed, for Hinton's Fourth Dimension was completely despiritualised into the field in which all spatial processes took place. All space was said to have a fourth dimension, i.e. an extension in time. The point in time which we call the present is nothing but our point of observation, for past and future are one. Forty years later, the visionary Dunne took up this speculative theory, and added a good pinch of fantasy to it, while physicists such as Einstein and Minkowski, by including it into their new world-picture, gave it a somewhat more prosaic meaning. Meanwhile, Schrödinger and de Broglie had introduced fifth and even higher dimensions into their wave theory, and mystifiers the world over were quick to turn this advance in physics to their own advantage.

They were given unexpected help by the cinema. The new art of conjuring up life from changing shadows, had shown that still frames could be made to give the impression of continuous progress in time, and, what was more curious, it appeared that by running a film backwards, time could, in effect, be reversed. The first of these two phenomena was used in support of Bergson's contention that continuous time did not really exist, and was no more than a sequence of individual moments from which the human eye constructed a continuum. The reason why it could do this, was that man's memory could be turned both backward into the past and also forward into the future. Thus every still in the film points clearly to its successor, and in life— just like in the film—the future is already contained in the present.

Still more revolutionary in its "philosophical" consequences was the technique of running films backwards. While the first impact of seeing someone dive out of the water, or a racehorse galloping back to the tapes, may cause great amusement, even films shown in this way appear to have an inner logic, and may give rise to the impression that psychological events may be similarly reversed. True the old objections to the reversibility of physical events—for instance, the fact that, having once melted ice into water, the water cannot be turned back into ice with the *same* amount of work—still held good, but man's faith in absolute irreversibility was dealt a severe blow by the cinema.

Further dimensions

Dunne drew on some of the new knowledge in constructing his new theory which, despite its mathematical embellishments was pure fantasy. Thus he developed the fantastic notion of a five-dimensional world which contained not only the entire past but also the entire future of the four-dimensional world. In waking existence, observers in this five-dimensional world—and that means all of us—behave just as if they lived in a four-dimensional world, but in their dreams they soar beyond it to survey the future and the past with greatly enhanced powers of imagination. Still, the five-dimensional world was by no means the ultimate world, since it contains a "real" time-dimension which can only be surveyed from a six-dimensional world, and so on *ad infinitum*.

This notion that time is multi-dimensional is also held by more down-to-earth philosophers than Dunne.[1] Thus Prof. C. D. Broad of Cambridge[2] has suggested a five-dimensional picture. To visualise the mechanism of precognition, we must imagine the second time-dimension as a line perpendicular to the horizontal time axis of the four-dimensional world. This perpendicular line can be perceived by men endowed with precognitive powers. Now, while the whole thing looks extremely convincing on paper, paper is, after all, at best four-dimensional. It tells us little about the ability of events to cast their shadows before them.

Paradoxically enough, this question is most readily answered in the affirmative by strict evolutionists, who are commonly no friends of E.S.P. No matter how they envisage the detailed processes of evolution, they are bound to assume that the future is somehow included in the present. Still, a given cause can have a great number of effects, and none of us would, for instance, be able to predict the exact effects of throwing a burning cigarette out of a train window. On the other hand, even the least com-

[1] Michel Souriau: *Le Temps* (Paris 1937), p. 55
[2] C. D. Broad: *Mr. Dunne's Theory of Time* in Philosophy X, No 38.

petent of detectives may trace the fire, once it has started, back to its original cause—in this case, the cigarette. Parapsychologists, however, claim that they can predict the effects of certain causes and, unlike biologists, they will apply their predictions to the individual rather than to the race.

Even so, the public seems to have lost interest in the performance of E.S.P. virtuosos. While they were as popular as football heroes only 30 years ago, few people will be able to tell you their names today. Even in variety shows they no longer command large fees for, unlike diviners in other fields, their stock is at very low ebb at this moment.

This is due neither to the fact that their powers have waned over the years nor to greater scepticism on the part of the public. The real reason is that means of communication have improved so greatly, that we need no E.S.P. to tell us what is happening, say, to our poor aunt in Australia. Most men prefer the telephone or the radio to keep in touch with the present.

Parapsychology, like washing powder, is subject to the laws of supply and demand—hence its decline. Possibly a new fashion may see it in full cry again, but if the present tendency continues it may well happen that man's parapsychological faculty will wither away even before science has had the final say on the subject.

CHAPTER 4

The Wheel of History

*A*LL NON-INSPIRATIONAL OR NON-INTUITIVE ATTEMPTS to look into the future are necessarily based on experience, i.e. on the past, and on the assumption that like causes will have like effects.

However, there are large spheres of human endeavour in which such simple empirical predictions are impossible or extremely difficult to make. Thus most historians would agree that past historical events cannot simply be projected into the historical future, i.e. that there is no such thing as the "lesson of history". Laymen, on the other hand, have never been content to consider the past as of no more than "historical" interest, and have tried instead to predict the future, on the questionable assumption that history repeats itself. Those who believe that they can, in fact, make historical predictions from past events, can, by and large, be divided into two groups: those who look upon history as a chain of cyclic events, and those who consider it to be linear, i.e. without beginning or end. Still, even the second group recognises periodic similarities in the appearance of certain segments of the line so that, when all is said and done, the two groups are not quite as radically opposed to each other as might be supposed. The only real difference is that the former look upon cycles as objective phenomena, and the latter as a mere working hypothesis—one of many possible approaches to history.

The conception that world history proceeds by cycles is one of the oldest and most persistent human beliefs. The greatest philosophers and the greatest dunces have always shared a common faith that what happened must inevitably happen again, even though there is not a shred of evidence to support this contention. In fact it is no more rational than the astrological belief that man's fate is determined by the revolutions of the planets.

According to Brahmism, for instance, the individual periods of a given historical cycle make up the calendar of the gods. In the same way that the "human" year was thought to consist of

27. Ancient Mexican calendar stone showing the four suns of
past ages, all of which ended in disaster, and the face of the
present, the fifth, sun god.

360 days (leap years excepted), so the divine year contained 360
human years. 120,000 divine years, i.e. 43·2 million human
years formed one "great period" the Mâha-Juga. The great
period was divided into four epochs of unequal duration but of
equal rhythm, and each epoch was preceded by a waxing period
and followed by a waning period, each $\frac{1}{10}$ the duration of
the epoch itself. Thus the Krita-Juga epoch, for instance, is
composed of a waxing period of 400 divine years, a main
period of 4000 divine years and a waning period of 400
divine years. A twinkle in the eye of Vishnu or Seva lasts two
million human years which, to all intents and purposes, is an
eternity.

In the Near East, religious concepts of time were a little more
down-to-earth, and were largely based on astronomical observa-

IX.   The Delphic Pythia (Greek vase).

X.   Forecourt of Delphic Temple (400 B.C.).

XI.   The 17th century first introduced "automation". Pascal constructed his calculating machine in 1641, when he was only 18 years old.

XII.   Calculating machine constructed by Leibniz in 1673.

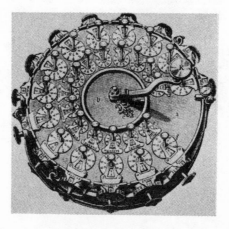

XIII.   More complicated calculating machine constructed by J. H. Müller (1782).

tions, on interpretations of holy texts, or on cabbalistic multiples of the basic number six or the magic number seven. The Babylonians spoke of a period of 3600 years, and the Jewish historian Josephus Flavius who lived in Rome during the first century A.D. tells us that ancient time was divided into periods of 600 years each.

The Sirius-cycle of 1461 years, the great astronomical discovery of the Egyptians, also led to the introduction of mythological and cyclical ideas of time: whenever the cycle was about to run its full course, the Phoenix would rise up in India—or, according to another version, in the north—to return to Egypt where, after having been burned to ashes in the Sun Temple at Heliopolis, it would be resurrected to new life. Within every 1461 years, not only heavenly but also terrestrial processes followed one another in rhythmical succession. Another Egyptian cycle consisted of 36,525 years, i.e. a hundred times as many years as the year has days. Once this cycle was completed, the golden age was said to recommence on earth.

The Greeks added little to oriental notions of time. They, too, were constantly searching for the Great World Year, the rhythmical unit of world history. From Plato's day, we know of a world cycle of 700,000 years, at the end of which everything starts all over again, and a later authority from the second century A.D. tells us that the Great World Year lasts 9977 ordinary years. Though the sceptics of the Platonic Academy rightly objected that such long periods were quite useless for all practical purposes of predicting the foreseeable future, the problem of the *kyklos*—the great cycle—continued to occupy the greatest minds of Greece. Thus, in spite of his famous parable of the river that could only be entered once, Heraclitus' "flux of becoming" was cyclic rather than linear. In the divine fire, opposing worlds consume each other, only to arise anew like the Phoenix. Similarly, the Pythagoreans symbolised the cycle of becoming by the wheel of re-birth. According to Plato, the "perfect" number which governed the "cycle of divine creation" was at one and the same time the basis of morals. Thus man was enjoined to live according to the system of numbers listed in the *Republic*[1] and elaborated in his *Timaeus*,[2] where we are told that

[1] Plato: *The Republic*, VIII.
[2] Plato: *Timaeus*, 47a.

man's gift of vision comes direct from God so that, as he beholds the cycles of the heavenly bodies, he may apply them to his own thoughts to which they are intimately related (Plate 15). Aristotle, approaching the subject from a mathematical and physical point of view, came to very similar conclusions. According to him, all perfect and durable motion was circular.

Whatever mental reservations Plato and Aristotle may nevertheless still have had on this subject were completely overruled by the Stoics, who were to exert the greatest influence on Greek and Roman intellectual life for more than 500 years. The Stoics believed that events recurred in an identical rather than a similar pattern, and took this belief quite literally. Thus we may read that "if the stars return to their position, a new Socrates and a new Plato will arise, and every individual will be reborn into the same circle of friends and fellow-citizens to suffer the same fate and to carry out the same activities. Every town, every village, and every field will be re-created just as they were".[1]

History repeats itself

With the rise of Epicurus, this philosophy met its first serious challenge. The Epicureans rejected the notion of the Great World Year and the doctrine of eternal rebirth as rank superstition. To them every man was a unique individual, and it was precisely for this reason that human life had value and significance. Now, if millions of individuals live unique lives, history cannot possibly repeat itself. In this way Epicurean philosophy may be said to be anti-historical, for if nothing can be gleaned from the past, it is best to live for the day alone.

It has been said that this stress of the uniqueness of the individual is a common bond between the Epicurean and early Christian philosophies. However, this apparent similarity is extremely superficial, since Christian philosophy is by no means fundamentally anti-historical. True, it rejects the idea of re-birth on earth, since life on earth, of which history deals, is not eternal but is followed by the life beyond, but there are never-

[1] Nemesius: *De natura homin.* Chap. 38.

theless historical parallels which generally result from man's sinfulness. Thus the earliest Christian philosophers, above all St. Augustine in his *De civitate Dei* (The City of God), expressed clear cyclic ideas of history.

St. Augustine's historical philosophy is largely based on Eastern notions of the kind found, for instance, in the Book of Daniel, where we are told that four kingdoms will arise, only to be destroyed through man's deceitfulness and error, until finally God sets up His Kingdom which shall never be destroyed.

Similarly, St. Augustine looked on all history, from Cain and Abel's fratricidal strife right up to the sack of Rome by the Goths (which he witnessed himself), as the struggle between good and evil. Thus Cain's murder of Abel corresponded to the killing of Remus by his brother Romulus,[1] and pre-Christian history could be divided into five periods, each of which ended in disaster. The sixth period which began with the birth of Christ would last until the Second Coming, the Day of Judgement, and the inception of God's eternal Kingdom, when good would finally triumph over evil.

The same historical outlook was reflected 200 years later by Bishop Isidore of Seville, and, with small changes, by subsequent Church leaders, for instance by the Jesuit Antonio Vieira, who in his curious *Historia de Futuro* predicted that the kingdom of his time, though not yet near its inevitable cataclysm, was bound to make way to God's perfect and eternal reign which, of course, would not be subject to periodic disaster.

During the Renaissance—and the word "Renaissance" means rebirth—Christianity, too, began to search for the Great World Year. Thus the Italian classicist Julius Caesar Scaliger, combining astronomical cycles with the 15-year Roman tax period (*indictio romana*—the unit of time of Papal Bulls to this day), arrived at a cycle of 7980 years. This cycle—which, after its discoverer, was called the Julian period, was said to have begun in the year 4713 B.C., so that in Scaliger's day another 1700 years were needed to complete it.

A later descendant of these earlier periodic historians was Friedrich Nietzsche, who in his *Will to Power* sang the praises of historical rebirth in beautiful dithyrambs. According to Nietzsche, "this world of stirring strength, endless and ne'er

[1] St. Augustine: *De civitate Dei*, XV, 5.

begun . . . this flood of fearless force, changing yet quite un-changed" turns simplicity into complexity, only to return to its original simplicity in time—to "joyful harmony, affirming itself in the uniformity of its orbits and years and blessing itself as never merely being, but always becoming—without satiety or tedium".

Nietzsche's faith in the ever-revolving cycle of life, his delight in the "luck of the circle", was, however, purely aesthetic and he never tried to apply it in any way. Some of his lesser disciples, on the other hand, have tried time and again to prove that history in fact follows a rigid cyclical pattern. In the case of such long cycles as, say, Scaliger's Julian period, their attempts are, of course, mere parlour games without any prac-tical value for predicting the future. But bolder men have tried to show that even within shorter periods, history has often repeated itself, and is therefore likely to repeat itself in the future, as well.

Cabbalistic numbers

The classic example of this kind of historical analysis is a book which was submitted to the French Academy of Moral and Poli-tical Sciences by one of its members: Gaston Georgel's *Rhythms in History*.[1] Georgel based his work on purely cabbalistic con-siderations: having come across the expression "7 x 77" in the Bible, he at once knew that historical events repeated them-selves every 539 years, or in multiples of that figure.

Georgel then put his revelation to the test, and—behold!—he was proved right, although there were slight deviations from the rhythm. Unfortunately, historical events can also be shown to "repeat" themselves at intervals different from Georgel's, depending on how we define this term, and the moment we apply any such schemes to real cases, we discover that their prognostic value is nil.

Take the case of the First World War, which was past history by the time Georgel's book appeared. 539 years earlier, i.e. in 1375–1379 we find ourselves in the middle of the Hundred Years War. At almost the same time, the period of Papal exile ended with the return of Gregory XI to Rome, and the death of

[1] Gaston Georgel: *Les rhythmes dans l'Histoire* (Paris 1937).

the Holy Roman Emperor Charles IV led to the division of the Habsburg Empire, to civil war, and to anarchy over large parts of the Western World. While these events might be compared with the collapse of the Austro-Hungarian monarchy in 1918, it would be difficult to find any other parallel with the First World War. If we go back roughly 2 x 539 years from 1914, we may find something slightly more reminiscent of the great territorial changes of our time: the partition of Franconia by the treaty of Verdun (843). Four times 539 years before World War I there took place the first of the Punic wars which can by no stretch of the imagination be likened to the First World War.

We should obtain much more convincing results if we used the ancient Egyptian Sirius-cycle of 1461 years instead, for if we count back 1461 years from the end of the First World War, we come to the middle of the fifth century, to Attila's great wars of conquest and to the Battle of the Catalaunian Plain (451)—the scene of the Battle of the Marne in World War I—which was of great historical importance. If we prefer to count back from World War II we are brought almost exactly to the year 476, which is considered the end of the Western Roman Empire.

These examples show that the difficulties of applying world-historical formulae lie not so much in solving as in posing problems. What exactly is it that we wish to compare? So-called world history, at least during long periods, is nothing but a sequence of political and cultural events and, however shrewdly we try to read a common thread into it, that thread must remain a philosophical or literary exercise. We simply change the scenery, as in a play, considering first Egypt and Babylon, and perhaps China as well, then Greece and Rome, then Northern Europe and, much later still, the New World. Archaeological finds may give us hints for setting up a pre-historical picture which, as its name implies, must be sketchy in the extreme. With little evidence and much fantasy we may seem to discover a few common links, but the actual facts, or at least our knowledge of them, is so small that we cannot legitimately consider the totality of historical processes as a unity with a discernible rhythm.

The search for a pattern in history has therefore assumed new forms in modern philosophy of history. Since past cultures were obviously not co-existent, some flourishing while others had hardly begun to exist, and some dead or dying while others were still at the peak of their powers, individual civilisations are now being compared as such, rather than in the context of civilisations as a whole.

Historical philosophers for the past 200, and descriptive historians for the past 100 years, have been tackling this task with growing enthusiasm. Historical events of two civilisations having been tabulated independently, they are compared with each other as if they were two organic beings placed side by side on a dissection table.

In fact, these investigations are not always strictly inductive, i.e. based on generalisations from the known facts; rather are the facts often made to fit certain *a priori* generalisations. In other words, the investigators "prod" their facts for the required evidence. Still, historians are not alone in using this approach, and some of the most important scientific discoveries were made in the same way.

The basic difference between modern analyses of history and the old search for a Great World Year, is the new approach to time. In the ancient cycle-notions, time was considered to be continuous and infinite, even though the individual cycles were thought to return to their starting points. A new cycle could never begin before the last one had finished, and while individual cycles ran an equal course, they were never simultaneous. Modern periodic theories, on the other hand, treat the history of individual people, or groups of people and cultures, as if they existed independently and simultaneously. They are not concerned with geographical space and are interested only in parallel phenomena taken out of their time context. Every historical cycle begins with the year A and ends with the year Z, where the actual duration of the interval A–Z is irrelevant.

Three stages of history

The first historian to use this method consciously and to turn it into a philosophic principle was the Neapolitan Giambattista Vico. In his *Principe di una scienza nuova d'intorno alla commune natura delle nazione* (Principles of a new science of the common nature of nations) which appeared in 1725, Vico saw the human spirit as the decisive driving force of all history. Now, this spirit develops equally in all peoples and in all countries. All people travel through three stages which Vico, basing himself on an Egyptian formula, called the divine, the heroic and the human. Thus in Greek history, the Homeric age was the heroic, and can hence be compared with our Middle Ages. In both epochs an aristocratic warrior caste ruled supreme over a predominantly rural economy, in both the ballad was thought the ultimate form of poetic expression, and in both human relationships were based on personal trust. Vico's point is that, if we recognise this principle, we can learn more about the Homeric age from a study of our own Middle Ages than from Homer himself.

Far-reaching though his conclusions were, Vico avoided speculations about future events, adding the rider that every independent cycle introduced novel and unpredictable factors. Less circumspect disciples preferred to ignore this reservation and insisted on using Vico's discovery for historical prediction. But the difficulties proved insurmountable, mainly because it is very difficult to determine what particular age—divine, heroic, or human—the present represents, and therefore by what stage it will be followed. This is true not only of history as such, but *a fortiori* of cultural trends.

Let us take an example from modern music. When Richard Strauss wrote the score for *Salome* at the beginning of our century, conservatives were not alone in considering him a revolutionary who was trying to upset all previous musical values. Using Vico's scheme, we would have to place him at the beginning of the third—the human—stage, if only because his realism was utterly opposed to, say, Wagner's romanticism. But only a year later Schönberg and Stravinsky produced works which, today, are considered the turning points in musical history, whereas Richard Strauss is called a late romantic.

Admittedly, some artistic phenomena recur so frequently that one can easily tell when one period is coming to an end and when a new period is about to begin. Thus the history of art demonstrates quite clearly that all great schools have simple beginnings which strike posterity as almost primitive. Once the new forms are perfected, mere technique gains the upper hand, first in a tendency towards exaggeration and pomposity and finally by emphasising mere decorative detail. As early as the 1750's, Winckelmann was able to trace this course of development in Greek art. Soon afterwards similar trends were shown to have existed in Gothic art, and even more emphatically in the phase which began with the early Italian Renaissance and ended with Rococo decadence. Even the apparently different architectural styles of the 19th century, which were little more than imitations of earlier styles, clearly reflect this trend.

Whenever we reach a "Rococo stage", we may be certain that the end is near, and that a new age is about to dawn. Though it is difficult to tell what this new age will bring, we can say with certainty that it will be a much simpler one, greatly shorn of pomposity. This is precisely what happened at the beginning of the 20th century when Cubism and functional architecture came into vogue, and the same thing is likely to happen when current stylistic trends have run their full course.

To a lesser extent, such trends can also be detected in political history, although with much greater difficulty. Nevertheless, Aristotle thought that he could devise a scale of political regimes: democracy is followed by tyranny, tyranny by oligarchy, oligarchy by democracy, and so on. Even though the Aristotelian scale based on the Greek city state is not universally valid, it does, nevertheless, apply to a number of modern instances.

But cycle-theoreticians are not satisfied with merely predicting artistic or political developments; their ambition is to predict the totality of events. One hundred years after the publication of Vico's *Scienza nuova*, a young French mathematician, Auguste Comte, published a theory of his own which, though very similar to Vico's, was apparently evolved independently. Comte, too, saw three stages in the development of Western civilisation: a theological age in which faith ruled supreme, a metaphysical age in which reason first rears its head and overthrows old institutions, and a third, positivist age in which scientific knowledge alone governs all actions.

Unlike Vico's human stage, however, Comte's positive stage had not yet arrived or was only just about to start, and 24-year-old Comte saw to it that its approach was hastened by constructing one of the most rounded and most influential intellectual systems[1] that has ever been devised. The second half of the 19th century was labelled the positivist era, and in some South American countries positivism became almost a state religion in which a "catechism" written by Comte himself took the place of the Bible. Alas, at the turn of the last century it appeared that far from having reached the promised stage of pure science, mankind was still bogged down in the first stage, and that much of what was considered positive knowledge was no more than naive faith and rank superstition.

Marx and Darwin

Auguste Comte's philosophy was much more messianic in character than that of his junior—Karl Marx, whose knowledge was aquired in more mundane ways. While every one of the four "progressive epochs", into which Marx divided past history with acknowledgements to Hegel, had laws peculiar to itself, it arose logically from the preceding epoch, and so would the fifth, the socialist epoch. That epoch seemed much closer to Marx than it did to most other people. Marx never looked upon himself as a messianic prophet promising pie in the far-distant future.

Nor is Marxism messianic in form, and it was only Marx's disciples and popularisers who gave it that character. For Marx, socialism was not an external act of salvation, but the inner consequence of an inevitable social catastrophe. Hence Marx never maintained that socialism would be the last possible stage of human development, or that the classless society would last forever. He was much too much an historian, and much too steeped in the historical philosophy of his time, to think that world history could proceed dynamically until the collapse of capitalism, and become quite static thereafter. This was a delusion which he left to his lesser followers and to his opponents who never tired of asserting that socialism was trying to replace true religion with the promise of paradise on earth.

Marx was not a believer in Platonic cycles, rather was he a

[1] Auguste Comte: *Cours de philosophie positive* (1839–1842).

linear historian. For him, history moved up a steep gradient. Still, he was not fool enough to ignore the fact that mankind's longing was often directed at the past and not at the future, and his own love for Greek civilisation often drove him in the same romantic direction: "Man cannot become a child again, unless he become childish. But does he not love the simplicity of children and must he not, albeit on a higher stage, strive to reproduce his childhood? Does not childhood reflect the character of every epoch? Why then should the historical childhood of mankind at its loveliest not exert a lasting charm, as a never-returning age? There are spoilt children and precocious children, and many ancient people were like these. The Greeks, on the other hand, were normal children."[1]

The later Marx, and particularly Engels, tried to adapt Darwin's theory of evolution to their own purposes. Thus, immediately after the publication of Darwin's *Origin of Species* (1859), Engels wrote: "Although crudely English, this book provides the scientific basis for our opinions." And 24 years later at Karl Marx's graveside, he added: "Just as Darwin discovered the laws of development of organic nature, so Marx discovered the laws of development of human history."[2] Even so, Marxism' marriage to Darwinism, like all hybrids, turned out to be rather barren, not only because Darwin was a liberal, but mainly because he regarded the struggle for existence as perpetual, while Marx and Engels considered the class struggle as a capitalist excrescence that would inevitably cease when the proletariat seized power. Thereafter anything might happen.

From Darwin's theory no predictions about the near future can be made. This is undoubtedly why it lacks popular appeal, for men expect a universal law to enable them to do just that. Darwin's disciple, Herbert Spencer, tried to correct this short-coming by propounding a general law of evolution that applied to natural as well as to political history. Spencer was a strict evolutionist and therefore an anti-revolutionary. All natural phenomena develop spontaneously and rigorously out of the preceding stages, and all attempts to accelerate this process are senseless. Evolution is completely continuous without beginning

---

[1] Karl Marx: *Grundriss der politischen Ökonomie* (1857–1858), p. 31.
[2] Karl Kautsky: *Materialistische Geschichtsauffassung* (Berlin 1927), Vol. I, p. 199 f.

or end. Hence Spencer's system included neither periods nor other rhythmical divisions.

Spencer's attempt to look on all historical developments as an uninterrupted chain of phenomena aroused immediate hostility. The most outspoken critic was the French philosopher Charles Renouvier who, in his spirited *Uchronie*, described a civilisation in which everything happens as logically and as rigorously as Spencer assumes, but in which the results are quite unlike those in the real world. Renouvier showed the absurdity of believing that history is an infinite continuum, and insisted that it was full of natural breaks. One such break was the emergence of great men. Renouvier's ideas, if true, would make political prognoses quite impossible, for who can predict the emergence of the next great man? Moreover, the "greatness" of men depends not least on the unpredictable durability of their success.

The Decline of the West

Since the beginning of the 20th century, the idea of discontinuity made its incursion even into science. Planck's quantum theory, and the biological theory of mutations showed clearly that nature herself could proceed by sudden leaps. This new approach had immediate repercussions on historical research, and the two most important historical works of that time Oswald Spengler's *The Decline of the West* and Arnold Toynbee's *A Study of History* both reverted to Vico's approach: history, far from being continuous, is a series of independent recurring cycles. Once these cycles are distinguished, there emerge general laws by means of which the future may be predicted scientifically.

Both systems were strongly influenced by biological notions, and this was held against them particularly by English historians.[1] Thus Spengler's "cultures" and Toynbee's 21 civilisations clearly assume that history is modelled on organic life: cultures and civilisations grow up from a primitive stage, reach

[1] R. G. Collingwood: *The Idea of History* (Oxford 1946), pp. 161–165 and 181–183.—W. H. Walsh: *An Introduction to Philosophy of History* (London 1951), p. 164 ff.

a mature stage, fall ill and die a natural or sometimes an unnatural, premature, death. Once we know what stage a given
culture or civilisation has reached, we can predict with a fair
amount of certainty how long it will continue.

Spengler, a mathematician by training but a man of wide
interests, came to very sad conclusions about the West: Western
culture was about to die of exhaustion. What was left in store
for it was no more than the typical decay phenomena of all late
cultures, followed by the inevitable stage of barbarism and then
by a new culture. It has been said that Spengler's scepticism was
merely a typically German reaction to defeat in war, but this
explanation cannot be seriously accepted, since the idea for his
great work had occurred to him before 1914. Seen in historical
perspective, *The Decline of the West* is really no more than one of
those interminable discussions about the problem of decadence
that were so fashionable at the turn of the century. While many
of Spengler's prophecies have already been proved wrong in
detail, it is too early to say that events have disproved his general
contentions.

Arnold Toynbee, a professional historian of astonishing
learning and scholarship, published the first of his ten volumes
during the depression (1934), and completed his work after the
Second World War, from which England emerged a greatly
weakened victor. Though his work reflects the critical mood of
the times, Toynbee's conclusions are far more optimistic than
Spengler's. Western civilisation may be endangered, but extinc-
tion is by no means round the corner.

Most modern propounders of cycle theories, like their
predecessors, carefully avoid setting up precise historical time-
tables, or else divide history into such long periods that no useful predictions can be made from them. Spengler was least
guilty in that respect, for in order to synchronise his cultures,
he had to determine the exact duration of the individual phases:
prehistory, early history, late history, and civilisation (decay).
Basing himself on the examination of older cultures and assuming
that, since the historical clock had always ticked at the same rate
and would therefore continue to do so in the future, he ventured
to make predictions beyond the year 2200.[1] Spengler was con-

[1] Oswald Spengler: *Der Untergang des Abendlandes* (76th–81st ed.,
Munich 1950), Vol. I, p. 68 ff.

vinced that the common belief that oriental countries, and particularly Far Eastern countries, were culturally inert, was an illusion, since, on closer examination, Oriental history proves to have been at least as stormy as Western history, and to have had comparable "cultures".

As a rule, modern nations take 200–300 years to reach their political peak, remain static for a somewhat shorter period, and then decline for another 200–300 years. On this basis, long-term predictions can easily be made. Thus, since England took 300 years to become the world's foremost power—from the reign of Elizabeth I to the Victorian era—the rise of the United States which began with Independence may be expected to continue for another hundred years.

However, all such predictions are highly speculative, not only because they are based on far too few comparative data but also because they seem to have no logical basis. Why should people tire after eight or ten generations rather than after twelve or fifteen? All attempts to derive such "ethnopolitical" natural laws from biological processes like youth, maturity, and senility, must strike the unprejudiced observer as highly questionable.

Father and Son

More plausible theories emerge from considerations of shorter periods, e.g. of one generation only. It is an incontestable fact that fathers and sons rarely have identical attitudes and temperaments, and since nations are made up of individuals, the succession of generations with different convictions and opinions seems to be a logical basis for making historical predictions.

In the 19th century, for instance, it was generally true to say that the respective heir to the throne would oppose the politics of his father. Where the latter was conservative, the Crown Prince would be liberal, where the father worked for international understanding, the son would usually be a rabid nationalist. Top-level changes usually led to changes of administrators, and thus the impression arose that all new generations make clean sweeps of the past.

We must, however, be quite clear that such changes are no

more than pseudo-biological processes. There is, in fact, no such thing as a clean break between generations. By and large, the same number of fathers die and the same number of children are born every year, and it is only after particularly bloody wars that a disproportionately large young generation may arise. In general, we may therefore say that changes of attitude from one generation to the next are purely sociological processes caused by periodic changes in fashion.

It was in this sense that Sainte-Beuve first used the term "romantic generation" to characterise the poets and writers who were in vogue in France after 1830, and it was from literature that the idea of self-contained generations later spread to other fields. Thus positivists tried to replace the customary division of history into centuries by a "natural" division into generations, and even quite recently, modern disciples of Auguste Comte have attempted to show that the three generations which succeed one another within every century always have distinct attitudes and ideas.[1]

If these positivist ideas were true, it would be the easiest thing on earth to make correct historical predictions. Unfortunately there is no evidence that the great bell of rejuvenation strikes every 30 years, and that those born between two strokes always fit into one of two categories. This rhythmical concept derived from literature was impossible to apply even to art, and art historians were forced to introduce a new notion of "generation": new artistic styles were said to arise regularly every 13–22 years by artists born at roughly the same time, so much so that the history of art could be divided into distinct periods based on the birth-dates of great artists.[2]

This "discovery", which caused something of a sensation in the twenties, did not remain a sensation for long. To consider the dates of birth of famous men as historical criteria for setting up an historical calendar seems questionable if only because a considerable number of poets, artists, philosophers, discoverers, inventors and statesmen only produce their most important works in later life, or change their style, approach, and form at

[1] François Mentré: *Rhythmes sociaux et historiques* in *Les Rhythmes et la Vie* (Paris 1947), p. 202 f.

[2] Wilhelm Pinder: *Das Generationenproblem in der europäischen Kunst* (1926).

frequent intervals. Picasso and Stravinsky, for instance, had quite a number of "periods". For this reason alone, great historical events, rather than great personalities, must be taken as the milestones of history, no matter how important these personalities are. Birth dates are best left in the hands of astrologers.

War and Peace

But what are great historical events? No one can doubt that the invention of the printing press and the discovery of America were more important historical achievements than even the most decisive wars. Unfortunately peaceful achievements of such scope are very rare and, indeed, occur far too irregularly for us to deduce any kind of rhythm from them. Moreover in troubled times like ours, it is wars rather than great inventions which seem to have the most striking effects on our lives.

Thus there is no historical problem that interests people more than that of the recurrence of wars. Unfortunately, history cannot provide the answer, not only because of the inherent difficulties of the problem, but also because war is a generic term, covering local skirmishes, large-scale battles, and international conflicts. Moreover, it is not always easy to tell when a given war began and when it ended. Even the Hundred Years' and Thirty Years' wars were not quite as long as their names imply, since they were interrupted by lengthy periods of relative peace. Large-scale wars are generally preceded and succeeded by small ones, politically inseparable from them—e.g. the Balkan Wars and the Allied War of Intervention in Russia before and after the First World War.

Because of these complications it seems much more logical to compare total periods of military intervention, rather than specific wars, and this is precisely what investigators of periodic war phenomena have usually done. From such investigations it would appear that during the 18th, 19th, and early 20th centuries, world-shaking military disputes occurred at approximate intervals of 50 years. Within roughly two hundred years, there were five long periods of armed conflict consisting of the War of the Spanish Succession (1701–14), the period of the War of the

Austrian Succession and the Seven Years War (1740–1763), the
Napoleonic wars (1796–1815), the Crimean War (1853–1856),
the German and Italian wars for unification up to the end of the
Franco-Prussian War (1871) and finally the First World War
(1914–1918). Unfortunately, this scheme breaks down if we
apply it to the Second World War or, for that matter, to the
16th and 17th centuries. In other words, the periodic nature of
wars which, for a time, was an article of faith with some historians, is just another historic fallacy.

Toynbee tried to repair the damage when he traced Western
history back to 1494. Proceeding rather arbitrarily, he set up
five great war and peace cycles, the first and last of which were
somewhat irregular. Every one of Toynbee's cycles consists of
two periods of war and two periods of peace which, in some of
the cycles, are preceeded by premonitory wars. This is how
Toynbee tabulated his results.[1]

*Successive Occurrences of the War and Peace Cycle in
Modern and post-Modern Western History*

Phase	Overture (1494–1568)	First Regular Cycle (1568–1672)	Second Regular Cycle (1672–1792)	Third Regular Cycle (1792–1914)	Fourth Cycle (1914–)
(1) Premonitory Wars (the Prelude)	—	—	1667–8	—	1911–12
(II) The General War	1494–1525	1568–1609	1672–1713	1792–1815	1914–18
(III) The Breathing Space	1525–1536	1609–18	1713–33	1815–48	1918–39
(IV) Supplementary Wars (the Epilogue)	1536–59	1618–48	1733–63	1848–71	1939–45
(V) The General Peace	1559–68	1648–72	1763–92	1871–1914	

If our present fourth cycle were to develop like the earlier
cycles, we should be able to look forward to a very long era of
general peace, but Toynbee himself was reluctant to make so
optimistic a prognosis, for, as he saw it, the Second World War
had been far too violent to be regarded as a mere supplement to

[1] Arnold J. Toynbee: *A Study of History* (London–N.Y.–Toronto
1954), Vol. 9, p. 255.

the First World War, and its outcome too indecisive for it to be looked upon as an epilogue. Moreover the respective intervals between the individual phases of the fourth cycle are out of phase with the corresponding intervals of the other cycles, even if we agree with Toynbee that the war phases have a tendency to grow shorter and the peace phases to grow longer. When all is said and done, Toynbee's scheme is a worse guide to the future than even the older theory of a fifty-year cycle was.

Perhaps we had best give up any idea of working with long war and peace periods altogether, and try instead to ascertain the length of specific wars and the peaceful intervals between them. If we do so, we shall find that, during the last 250 years, there have been roughly two years of peace for every year of war.

The 13 years of the War of the Spanish Succession (1701 to 1714) were followed by 26 years of peace; the 23 years of the Silesian wars (1740–1763) which were punctuated by fairly long peaceful intervals, were followed by 33 years of peace; the 19 years of the Napoleonic Wars (1796–1815) were followed by 38 years of peace which continued until the Crimean War (1853); the subsequent 18-year war period which lasted until the end of the Franco-Prussian War (1871) was followed by 40 years of relative peace until the war between Italy and Turkey (1911). From then on Eastern Europe was in an almost constant state of war right up to 1920. This nine year war period gave way to 18 years of peace. The Second World War lasted for six years, or rather for almost eight years if we include Hitler's annexation of Austria and Czechoslovakia. If the last war, too, were to be followed by a period of peace twice its own duration, a new war ought to be expected by 1960.

The fact that war and peace are in the approximate ratio of 1 : 2 is no mystical accident, but can be explained in physiological and psychological terms. Nations like individuals must recuperate after long periods of great strain, and the human organism needs roughly twice as much time to recover as it takes to lose its strength. This explanation is far more convincing than the old contention that one generation will never fight two wars, since many men have been known to volunteer for as many as three wars, provided only that the intervals were long enough for them to regain their strength and equanimity.

Large states and small

The rhythmical alternation of war and peace is closely related to another periodic phenomenon. For a number of decades successful wars are followed by a drive towards amalgamation with the consequent disappearance or annexation of smaller and weaker countries. The national resentment of these weaker countries then grows stronger and stronger, until finally the large states are forced to decentralise. The phase of decentralisation continues until the nationalism of the young states becomes so aggressive that peace and economic stability are threatened even more than they were by centralised states. Then the pendulum swings back again.

The phases of this development do not necessarily coincide with periods of war and peace, and many countries have gained independence without war or even revolution—for instance, Norway when she seceded from Sweden. On the other hand, even wars of conquest have often ended in the dissolution of established empires and the formation of countless new states. The popular belief that scientific progress leads to greater centralisation is not borne out by past events. What really happened during the last 200 years can be summarised as follows:

American Independence (1783), was followed in 1787 by a marked period of centralisation which continued until the first decade of the Napoleonic wars. Scores of minor states disappeared, and the few new states created by Napoleon were mere vassals without real independence. In 1810, the trend began to be reversed, first in South America, where a whole series of new states were set up right up to 1822, and then in Europe (Greece, Belgium 1830). With the German Customs Union (1833) a new centralisation period was begun. This period culminated in the unification both of Italy and of Germany and lasted until 1871. From then on, self-determination, particularly in central and eastern Europe gave rise to the founding of the Balkan states in 1878, Norway's declaration of independence in 1905, Albania's in 1912 and Ireland's in 1921, together with the formation of Czechoslovakia, Yugoslavia, the restoration of Poland, the foundation of the Baltic states, of Syria, and of Iraq (1918 to 1920). A new centralistic wave began with Italy's annexation of Abyssinia in 1936, Germany's of Austria and Czechoslovakia

(1938–1939) and Russia's of the Baltic states during the Second World War. Since 1947 (Independence of India, Pakistan, Indonesia, Morocco, Tunisia, the formation of Israel, the division of Indo-China) there has been another great wave of independence.

Thus the last 170 years have known three Centralisation and Decentralisation cycles, viz.:

Period	Characteristic	Duration
1787–1809	Centralisation	23 years
1810–1832	Decentralisation	23 ,,
1833–1877	Centralisation	45 ,,
1878–1921	Decentralisation	44 ,,
1922–1946	Centralisation	25 ,,
1947–	Decentralisation	—

The present period of decentralisation is characterised by anti-colonialism and anti-imperialism. Foreign ideologies are increasingly being challenged (e.g. in Hungary in 1956), and we may be certain that this period has a very long time to run yet.

CHAPTER 5

Wishing and Choosing

*T*HE WORD "EXPERIENCE" CONTAINS AN IMPLICIT EXPEC-
tation: the assumption that past successes or failures are
yardsticks for the future, as well. Certain materials will continue
to wear well, friends will continue to be amicable, committees
will continue to squabble, and so on. The moment, however,
we put this tacit assumption to the test, we find that many of our
"experiences" are based on a very small number of instances,
or on only a single one. For instance, the man whose washing
machine is faulty and who wants to replace it with a new one,
may be said to know infinitely more about the old than about the
new machine (the ratio of his knowledge about them is 1 : 0),
even though his original experience was purely negative.
However, this purely negative conclusion may be false for he
may not have known how to use the original machine correctly
or for the purposes for which it was designed. In any case,
he would be quite wrong to generalise from an exceptional
case.

This is a difficulty encountered in any one of countless
decisions that face us with alternatives. If the decision, i.e. a
particular purchase, is important enough and if we have time
enough, we may consult someone more experienced, but
generally no such person is on the spot, and we are forced to rely
on the salesman or some other interested party. Only if the
salesman looks particularly unreliable do we generally ignore
his advice and rely on our own experience, however meagre.

Freedom of choice

Pseudo-experiences, i.e. experiences based on insufficient
evidence, play a very important role in political, and particularly in economic life. It is due to them that mankind makes so

many false predictions and is so often disappointed even where it would be relatively simple to have genuine experiences and to form correct judgments. A very good example is our ignorance of the quality of most of the goods we purchase in shops. While the state often relieves us of worry in that respect, for instance in the case of dangerous drugs, in the assaying of metals, and in seeing that weights and measures are standardised, it generally prefers to allow us to learn by our mistakes. Only in technical colleges and particularly in domestic science colleges are young men and women taught anything at all about the quality of materials, and most men, no matter how educated, will make their way in the world without the slightest inkling that, as far as common purchases are concerned, they are at any swindler's mercy.

Undoubtedly, this not an accidental fault of our educational system, but reflects the democratic wish that human beings must be allowed to choose freely, at whatever risk to themselves. And every choice contains a risk: the risk of choosing wrongly. The less experienced a man, the more his choice becomes like a gamble—he must trust to luck, to price differences, or to the good faith of others.

The wide variety of choices is most certainly one of the greatest attractions of large shops. True the choices are not quite as large as some would have us believe, for consumer research has shown clearly that we shop according to fairly rigid patterns. The vast majority of customers are conservative and buy what they have always bought. This is just another reason why purchasers have very much less experience than they usually believe. Freedom of choice is widest in women's dress shops, but here fashion rules too supreme to leave very much room for individual decisions.

Client motivation

Nevertheless, the range of consumer goods that is subject to sudden changes of demand is large enough for thousands of manufacturers and merchants to ask themselves year in and year out what it is that the public really wants. The correct answer to this question is a matter of life and death for any progressive business, particularly in times of prosperity and growing individual incomes, when large sections of the population buy goods that they could not afford before, and thus face entirely new choices.

During the prosperous twenties, industrialists, and American industrialists in particular, began to take a keen interest in this subject and their interest did not diminish when times became so bad that salesmen had once again to go chasing after customers.

Surprisingly enough, neither manufacturers nor merchants knew very much about the public's real needs. To bridge this gap, a new science—consumer research—was born between the two world wars. Experts began to investigate what goods were in demand, which markets were saturated, which sections of the population were potential customers for which products and what individual wishes they had.

In the course of a few years, an entirely new technique for answering these apparently trivial, but in practice fairly complex, questions was developed. Whole mountains of questionnaires were sent out—some quite straightforward, others less so. Thus, General Motors did not enquire what cars their potential customers would most like to own, but presented an illustrated list of technical innovations and asked the public which of these interested them *least*.

Written questionnaires were frequently supplemented by personal interviews, and most firms used all their ingenuity to consult the largest possible number of people. However, after some time it emerged that more significant results could be obtained from interviewing a relatively small number of carefully chosen people rather than a very large unrepresentative mass. Quality was found to be more important than mere quantity—where quality did not of course mean intellect or education, but representative opinion.

But what are the criteria whereby a given individual's opinion is judged to be representative of a large group? Though this question has been discussed time after time and at great length, no one to this day can tell you precisely what the ideal guinea pig must look like. The beloved "man in the street", the "average American", the "average buyer", and the "average driver", are mere phantoms with no real existence. It is the experts' job to find people who resemble this phantom as closely as possible, i.e. people whose tastes, inclinations, and wishes best reflect those of the public at large. In this way the organisers of questionnaires can save much time and trouble, time being the more important factor of the two. A car manufacturer who is about to launch a new model, cannot afford to waste time on analysing a mass of questionnaires, since, by the time he has tabulated all the results, the new model may well have become outdated.

All such questionnaires are, after all, simply an effort to take stock of public opinion at a given moment, and not at some future date, though the results are, of course, to be used for practical actions in the future. It is here that the main difficulty of consumer research lies, for if the results of questionnaires lead to mere short-term prognoses, the enquiries must be repeated at frequent and regular intervals, which involves a great deal of labour, expense, and delay.

Straw votes

In about 1930, consumer research methods were applied to American politics, as well. Since elections are not normally held every day, not even professional politicians can always tell how the electors feel during the interval. The circulation figures of politically biased newspapers cannot help them here, for the political complexion of a given paper is no true guide to its readers' opinion. Since American political parties only really spring to life during elections and play a small part in public life at other times, little is known about a given candidate's chances before nomination. Candidates and their agents are therefore most anxious to test the mood of the electorate before they rush into very costly campaigns. For instance, they would like to know which seats are safe, and which must be made safer by increased propaganda. But even the electors themselves, and particularly those who are not very interested in politics at normal times, take a sudden interest in their fellow citizens' opinions and in their candidates' chances as the election date approaches.

Newspapers and journals have always tried to satisfy their readers' curiosity in this respect, publishing forecasts weeks or even months before the poll. Since the readers were not particularly interested in mere editorial opinion on this subject—in democratic countries, an editor's voice counts for no more than that of Tom, Dick, or Harry—the papers concerned had to organise public opinion polls, or "straw votes".

The first "straw vote" was organised by the "Harrisburg Pennsylvanian" before the 1824 Presidential Election.[1] At that time, communications were such that it was impossible to get anything other than local opinions in good time, and the "straw votes" were therefore bound to differ widely from the actual election results. The public looked upon them as a kind of parlour game in which they participated with relish though with little faith. Many years later, when the great *New York Herald* organised a similar poll, the predictions were still so wide of the mark that they might just as well have been drawn out of a hat.

But as the numerical gulf between Democrats and Republicans began to narrow, and as winning an election was often a matter of only a few votes, papers tried desperately to satisfy their readers' curiosity in more reliable ways. Elections results had become almost a lottery, and more and more people had begun to gamble on them. Wall Street would give the odds every day, and everyone had a glorious time—except, of course, the losers. Things changed again in the twenties when during three successive presidential elections—1920, 1924, and 1928— the Republicans emerged so obviously victorious that the outcome seemed a foregone conclusion, and the odds offered ceased to be worth taking. Instead people began to bet on what percentage of the votes a given candidate or party would obtain, and a great deal of money changed hands in those days of general speculation.

The press was keen not to let its readers down, and plied them with well-meant tips. Before the 1928 elections, no less than 85 newspapers and journals made private enquiries, generally by means of questionnaires. Others preferred to simplify the procedure by ringing up every tenth or twentieth

[1] Albert B. Blankenship: *Consumer and Opinion Research* (N.Y.- London 1943), p. 4.

subscriber in the local telephone directory, while yet others sent out special reporters to interview voters at home or in the street. The principle common to all these enquiries was that the more people were interviewed, the better the results would be. In contradistinction to consumer research, opinion research stressed quantity rather than quality—after all, everyone over twenty-one years of age was equally entitled to cast his vote.

In fact the questionnaires did anything but reflect the real opinions of the total electorate. Telephone enquiries, for instance, completely ignored the many people who were without telephones, and questionnaires, which were generally sent to regular newspaper subscribers whose addresses were easily obtained, but who usually belonged to the middle classes, told one little about the intentions of, say, the workers. In consequence, the electoral chances of the conservative candidates were generally over-estimated—this happened not only in American elections.[1] Still, the erroneous belief persisted that the greater the number of questionnaires, the more accurate the results would be. The record was held by the American monthly *Literary Digest* which sent its readers millions of postcards with short and pointed questions before every election, and received many hundreds of thousands of replies. In fact, in 1932, before Roosevelt's first electoral victory the *Literary Digest's* forecast was out by only 1%.

The Gallup Poll

In view of such striking achievements, it seemed rather impertinent for the young American journalist George Gallup to claim that large numbers were irrelevant, and that equally accurate or better predictions could be made with a small but very carefully selected sample of the population and a small team of skilled interviewers. While Gallup's approach may not have been entirely new, there was nevertheless a radical difference between the old method of asking a few hundred people which vacuum cleaners they preferred and predicting the political opinions of the U.S. electorate by similar methods.

[1] H. J. Eysenck: *Uses and Abuses in Psychology* (London 1955), p. 153.

For while the manufacturer merely takes the public pulse and may or may not act accordingly—it is, after all, an open question whether his actual successes were due to his acting on the advice of opinion polls, or to other factors, e.g. good ideas, good organisation, good marketing, etc.—political opinion polls stand or fall by the results, and the organisers must take full blame for their errors.

No wonder, therefore, that George Gallup was met with great reserve when he suggested to a number of American newspapers that they apply his system to the 1936 presidential election. It took him a long time to convince the editors that his system was much cheaper than the customary mass enquiries, and that surprisingly accurate predictions with his method had already been obtained, using a single interviewer and a mere 200 samples.[1]

In the end, 35 newspapers agreed to subscribe to his American Institute of Public Opinion, with the proviso that if his predictions about the presidential election of November 1936 proved less accurate than those obtained by the tried method of the *Literary Digest*, he would have to refund the entire cost of the investigation.[2] Fortunately for Gallup, it never came to that, for although the *Literary Digest* broke its own record by obtaining two million replies to its electoral postcards, its prediction was out by 19% while Gallup's prediction was out by less than 1%. Moreover, the *Literary Digest* had predicted that the Republican candidate A. M. Landon would obtain 56% of the total votes cast, when Franklin D. Roosevelt was, in fact, re-elected with an unusually large majority. Gallup was one of the few political prophets who had predicted this result correctly, at a time when most political experts were convinced that Roosevelt's New Deal was so unpopular that the Republicans were bound to oust him.

Because of this striking achievement Gallup's name was suddenly on everyone's lips. Not only was he the prophet of the moment, but it was generally conceded that he had founded a new and most important scientific method of prediction. The American Institute of Public Opinion was suddenly showered

[1] George Gallup: *A Guide to Public Opinion* (Princeton 1944), p. 16 f.
[2] Pierre Lazareff: *L'Opinion publique: comment la déceler?* Les Annales (Paris) January 1956, p. 26

with money and commissions, and the "Gallup Poll" became a generic concept for public opinion polls the world over. That same year, a British Institute of Public Opinion—the British Gallup Poll—was founded under the auspices of the *News Chronicle*, and France, Australia, Canada and Sweden quickly followed suit. In all these developments, the American mother institute not only took pride of place, but continues to play the leading role.

Red beans and white

What are the secrets of Gallup's success, and within what limits can his system operate efficiently?

George Gallup, who likes to romanticise his own career, tells us that the whole idea came to him while he was a student of psychology at Iowa University. During an experiment with a bag of red and white beans, he was struck by the fact that, twice in succession, he pulled out handfuls of beans whose colours were in the same ratio as those of the entire bag (3 : 7). Beans have therefore played the same role in Gallup's life, as the famous apple is said to have played in Newton's though, strictly speaking, there is a difference, since Newton's discovery was the result of an inevitable physical process, while Gallup's was not. Had he put his hands into the bag a few more times, he would have been most unlikely to have continued to pull out red and white beans in the same ratio. Thus Gallup's original discovery was sheer luck, and luck is precisely what he insists must be obviated in scientific polls.

In fact, it was the older methods of predicting election results which had acted as if the whole enquiry was a giant bag of red and white beans mixed in a fixed ratio, and that, short of counting the entire contents of the bag, it was best to count as much of it as possible. This sounds very logical but is an error in fact, for even if as many as 50% or even 66% of the beans had been counted, little could be said about the rest—the beans may not have been thoroughly "shuffled". The whole process is reminiscent of the old story about the peasant who, having been paid £100 in cash, counted the first 70 notes and then put all the money in his pocket saying that since the count was correct so far, he had no reason to suspect the remainder.

Unlike these earlier prophets, Gallup based his investigations on sociological rather than purely arithmetical considerations. To him, the electorate was not an amorphous mass of Republicans and Democrats, as the election figures might have led one to believe. In reality the electorate was made up of different social strata with different political trends. Thus farmers vote differently from industrial workers, the North votes quite unlike the South, Negro preferences differ from those of the Whites, employers have other interests than employees, and so on. Then there are differences of age and sex, for it appears that older people and most women usually vote for conservative parties.

We could continue this list of biological, economic and social differences which affect election results *ad infinitum*. For practical purposes, however, some of the finer distinctions must be ignored, for though the census figures show the composition of the electorate according to age, sex, vocation and to some extent according to income, there are other factors for which we have no up-to-date statistical data. To carry out comprehensive private investigations of all these factors before every election would take up far too much time and money.

It is therefore quite impossible to construct a true mirror image of the entire electorate in the opinion poll laboratory, but even a slightly blurred image is always better than no image at all. Gallup therefore samples his subjects mainly according to six factors: state, size of community, age, sex, income, and political affiliation. Other factors may also be taken into account from time to time, e.g. the national origins of electors during the last war.

Only when the structural composition of the electorate has been adequately reconstructed, can the purely arithmetical question of how many people in every state, in every income group, etc. must be interviewed, be solved. Once this is done, probability laws take over, and the more people are interviewed the more exact the estimates will be. However, above a certain maximum, the accuracy increases by no more than a fractional percentage. Whenever errors of 1–2% are permissible, a few thousand questionnaires will accurately reflect the opinions of the total U.S. electorate.

Predicting elections today

Gallup maintains that, with correct sampling, the predictions made on the basis of only 100 questionnaires would not be out by more than 15%, those made on the basis of 900 questionnaires would reflect electoral opinion to within 5%, while 10,000 questionnaires would involve a margin of error of only 1·5%.[1] Beyond that figure, the margin of error decreases so insignificantly that, in election forecasts, it may be safely neglected. Before the 1936 elections, when Gallup was still on probation, he interviewed no more than 3000 out of 80 million eligible and 45 million actual voters. In other words, though only one in every 27,000 eligible voters (or one in every 15,000 actual voters) was consulted, the results were exceptionally accurate.

True, not all Gallup's predictions were as accurate as that, for of the 114 election forecasts made by the Institute between 1936 and 1944, only 19 were out by less than 1%, 39 were out by between 2 and 3%, nearly half were out by more than 3%, and six were out by as much as 10–15%.

The Gallup system had its greatest setback during the 1948 presidential election in which Truman and not Gallup's favourite, Dewey, was elected. Actually, the error was not all that great, for though Truman was 9% ahead of Dewey, two outsiders had obtained 10% of the votes so that the victor did not gain an absolute majority over his opponent—a rare event in U.S. politics. Before Eisenhower's election in 1952 and re-election in 1956 there was little doubt about the outcome, and Gallup did in fact make fairly accurate forecasts.

The American results were excelled by those obtained by the British Institute of Public Opinion which, using the same methods, managed to forecast a number of Parliamentary elections within a margin of error of only 0·5%. In France, too, the "Institut Français d'Opinion Publique" managed to forecast parliamentary results with a margin of error that rarely exceeded 2%.

Having had more than twenty years experience of Gallup polls, we may say that Gallup's method of sampling the electorate has proved most successful. Despite a few failures, the results go far

[1] G. Gallup, op. cit., p. 17.

beyond any previous expectations. Before Gallup, political predictions were no more than shots in the dark, and it is thanks to his achievement that we can nowadays speak of scientific forecasts in this difficult field. This is a significant advance, indeed.

The art of prediction

No doubt, current methods of taking the public pulse are capable of vast improvement. While Gallup and his disciples have written a great deal about the basis and workings of his methods, they have kept the details of their sampling procedure a strict trade secret. But even if this secret were ever wrested from them, they have little to fear from unfair competitors, for election forecasting is an art rather than a strict science.

And Gallup is an excellent teacher of that art. He has personally trained a large staff of assistants and can throw an army of interviewers into any strategic point, if speedy analyses are needed. In the United States alone, there are about 1,000 interviewers, mainly part-time, who must not only know how to ask questions but must also be very familiar with local conditions, in order to select their samples. The Institute merely indicates how many persons in every category have to be interviewed, and the final choice is left to the interviewers' sole discretion, provided that they do not question the same voter more than once a year.

Since the personal qualities of interviewers are of the utmost importance, there is always the danger that, no matter how careful the choice of personnel, a subjective note may be introduced into the results. Governments try to avoid this pitfall by prescribing to Census officials exactly whom they are to interview, but this merely shifts the problem to a higher level.

Moreover, official sources generally prefer "area sampling" to Gallup's "group sampling" and the choice of area is, of course, a matter of personal judgment. Area sampling is, in any case, the costlier and more laborious of the two methods, and for that reason alone avoided by most Private Opinion Poll Institutes.

It is difficult to say which of the two is generally preferable since, apart from election forecasts, the accuracy of predictions can be evaluated in only the rarest of cases. In commercial enquiries the predictions can be checked to some extent at least against sale results, but in social enquiries no such criteria exist. Despite this fact—or precisely because of it—Americans have tried to apply Gallup's technique to every possible sphere. Thus polls are taken not only of public opinion about proposed legislation and about the international situation, but also about belief in the immortality of the soul and the Day of Judgment. There is no means of making sure how representative the replies are of public opinion as a whole, since it is unlikely that any government will hold referenda on these topics.

Is democracy endangered?

Many opinion polls are simple investigations rather than fore-casts, let alone methods of propagating ideas. Nevertheless, they may have a persuasive effect and considerable repercussion on the future. When Gallup avers that 75% of the American people believe in life after death, this may go a long way towards persuading some of the sceptics, and when Kinsey in his famous investigation of the sex life of the American adult (which was based on the Gallup system)[1] concludes that 50% of American women have pre-marital relations with men, the other 50% may be inclined to become less chaste. Such effects are un-avoidable, particularly in a country as conformist as the United States.

"A whole town cannot lie", Sartre has an American Senator say in one of his plays—least of all, we might add, if its opinions are confirmed by a Gallup Poll. We need, therefore, not be sur-prised to learn that most of the people's elected representatives pay great heed to opinion polls, though some are too proud to bow to the popular will. Still, if they will be pig-headed, they must not be surprised if they are thrown out of office.

It is for this very reason that Gallup Polls have been decried as exerting an improper influence on American politics. Gallup himself has hotly contested this imputation. Polls, far from

[1] A. C. Kinsey *et al*: *Sexual Behaviour in the Human Male* (Philadelphia 1948); *Sexual Behaviour in the Human Female* (Philadelphia 1953).

endangering democracy, may well be a democratic method of enabling people to have their say even outside the voting booths. Such a system, has, in effect, been used successfully in Switzerland, where all important legislation is decided by popular vote.

Meanwhile, public opinion polls are increasingly being applied to non-political events, even outside the United States. Thus the church of St. Sulpice, one of the largest in Paris, called on the *Institut Dourdin* (which uses Gallup's methods) to organise a poll on "What non-believers think about us". The result of the poll was published in the church magazine and was made the subject of three sermons by the priest, who assured his readers that he had derived great spiritual benefit from the replies.[1] The *Institut Dourdin*, however, also plays a more secular role, and has organised discreet polls about the popularity of a number of stars of the stage who were worried about their next public appearance.

But no matter what the subject of the enquiry, all such polls are based on the same principle: correct sampling, and the assumption that public opinion will not change radically until, say, the next election, referendum, or other specific event. Only in very rare cases is it assumed that public opinion will remain unchanged for a longer period.

Opinion polls therefore predominantly aim at short-term prognoses, and generally make no attempt to predict public attitudes in, say, two or three years' time. Even so, periodic questionnaires on specific subjects may well provide the key to trends of opinion, and thus lead to successful long-range forecasts. In this way public opinion polls would cease being a static and become a dynamic technique instead.

[1] *Les Annales* (Paris), January 1956, p. 28.

CHAPTER 6

Weather Prophets

METEOROLOGISTS ARE THE ONLY PROPHETS EMPLOYED by the state, which prefers to leave other methods of prediction, e.g. public opinion polls and economic forecasts, in private hands even when it does make use of them. Weather forecasts, however, are needed by so many people that it is only right to expect the taxpayer to foot the bill.

But though their services have always been in great demand, meteorologists have one of the most thankless jobs imaginable. The errors of other prophets are often overlooked, but weather forecasts can be read and checked by anyone old enough to read a newspaper, and few men are prepared to make allowances when their favourite football game or picnic is washed out despite forecasts to the contrary. Even people whose activities are fairly independent of weather conditions will become terribly angry about false weather forecasts, often accusing the meteorologists of robbing them of a precious day in their lives. This is true even if the promised rain turns out to be sunshine. Men are inclined to remember one false forecast and forget a host of correct ones.

Perhaps all this violent carping is no more than a reflection of the great esteem in which the public really holds its weather prophets, or else it is a relic of those days in the not too distant past when meteorologists used to be quite wrong most of the time. For although weather forecasts fell into the province of most ancient court prophets, scientific meteorology is a very young discipline. It was only in the middle of the 19th century that international weather stations were first set up, and without these stations even the shrewdest local observations were bound to be as good as useless.

Astro-meteorology

The reason why scientific meteorology grew up so late, is the direct result of its having been reared as the step-child of astrology. Even the greatest minds of antiquity thought it self-evident that weather conditions were governed by the stars, and it never occurred to them that the earth had an atmosphere of its own. The term "atmosphere"—circle of mist—was, in fact, only coined towards the end of the 17th century. Before then the "air" surrounding the earth was thought to be completly devoid of matter.

To the minds of the ancients, clouds, rain, thunder and lightning were all controlled by the gods—in Greece, by Zeus himself. *Meteorologia* was the doctrine of transcendental and particularly of celestial phenomena—not, as we might have thought, of meteors.

The Greeks were nevertheless too shrewd to rely on astrological weather predictions, and none of the oracles were expected to prophesy droughts or periods of plenty from the constellations, as, for instance, Babylonian prophets were. If a prince from distant lands absolutely insisted on being told whether meteorological conditions would be propitious for a future campaign, the priests would oblige, but on the whole they preferred to steer clear of this equivocal subject altogether. Even when Alexander's campaigns led to closer contact between Chaldean astrologers and the Greek oracles, the latter continued to give the weather a wide berth, and to stick to less risky horoscopes.

Astrological weather prediction only began to come into its own in the Middle Ages. Forecasts were generally made for months or even years ahead on the assumption that "conjunctions" (which could be worked out well in advance with the help of tables) always caused catastrophic weather. It was this assumption which enabled John of Toledo to make the predictions which, as we saw, caused universal panic towards the end of the 12th century. Although none of his prophecies, viz. that the conjunction of the seven planets under Libra would cause terrible storms which would lay waste cities and ruin the entire harvest, were ever fulfilled, similar prophecies continued to be made, all based on the same assumption.

Astrological, like other, prophecies, if repeated often enough, must occasionally come true, but astrological weather prophets were singularly unfortunate in that not a single one of their

28. Title page of one of many pamphlets proclaiming a flood in 1524.

promised catastrophes ever occurred. The greatest sensation, but also the greatest flop, came in the year 1524 when, on the basis of a prediction made in Johannes Stöffler's Almanach 25 years earlier, a great flood was expected on the 2nd February. On that date a number of planets were expected to meet under Pisces. The matter was keenly discussed and no less than 137 pamphlets about it were published. Though some weighty voices objected that God had clearly promised mankind never again to destroy the earth with another great flood,[1] many people deemed it wiser not to rely on a promise made so long ago and to imitate the example of Noah instead. Huge arks were

[1] Genesis 9, 11.

built in Toulouse, and though no provision was made to house "every living thing of all flesh" in them, enough provisions were hoarded to enable many citizens to weather the expected flood. In a number of ports, all available ships were requisitioned and the local population quartered on them.[1]

The Margrave of Brandenburg, who lacked a fleet or enough funds to float an ark on the river Spree, was forced to take his court and most of his loyal subjects to the Kreuzberg, a small hill south of Berlin. Now the Kreuzberg is no Mount Ararat and its 150 ft. peak could hardly have been expected to offer the population much shelter. Fortunately, the astrological gods had once again sounded a false alarm and the Margrave, together with his retinue, could return home without even a wetting. Oddly enough, the whole episode was forgotten only a few decades later, so much so that the great and highly learned Melanchthon, in his public lectures on the usefulness of astrology, supported his arguments with the claim that Stöffler's predictions were fulfilled in 1524.

Florentine illumination

But not everyone was as tolerant of astrologers as Melanchthon. Thus the 15th century Italian classicist Pico della Mirandola wrote: "For a whole winter, I have taken observation of daily weather conditions and checked these against astrological predictions. May fate punish me if I do not speak the truth: on the 130 days or more that I made my observations, there were no more than six or seven days in which the weather agreed with what was written in astrological books."[2]

Absurd though astrological weather forecasts were, they had the beneficial effect of inducing critics to make regular notes on the weather. While this was a purely negative measure, these records were to lay the foundation of a future science.

The first steps in scientific weather research were taken in

[1] Rudolf Thiel: *Und es war Licht* (Hamburg 1956), p. 67 f.
[2] Giovanni Pico della Mirandola: *Selected Writings*. German ed. by Arthur Liebert (Jena 1905), p. 261.

29. Evangelista Torricelli, the inventor of the
barometer (1643).

Galileo's workshop. Galileo himself had invented the thermometer, and in 1643 one of his pupils, Evangelista Torricelli,
invented a handy apparatus for measuring atmospheric pressure,
the Torricelli tube, which was, in fact, the first barometer. The
news about this miraculous tube took Europe by storm, and only
five years later, Pascal proved experimentally that atmospheric
air could actually be weighed, i.e. that it consisted of matter.
However, his ideas ran so much counter to popular belief, that
another century was to pass before they were generally
accepted. Still, there was no disagreement about the practical
usefulness of the barometer, for when the mercury column
rose, a clear sky, and when it fell, mist and rain, could
generally be expected. As observations proceeded, it became
clear that the barometer did not, in fact, work quite as simply

as all that, and that other factors, as well, had to be taken into consideration.

One of the most striking aspects of barometric weather forecasts was that they introduced realistic concepts of time into meteorology. While astrologers had prided themselves on their ability to make weather forecasts for centuries ahead, the new science concentrated on tomorrow's weather instead. Hours had taken the place of eons, and weather forecasts had become less fantastic, if less imposing. Thermometers and barometers had found their way into most households, and now even the most illiterate people could foretell (or thought they could) the temperature and next day's weather, and act accordingly.

The three great L's

Professional meteorologists were the first to suffer, since their services seemed to have become redundant. Then three famous French scientists, Lavoisier, Lamarck, and Laplace, began to repair the damage. Unlike the three great B's of music—Bach, Beethoven, and Brahms—the three great L's of science were contemporaries—all three were born in the 1740's—and close friends. They came to meteorology by quite different paths: Lavoisier from chemistry, Lamarck from botany, and Laplace from astronomy.

The first start was made by Lavoisier, who set up a chain of weather stations in France from which he received regular reports. Lavoisier became a very wealthy man, when the French government rewarded him for his scientific experiments by appointing him one of its *fermiers généraux* and commissioners of powder. This sinecure was to prove his downfall, for the French Revolution sent everyone of the 28 *fermiers généraux* to the guillotine. No exception was made for Lavoisier for, as the prosecutor-general put it, the republic needed no scholars.

Lavoisier's death was at one and the same time the defeat of the first attempt to set up a scientific meteorological institute. Lamarck lacked the financial means to keep Lavoisier's weather stations going, and was forced to rely on his own observations. Fortunately, he was an outstanding observer. At home in the plant and animal kingdoms like few others, he now directed his keen eyes towards the sky—not at the stars, which he left to better mathematicians, but at the clouds. While millions of people had done just that before him, and like Hamlet had been content to see that clouds looked now like camels, now like weasels and now like whales,[1] no one had ever thought of classifying clouds according to their shapes and other characteristics. This was to be Lamarck's achievement, for though it took meteorologists almost a hundred years to agree on an international system of cloud classification, it was Lamarck's language that they eventually employed—with modifications.

To keep track of his observations, Lamarck began to compile weather charts with the assistance of Laplace, one of the greatest mathematicians and astronomers of his day. These two men made a unique team. Lamarck, always concerned with concrete facts, was convinced that all nature was purposive and that the art of living was the art of adaptation. Thus, in 1809, in his *Philosophie Zoologique* he put forward the thesis that nature improved the organisation of animals gradually, and that all animals were modified in form and habit by their environment. No wonder that he was so interested in climate and weather conditions.

Laplace, on the other hand, took a more exalted and abstract view of nature. For him, all research was the discovery of universally valid laws. He was the strictest determinist of all time, and it is he who coined a phrase that was to remain on the lips of scientists for a whole century: "A mind which, at a given moment, had full knowledge of all the forces vitalising nature, and of the position of all the beings of which nature is composed, and which would, moreover, be broad enough to submit these phenomena to analysis, would be able to apply one and the same formula to the motions of the celestial bodies and the lightest atoms alike. Nothing would be uncertain for such a mind, and past and future would be immediately present."

Though Laplace was fully aware that his ideal was unattainable, he nevertheless suggested that it be used as a guiding principle in all research. It was with this aim in view that he developed his celestial mechanics, in which everything worked like a clock that needed no one to wind it up. Applying his ideas

[1] *Hamlet*, Act III, Scene 2.

to meteorology, he produced laws ·and calculations whose accuracy ·continues to astonish scientists to this day. The decrease of air pressure with increasing height—a phenomenon that had long been known to all mountaineers—was calculated precisely up·to a height of 30,000 meters where, in fact, the stratosphere throws Laplace's calculations out of gear. It was his realism which persuaded meteorologists not to waste their time on idle speculation. His *Annuaires météorologiques* (1800– 1812) were full of practical advice.

On the opposite side of the English Channel, as well, people had begun to take a keen interest in practical meteorological problems, particularly as they affected navigation. The weather in London or Manchester was no grave problem since, after all, most people could afford to carry umbrellas on their arms, but storms on the ocean wasted ships, lives, and a great deal of money. Though Parliament had repeatedly offered high rewards for discoveries and inventions that would contribute to the safety of ships and seamen, no one came forward with any practical means of predicting gales off the coast, let alone on the high sea. By the time Queen Victoria ascended the throne in 1837, this danger was no smaller than it had been 250 years earlier, when a storm, by destroying the Spanish Armada, made England the world's greatest maritime nation.

The debacle of Balaclava

The main trouble was the same on both sides of the Channel: ignorance of weather conditions in the rest of the world. By means of weather charts which were by then being drawn up in many parts of the world, a wealth of data had been accumulated, and it was known roughly how long it took for high pressure and low pressure areas to disperse, with what speed high winds travelled cross-country, and so on. But all this knowledge was useless for the simple reason that it could not be applied quickly enough. Even had the number of weather stations been increased tenfold, little advantage would have been gained, since the main fault lay in the slowness of communications. A whirlwind travels with an average speed of 30 m.p.h., i.e. four times as quickly as even the fastest coach, twice as quickly as the fastest dispatch rider. Even trains travelled much too slowly and too irregularly to carry news of storms before they broke.

This shortcoming was only remedied with the invention of the electric telegraph, or rather 15 years later when enough cables had been laid and enough equipment constructed. During the 19th century, sufficient progress had been made for every progressive town to have a telegraph office. Even then a major catastrophe was needed before governments realised the need for international exchanges of weather information.

On the 14th November 1854, during the Crimean War, French and British men o' war at anchor in the harbour of Balaclava were overcome by a sudden storm which endangered the success of the entire expedition. Paris was in an uproar, and in his desperation, the Minister of War, the Maréchal Vaillant, instructed the famous astronomer Leverrier, whose calculations had led to the discovery of Neptune, to devise a means of averting similar disasters in the future. Leverrier's considered reply was that he could only undertake that task if he could rely on a well organised network of weather stations, and the Maréchal granted Leverrier's demand.

By making inquiries from various scientific institutes, Leverrier managed to plot the route of the atmospheric disturbance that had led to the Balaclava disaster, and his map in itself was so convincing an argument, that even countries opposed to an international weather bureau, became converted. Observatories all over Europe began to wire daily weather reports to Paris and, in return, were warned by Paris of any storms moving in their direction. When Paris wired its first reports to the world at large on the 1st June 1860, the event marked a milestone in the history of scientific prediction.

An organisation had at last been set up that meteorologists had vainly tried to establish for generations. Oddly enough, this great advance did little to prevent meteorology from remaining stagnant for the next fifty years—it looked much the same in the early 20th century as Leverrier had left it in the middle of the 19th century.

Meteorologists will explain that this failure was the result of their art having fallen into the wrong hands, viz. into those of statisticians, instead of great mathematicians like Laplace. For a number of decades it was most fashionable for meteorological institutes, which had by then begun to lead a separate existence from astronomical observatories, to calculate nothing but averages. Average temperatures, average rainfall, average snowfall, average hours of sunshine, and so on, were recorded in every village worth its name, and favourable results were pasted up in large letters on all public places by way of advertisement. While this attracted holiday-makers, meteorology was becoming stifled by all these averages which had little predictive importance.[1]

Still, this insistence on averages alone could not have been the main reason why meteorology failed so badly, at a time in which all other branches of applied science made such great strides. The real reason was probably that the public demand for weather forecasts had greatly fallen off. The 19th century was largely an urban age, people lived in strong stone houses with strong roofs that no storm could dislodge; they dressed in protective clothes, and travelled by omnibus, tramway, or train which ran irrespective of weather conditions. Even ships had less to fear from the weather than before. In short, the weather had lost most of its threatening character, and was no longer worth bothering about a great deal.

War in the air

Things took a new turn with the advent of the aeroplane. Flying was not merely a triumph of mechanical genius and engineering know-how, but of meteorology, as well. Without prior research by meteorologists, the Wright brothers could never have hoped to keep their primitive equipment in the air for even a few minutes. Flying might have remained a mere sport, had not the First World War forced governments to call in their meteorologists.

The great meteorological contribution to aerial navigation was not made by any of the countries at war but by neutral Norway, where after years of careful observations, Vilhelm Bjerknes, a meteorologist attached to the Bergen Geophysical

[1] André Viaut: *La Météorologie* (Paris 1954), p. 8.

Institute, became convinced that there was something radically
wrong with all previous methods of weather-forecasting. Now,
since the first half of the 19th century meteorologists had
mainly concentrated on the study of cyclones, by which experts
mean a system of winds rotating around a centre of minimum
barometric pressure. Leverrier had made it a common dogma
that all cyclones were dangerous, and his thesis seemed completely corroborated when the Dutch meteorologist Buys-
Ballot formulated his general laws of storms (the Ballot Laws).
From then on, the prediction of storms seemed to be a matter of
pure calculation.

The only fly in the ointment was that the calculations did not
lead to particularly good forecasts, and it was for this reason
that Bjerknes opposed the cyclone theory with an entirely new
conception: the weather was decided, not by individual cyclones
but by general movements of air, particularly from the poles.
Vilhelm Bjerknes, and his son Jacob who formulated the new
theory even more precisely,[1] thought and wrote in the language
of their time, i.e. in World War I jargon, and their scientific
dicta read like so many military proclamations. The sky is in a
state of war, in which huge armies of cold and warm air face
each other in close battle formation to vanquish or to be vanquished, according to fixed strategic rules: if a cold front is
brought to a halt by a warm front, rain is formed behind the
former and if a warm front is halted by a cold front, rain forms
ahead of the warm front. If equally matched fronts face each
other, the outcome depends on their temperature differences.
In all cases the fronts are accompanied by specific cloud forma-
tions, so that their nature can be ascertained quite simply.

The Norwegian theory proved particularly useful for aerial
navigation. Before take-off, all pilots are handed a weather
chart on which the fronts they will meet are carefully recorded.
Such weather charts are, moreover, not used by airmen alone,
but have become one of the essential tools of all meteorologists.
Thus the entire meteorological system of the United States was
reorganised by Carl-Gustaf Rossby, one of Vilhelm Bjerknes's
pupils, to conform with the Norwegian system, and even French
meteorologists, who still base their predictions on the old cyclone

[1] W. J. Humphreys: *Ways of the Weather* (Lancaster, Pennsylvania
1944), pp. 387–390.

theory, have learnt to accept a great deal of the frontal theory, as well.

Naturally, theory is not the be all and end all of weather forecasting. Careful observations, accurate calculation, and an efficient system of international communications are as necessary today as ever they were. And communications continue to be the greatest bugbear, since as a result of bad international relations, meteorological co-operation has been steadily decreasing. Apparently the fronts of the Cold War are more intransigent than those of the atmosphere. Even so, regular weather reports are broadcast from eight centres: Arlington (U.S.A.), Rio de Janeiro, Rugby (England), Moscow, Vladivostok, Nairobi, Delhi, and Guam. Airmen, in particular, are well looked after, for more than 1200 meteorological forecasts are broadcast daily in international code.[1] Shipping, too, is kept in touch with meteorological development by nine floating weather-stations and 22 weather ships. The Communist bloc does not participate in this maritime service.

Freddy, the frog

On the whole, weather predictions have improved by leaps and bounds, though, in some respects, they have remained bogged down in uncertainty. Thus mountain-weather forecasts are still so unreliable that false forecasts often outnumber correct ones for weeks on end. According to the very reliable evidence of Councillor Robert Heindl, a leading Bavarian criminologist who lives just outside Munich and who made detailed records of rainfall, air temperature and hours of sunshine at 6 a.m., noon, and 6 p.m. from the 24th July to the 23rd August 1956, in order to compare his entries with the official weather forecasts for Southern Bavaria, not a single prediction was correct from 24th July–7th August. For the next two weeks, the Central German Meteorological Office predicted a persistent stable and dry spell, whereas Heindl noted rains, storms and even a monotonous drizzle. For three successive days, rain fell uninter-

[1] Eugène Pepin: *Géographie de la circulation aérienne* (Paris 1956), p. 110.

ruptedly. Our criminologist concluded from all this that his frog
Freddy seemed a better judge of the weather than all the
meteorological experts put together.[1]

Official weather forecasts like these remind us of Pico della
Mirandola's predictions made 500 years earlier. While we hold
no brief for frogs, let alone for astrologers, we cannot help
marvelling why meteorology has failed to make sufficient progress these last 500 years, to be able to predict mountain weather
accurately for even the next 24 hours.

In lower altitudes, on the other hand, it is quite usual to find
that 24-hour weather forecasts are correct over long periods,
and that the general trend of the weather is rarely miscast. But
even here, there are occasional errors in the time interval:
a change in the weather predicted for the next day may only take
place in two days, and vice versa. In Rio de Janeiro, where
meteorologists are particularly brave and fly coloured weather
flags from the tallest sky-scraper, people have often seen the
white, good weather, flag being hauled in almost as soon as it
was hoisted, and just before their city was turned into a second
Venice by a tropical downpour. But then Rio de Janeiro has an
exceptional position: not only does it lie on the sea, but it is
surrounded by a chain of mountains.

Still, many false weather forecasts are less due to adverse
geographical conditions, than to miscalculations. Weather
forecasts are based on countless factors, some of which—e.g.
temperature conditions—are so well-known that conclusions can
be drawn from them directly or by simple calculation. Other
factors, however, are so complicated that general weather predictions always involve a large subjective element, and the day
still seems far off when rules of thumb will enable every trained
meteorologist to predict the weather purely mechanically. As
it is, meteorology continues to be the application of known laws
to more or less unknown events.

Doubling the scope

Large meteorological institutions with sufficient equipment

[1] *Süddeutsche Zeitung* (Munich), 30th August 1956.

have more recently tried to extend weather forecasts not only in space but also in time. As late as 1920, no weather bureau would dare to make forecasts for more than 24 hours, and it was only in 1930 that the *Météorologie nationale* in Paris, which did pioneer work in this field, began to make 36-hour forecasts. In 1939, forecasts were extended to 48 hours, and since 1949, Paris and many other centres habitually make forecasts for two to four days ahead, though those for the last two days are usually couched in general terms.

While it may be said that this increase in the scope of meteorology represents a considerable achievement, this achievement pales into insignificance when compared with the rate of development of other branches of technology. From this fact alone we can conclude that the obstacles which meteorologists still have to surmount in applying their theories to natural processes, remain enormous. Their achievements in the aeronautical field are largely due to the fact that all forecasts are short-term: the weather charts for the guidance of pilots are compiled every three hours and all unforeseen changes are radioed out immediately. The faster an aeroplane, the simpler the task, particularly when there is a world-wide net of special radio stations. Moreover, radar nowadays enables aeroplanes to spot approaching storms and cyclones without outside assistance.

Compared with such short-range forecasts, our daily weather service must be considered a long-term forecast, and 48-hour forecasts as almost prophetic. In fact, 48 hours continues to be the upper limit of normal weather forecasts, since neither the Norwegian nor the cyclone theory can hope to make longer predictions, except under particularly favourable atmospheric conditions.

Such favourable conditions exist, for instance, when we know the velocity with which a "low" is travelling, in which case accurate forecasts for four or even five days can be made. Take the following actual forecast: "The atmospheric disturbance over the N. American Lakes at 1 p.m. on 12th January will have reached Newfoundland by 1 p.m. on the 13th January, and will have reached Europe via Ireland on the 15th, and via N. France early on the 17th January." To make this forecast, the weather staion in question knew no more than that an area of low pressure was travelling at about 36 m.p.h. eastwards along 50°N. Actually, such forecasts often go wrong, and even when the facts bear them out in detail, this is usually due to luck rather than to brilliant meteorological deductions.

Be that as it may, forecasts of the kind just mentioned are, in any case, within the technical scope of modern meteorology, whereas long term forecasts (one to three months) are not, since unlike short term forecasts, which are based on the analysis of concrete atmospheric phenomena, they are generally derived statistically, i.e. on the basis of past observations.

Geographically speaking, we know a number of centres of activity from which cyclones (depressions) and anticyclones (high pressure) take their origin. Anticyclones are usually formed in the Azores, the Bermuda Islands, Siberia, the central part of North America, while cyclones arise from Iceland and to a lesser extent from the Mediterranean. Now, we know that these regions are meteorologically related, i.e. high pressure in one will be accompanied by low pressure in another. Thus a depression between Iceland and Norway is usually accompanied by a high pressure area between the Azores and the Mediterranean, and if the winter is particularly severe in Northern Europe, it is usually very mild in North America and very cold in Mexico. But though theoretical considerations show that this compensatory process is somewhat similar to the simultaneous fluctuation of a liquid in the two arms of a U-tube, the phenomena are not quite simultaneous or not always equally strong. Thus Mexicans might be wrong to discard their heavy overcoats the moment they hear of a freeze-up in Canada.

Side by side with these more or less compensatory phenomena, meteorologists can also base their long term predictions on the occurrence of well-known sequences of events, most of which are still unexplained and simply taken for granted. One of the most curious of these is the relation between rainfall at distant points. Thus some meteorologists believe that there is a connection between the rainfall on the Faroe Islands and that on Berlin, the January–March rainfall in the former being a fairly accurate indication of the April–September downpour over the latter.[1] Berliners would therefore do well to look to the Faroes when deciding on the purchase of rainwear.

[1] René Valmar: *Pour prévoir le temps* (Paris 1953), p. 151.

Weather-lore

Although official weather prophets proclaim their opinions through wireless sets the world over, millions of people, most of them countryfolk, prefer to be their own weather prophets. Country weather-lore may differ from country to country, and from region to region, but it is always based on a mixture of ancient superstititions, relics of antiquated science, and very shrewd observation.

Countryfolk take their weather forecasts where they can. Their favourite assistants are birds, bats, flies, bees, spiders, worms, frogs, fish, cats, dogs, sheep, cattle—there is hardly a species of animal which does not serve the farmer as a weather prophet. And, in fact, animals do their job extremely well, for they are much more sensitive to weather changes than human beings. Certain animals are good-weather prophets, others are bad-weather prophets, and some combine both roles. Thus croaking frogs generally indicate good weather, unless they croak unusually loudly when a storm is to be expected. Bad weather is also imminent when toads and salamanders come out at night. Bees, on the other hand, retire to their hives before storms, and swarm in the early morning of bright days.

All these omens are usually short term warnings, for they occur only a few hours before the event. On the other hand, if cocks crow in the afternoon they are said to herald rain next day —a fairly long term prediction. But then cocks are so notoriously unreliable that, according to an adage: "If the cock begins to crow, we may have sunshine, rain, or snow."

More reliable still than the behaviour of animals, is the behaviour of certain plants which react to moisture in the air. The most famous of these "hygrometric" plants is the Scarlet Pimpernel, which the botanist John Gerard called a weather prophet as early as 1597, and which closes when rainy or cloudy weather is imminent. Since Gerard's day, a host of such "weather flowers" has been discovered, quite apart from artificial "flowers" saturated with chemicals, e.g. cobalt chloride, whose colour changes with the humidity of the air.

A third, and probably the oldest type of "natural" weather prediction is based on the direction of the wind. Every peasant has some knowledge on this subject, but to master it he must

XIV. Two Tarot-cards used for fortune telling. Tarot, like so many
other card games, is of Central Asian origin.

XV. Two of the cards used by Mlle. Lenormand (1768-1843) who
allegedly predicted Napoleon's rise and fall to him.

XVI.   A seance being conducted by the great Hanussen. The method illumination was new, the rest as old as the hills.

XVII.   Mrs. Günther Geffers being consulted by German detectives to solve a criminal case. She always "worked" in a trance.

also have keen eyes. Though proverbs about the wind, of which there are a vast collection, are rarely reliable, the wind is one of the best empirical criteria for judging weather changes.

Unfortunately traditional weather-lore can at best hope to tell the farmer his immediate meteorological future, when country-folk, more than anyone else, need predictions that not even scientific meteorology can provide at present. They would like to know many months in advance what the weather will be like at harvest time, whether the next winter will be particularly severe, the next summer dry, if there will be spring frosts, etc. Though most of the rules of thumb they use are based on past experience, popular weather-lore is like scientific meteorology in that the accuracy of both falls off rapidly the longer the term of the forecast.

Inasmuch as they are not based on some miraculous event in the far distant past, common-sense forecasts for the next season or for the next year work in much the same way as professional forecasts: they are either based on the principle of compensation or in the belief in cycles. There is a very widespread belief that within twelve months—not necessarily twelve calendar months —the total temperature is always constant, and that, for instance, a severe winter is followed by a very hot summer. Similarly with humidity—a dry winter is usually followed by a rainy summer.

The other idea, viz. that the weather is governed by periodic influences, comes to meteorology from astrology. The popular weather planet *par excellence* is the moon, every one of whose phases is said to have a special significance, the new moon, in particular, bringing weather changes. Careful investigations over the years have, however, shown that the moon has no perceptible influence whatsoever on the weather.

Sunspots

Meteorologists do, however, recognise the effect on the weather of other periodic phenomena. The most important of these is the sunspot cycle with a mean period of $11\frac{1}{2}$ years. While the exact causes of sunspots are not yet fully understood,[1] there are never-the-less a number of brilliant hypotheses on the subject. Formerly sunspots were considered to be solar clouds (Kirchhoff), slag deposits (Zöllner) or electro-magnetic storm centres (Hale), but recently they have been thought to be associated with atomic processes (Bethe). But none of these hypotheses satisfies astronomers or meteorologists completely.

Now this lacuna in our knowledge would not necessarily affect practical prediction, were it not that no one can foretell precisely when sunspots will appear with enough intensity—weaker sunspots are invariably present—to influence the earth's atmosphere appreciably. In this respect, uncertainty has become even greater than it was, for in 1843, when an amateur astro-nomer—Samuel Heinrich Schwabe—discovered the periodic rise and fall of sunspots, it was thought that he had found a perfectly periodic phenomenon. But subsequent investigations and also historical research—sunspots have been known in Europe since the beginning of the 17th century, and the first Chinese records go back to A.D. 188—have made it clear that the spots are by no means as regular as, for instance, the movement of the planets. The $11\frac{1}{2}$-year cycle is only a very rough arithmetical average, and sunspot maxima may occur at intervals of from 7–17 years—much too great a discrepancy for any kind of weather forecasting. Moreover the periods seem to be growing longer.[2]

Meteorologists were not alone in being fascinated by sunspots, and all manner of people tried to relate them to all sorts of terrestrial processes—from plagues of insects to South American revolutions. Above all, sunspots were thought to have a direct effect on economics.

In 1878, the English economist W. S. Jevons drew attention to the fact that the occurrence of economic crises coincided almost exactly with the sunspot cycle. Clearly the two were related. The American economists Warren Persons and H. L. Moore then pursued Jevons's thesis and tried to make it more plausible, by investigating the influence of sunspots on the weather and hence on grain prices. If the sun is very disturbed and full of spots it was said to have an adverse effect on the

[1] H. T. Stetson: *Sunspots in Action* (N.Y. 1947), p. 132.
[2] Albert Ducroq: *La Science à la conquête du passé* (Paris 1955).

weather and hence on harvests, whereas a bright sun was said to have the opposite effect. Sunspots therefore tend to drive grain prices up as a result of poor harvests, while the absence of sunspots and the consequent good harvests tend to depress the grain market—in theory, but not in practice.

There is a much closer connection between sunspots and large-scale storms, but even then only in certain localities. While sunspots seem to be associated with storms in Siberia, Scandinavia, the West Indies, the south-eastern part of the United States, and the South Pacific, they are less so in neighbouring regions, and they may even have the opposite effects in other parts of the world. Some meteorologists even maintain that Europe has the worst storms when sunspots are at a minimum.

Since sunspots have proved such unreliable guides, people have looked for other periodic effects on the weather. At the moment, 22-23 and 44-46 year cycles (twice or four times the mean sunspot cycle) are in great vogue, mainly on the evidence of certain anomalies in the annual rings of old trees, and increased periodic deposits in some African lakes. In the U.S.A. where cycle theories are particularly fashionable, they have been used to predict a severe drought for 1975, and an even severer one for 2021.[1]

It is due to these new cycle theories, that Brückner's famous theory, which was once considered to be unassailable, has fallen into oblivion. On the basis of painstaking research into older weather reports, Eduard Brückner[2] put forward the thesis that the European climate has been subject to periodic fluctuation for at least 1000 years, with individual cycles lasting for about 35 years, i.e. about three times as long as a sunspot cycle. In the first half of each cycle the weather was mainly warm and dry, and in the second half mainly cold and wet. Since Brückner's individual cycle was, however, merely a statistical average, it could never be applied in practice: a current cycle might take anything from 20 to 50 years to run its full course.

[1] George Kimble and Raymond Bush: *The Weather* (N.Y. 1944), p. 178.—I. R. Tannehill: *Drought. Its Causes and Effects*. (Princeton 1947), pp. VII and 175.
[2] E. Brückner: *Klimaschwankungen seit 1700* (Vienna 1890) and *Klimaschwankungen und Völkerwanderungen* (Vienna 1912).

The long summer

The most awkward thing about weather cycles is not so much their vagueness as their great number. Thus an English meteorologist noted in 1936, that there were 130 different cycle theories, with cycles varying from 14 months to 160 years.[1] With such a wealth of cycles, anything or nothing at all, can be explained. Possibly, the most complicated weather processes result precisely from the interference between two or more such cycles, but a graph of all the combined cycles would look more like a maze than like a useful chart. Cycle theories must be simple, for if there are too many independent wheels turning at different rates, the human mind, too, begins to spin in a circle. While any or all of these cycles may, in fact, exist in nature, their very interactions would make them too complex to be of practical use. It is for this very reason that meteorologists are increasingly returning to linear theories, and concentrate on actual trends rather than on the periodic return of past phenomena.

It is generally conceded today that there are, in fact, long term meteorologic trends. Our climate has undergone considerable changes not only in the ice age or in prehistoric epochs, but also within historical times. At this very moment there is a marked tendency towards warmer weather, for while summer temperatures have not changed a great deal, our winters have become milder.

Apparently, this tendency began in the middle of the 19th century, though, in view of the sparsity of records and systematic observations, it is impossible to be certain. What is clear, is that the tendency was too gradual and irregular to be observed by untrained men until the beginning of the 20th century, when the winter temperatures, particularly in northern regions, increased so much that no one could mistake the fact, particularly since marked changes in the economic field and in our habits have resulted from it. In Western Europe, the average winter temperature is 5°F. higher than it was in the second half of the last century, and in Spitzbergen the increase is as much as 16°F. The coast of Iceland has become clear of drifting ice, and the edge of the main area of Arctic ice has receded towards the

[1] Sir Napier Shaw: *Manual of Meteorology* (Cambridge 1936).

pole by some hundreds of miles.[1] But even more temperate
European and N. American areas have undergone considerable
climatic changes. Thus Washington has 35% fewer days of
frost than it had towards the end of the last century, and the
same tendency seems to govern the climate in the Southern
hemisphere, at least in so far as we can tell from the rather
scant data.

We must leave it to the authors of utopian novels, to paint
life in a world completely free of ice, where sunbathers can relax
on the shores of the polar sea and take an occasional dip. All we
can say is that this tendency towards warmer winters may well
continue for another hundred or possibly another two hundred
years, with marked repercussions on agriculture, emigration,
fuel consumption, and so on.

But how sure can we be of this tendency when January 1940
brought a sudden spell of severe cold, and when the two subsequent winters were extremely cold as well? Some weather prophets became so frightened that they proclaimed the end of a
90-year-old trend, and the beginning of a new phase of increasingly colder weather which would most probably last for just as
many years. Since then their gloomy prophecies have been
silenced by the events, for, though there have undoubtedly been
severe winters, milder weather has clearly been the rule during
any recent 10-year period. Quite possibly this trend is one of
those long cycles spanning a few centuries which can also be
reconstructed from old Chinese and European weather reports.
In any case, we may take it that the big thaw has set in, and that
there are no signs of a new "ice age", or of a glaciation of the
kind that occurred in the 17th century.

[1] C. E. P. Brooks: *Climate through the Ages* (London 1950), p. 376.

CHAPTER 7

Matters of Life and Death

*I*N PRACTICALLY NO OTHER FIELD ARE PREDICTIONS AS frequent as they are in medicine. While even meteorologists are not normally expected to publish more than one daily bulletin, doctors must prognosticate the whole day long. The fact that they do not have to make their pronouncements public, does nothing to diminish the gravity of their responsibility, since the patient whom a doctor tells whether he will recover quickly or whether he will have to count on a long spell of suffering, listens to every one of his words and to every shade of meaning as if the doctor were an oracle.

Moreover, when it comes to an operation, not only the patient but his dependents also, become intimately concerned in the problem. It is before the dependents that the doctor must weigh up the risks involved in an operation or its omission, and if he makes unequivocal pronouncements he runs the risk of gaining the reputation of recklessness. If, on the other hand, he is careful to put forward all the pros and cons of the case, he may undermine his own authority, and thus the patient's faith in him and his cure. Medical prognosis is therefore very much like diplomacy—the doctor cannot simply discuss the objective facts, but must dress them up in such a way as to make them palatable to his audience.

Nor does that exhaust the range of his prognostic activities. National or private insurance authorities must be told how long a patient is likely to be incapacitated, Life Insurance Companies demand clean bills of health which involve long range prognoses, immigration officials may make similar demands, and in many countries pre-marital health certificates are obligatory. All these, though based on purely diagnostic investigations, are in fact implicit prognoses, for otherwise they would be a waste of time.

Hippocrates' teaching

One might have assumed that so wide and important a branch of medicine would play a correspondingly large role in the education of medical practitioners and in medical literature. In fact, while diagnosis and pathology represent large and independent branches to which countless books and investigations are devoted, prognosis is a mere step-child, and is practically ignored by teachers and students alike. Thus an investigation of 100 English, French and German text books on general medicine and on the most important special branches of medicine, showed that less than 1% of the subject matter was devoted to prognosis. In the great majority of these books, the words "prognostic" or "prognosis" were found neither in the table of contents nor in the index. Nor has much special literature been published on the subject, so much so that, in Germany and Austria for instance, no more than three comprehensive works on prognosis have appeared during the last 50 years.[1] Actually, things were not always like that, and until quite recently, prognosis was much more greatly emphasised in medical literature. This was in the great tradition of Hippocrates, who founded scientific medicine almost 2500 years ago. Hippocrates himself wrote two books on the subject of prognosis and enjoined his students to pay very particular attention to them since, without prognosis, they could not hope to gain their patients' confidence. True most of Hippocrates' prognostic ideas are of only historical interest today, for he concentrated chiefly on facial expression, posture and movements. Thus sleeping with an open mouth and outspread legs or gesticulation in sleep were unfavourable signs, and the *Facies Hippocratica*—a prominent nose, sunken eyes, sunken temples, tense skin and yellow or black complexion —was a criterion of impending death. However, Hippocrates did not restrict his prognostic comments to such external factors alone. One of his favourite methods (which caused more confusion than enlightenment) was to make prognoses from the appearance of the patient's urine. According to his pupil Theo-

[1] T. Brugsch: *Allgemeine Prognostik* (Berlin-Vienna 1918), H. Curschmann: *Lehrbuch der speziellen Prognostik innerer Krankheiten* (Stuttgart 1942) and H. Winter; *Die Individualprognose in der inneren Medizin* (Vienna 1950).

philus, whose dictum on this subject became the dogma of many
generations, cloudy and reddish urine on the fourth day of a fever
was a clear sign that the crisis would set in on the seventh day.[1]
Particularly under the influence of Arab physicians, the inspection of urine became a medieval criterion for distinguishing
"serious" medicine from quackery and magic.[2] From urine
inspections, not only the shrewdest diagnosis but also the most
far-reaching prognoses could be made. Characteristically, the
moment that serious science discarded this questionable method,
charlatans took it over to inflict it on mankind to this day.

It is quite understandable that the many errors and fallacies
of past methods have made medical practitioners sceptical of
prognoses as such. Unfortunately, this scepticism is misapplied,
for doctors simply cannot help prognosticating in practice
and, short of learning this art from reputable sources, they
must rely on their own intuition and on their own limited
experience. There is little to guide them in the literature, and
what statistical data there are—except in surgery which occupies
a special position—are still so utterly inadequate and contradictory as to be merely confusing. For this reason many
practitioners—and the leading and most experienced doctors
among them—make a virtue of necessity by maintaining that
prognoses differ from case to case. And so they do, but if we
were to apply that criterion to diagnosis and to therapy, there
would be no medical science based on scientific principles at all.

In fact the difficulties of modern medical prognosis are
largely social. With the decline of the family doctor, the number
of medical practitioners who observe their patients from birth to
death is growing smaller from year to year, and hospitals and
casualty wards have such a great turnover of patients that they
can do little to observe the development of a given ailment.
The specialists, who, after all, write most of the literature,
are even less likely to be able to carry out long term observations, since the moment their patients improve, specialist
services are generally dispensed with. This lack of continuous
contact between doctors and patients makes it extremely
difficult to develop a science of prognosis—medical congresses
and exchanges of views notwithstanding.

[1] M. Weiss: *Diagnose und Prognose aus dem Harn* (Ulm 1954) p. 19.
[2] Douglas Guthrie: *A History of Medicine* (London 1945) p. 90.,

1001 *diseases*

All medical prognosis must consider three main factors: the aetiology of the disease, individual characteristics of the patient —constitution, hereditary defects, age, sex, habits, and social position—and the possible means of therapy. The most basic question is that of the aetiology, i.e. whether the causes (and the development) of a given disease are so general as to allow predictions from past experience. If that is the case, the prognostic problem is as good as solved in the majority of cases. Unfortunately, things are not as straightforward as laymen commonly believe. It is a fallacy to think that once a doctor has made his diagnosis, the rest follows automatically—the typical course of many diseases is largely unknown. There are so many possible developments that not even the most experienced doctors can speak of a norm. At best, they can distinguish a a number of typical, though uncertain, pathological expressions of the same illness. Moreover, the number of diseases has increased tremendously, at least in name. There are now over 1000 medical conditions, endemic illnesses excluded. In establishing a "new" condition, its discoverer need not specify its exact aetiology; all he need do is to show that the acute phases are clearly distinguished from those of any other illness. The prognosis in each and every one of them must therefore be established after a great deal of laborious research, which usually takes a few decades, and often tells us no more than that one disease may have a number of different results.

In contradistinction to other branches of science, and modern physics in particular, where recent theoretical revolutions have led to a general drive towards unification, medicine is undergoing a period of decentralisation, i.e. of compartmentalisation. Undoubtedly, this decentralisation has many advantages, and no one in his right senses would desire medicine to revert to the rigid dogmatism from which it suffered until the 17th century, and which threatened to make its come-back at the beginning of the bacteriological era. Even so, so unexplored a field as medical prognosis could only benefit from a set of guiding principles.

Luckily, prognosis can never be completely wild and fancy-free, for it is bound to a factor independent of all changes of theory and practice: time. To prognosticate means to predict in time rather than to prophesy about the dim distant future. Thus medical prognosis is unconcerned with the average age of man in the year 3000, or with what fatal diseases will arise at that time. Its proper field is the prevention and cure of diseases, here and now. True, medicine can tell us much that might conceivably affect the health of future generations, but it does so only by the way.

For that very reason, medical prognoses are so often terribly pessimistic. Thus a wave of gloomy predictions was made some 20 years ago on the course of infective diseases, only to be upset by the discovery of sulphanilomides and antibiotics. It might be argued that, medical knowledge being what it was, these discoveries could not possibly have been foreseen by anyone, and that the predictions were therefore quite logical at the time. However, this is a form of logic that does not strike us as particularly revealing.

All the same, not even modern doctors can act any differently, for they, too, must make static predictions, i.e. assume that there will be no radical changes in therapy within the next thirty years. Dynamic forecasts so characteristic of those economists who speculate about economic changes in A.D. 2000, are quite outside the scope of medical prognosis, since the sensitive objects of its enquiries would resent mistakes most emphatically.

Infections

Even so, doctors can afford to be somewhat more daring in some of their forecasts than meteorologists, for unlike the latter, they can make accurate or highly probable predictions about a host of phenomena. One striking exception is the case of coronary thrombosis, for although some of its predisposing factors are known, it is still impossible to predict whom it will afflict fatally. All we know is that 40% of all cases die within the course of a few days, and that people with distended hearts, severe diabetes, syphilitic aneurysms, and certain pulse anomalies are unlikely to recover.

But apart from severe heart attacks, doctors nowadays confront acute diseases with far greater certainty than ever before. Not only can they intervene in time, but they can also predict expected changes in the overall picture of the disease from day to day, and know when the crisis and final recovery will set in. Still, the possibilities of correct prognosis differ from illness to illness.

Simplest of all, are prognoses of infections, since the germs responsible usually develop with clockwork precision. In most infections it is therefore relatively easy to predict the interval between the actual infection and the appearance of the first symptoms: 2 days in diphtheria, 2–4 days in scarlet fever, 14 days in measles, 10–21 days in typhus, and about 3 weeks in syphilis. Admittedly this knowledge is rarely of practical value to the patient, since few people can tell that they have been infected and thus rarely consult their doctors before the onset of the symptoms. However, once an infection has been diagnosed, its course can be predicted much more accurately than that of most non-infectious diseases.

Some infections follow a fixed rhythm, and malaria sufferers know precisely when to take quinine against the next bout of fever. Still, only a doctor can tell them whether their malaria is due to *plasmodium vivax* or the much more dangerous *plasmodium falciparum*, and predict the future course of the disease accordingly.[1] In the prognosis of pneumonia it is also a matter of importance whether the disease has been caused by pneumococci or by far more dangerous streptococci. Moreover there are distinct types of pneumococci of which some are more virulent than others.

In these, and in a number of other diseases, the microscopic picture is therefore an excellent prognostic criterion. In other cases, chemical investigations replace the microscope, but in neither case is medical prognosis advanced enough to rely on such objective tests alone. Laboratory investigations must always go hand in hand with direct observations of the patient which, in most cases, are still based on methods used in Hippocrates' time.

In one of the most recent works on prognosis, for instance, the section on pneumonia contains the following "hints" about the

[1] C. F. Craig and E. C. Faust: *Clinical Parasitology* (Philadelphia 1945), p. 21.

patient's appearance and behaviour: "Subicteric (i.e. slightly jaundiced) colour is a sign that the disease will run a violent course, but, like the delirious state which accompanies lobular pneumonia, its prognostic value in individual cases is uncertain. Deliria accompanying lobar as distinct from lobular pneumonia, on the other hand, are usually certain signs that the outlook is poor. Similarly, meteoristic distensions of the abdomen accompanying pneumonia, must be evaluated very carefully." Side by side with these pronouncements, the author—who, by the way, is a leading Viennese physician—also gives prognostic advice that might well have stemmed from an Aesculapian priest in ancient Epidaurus: "If a case of pneumonia is unusually bothered by flies in a well-aired ward, the prognosis is bound to be bad. The same is true also of a number of other diseases, and particularly of jaundice. While I would hesitate to explain this fact, it is particularly striking when a number of patients suffering from the same disease share a ward, and when some, and not others, are bothered by the flies.[1]

Modern difficulties

If medical prognosis seems more speculative today than it was fifty or a hundred years ago, this is due to the paradoxical result of recent medical advances. Once a typical disease has been diagnosed, it is, of course, fairly easy to predict the subsequent stages, but unfortunately non-infectious diseases are rarely typical. While they are much better understood than they were, say, 100 years ago, the new knowledge consists largely of details that do not greatly affect prognosis, or of the introduction of countless complications where no complications were previously suspected. Hence, many doctors can no longer see the wood for the trees, and while it seems likely that our present analytical stage will once again give way to a new synthesis, that day seems very far off.

Medical advances have had yet other repercussions on the art of prognosis. During the past 100 years medical science has managed to eradicate some of the most murderous diseases

[1] H. Winter: op. cit. pp. 61–62.

almost completely, and to reduce the severity of a host of others. During the second half of the last century acute infections were being vanquished by such sanitary measures as running water and public drainage. Cholera and typhus were overcome in that way, while compulsory vaccination put an end to smallpox. Finally, puerperal fever was banished from hospitals and homes by antiseptic measures. During the first half of our century, there began the great battle against the chronic infections: syphilis and tuberculosis, and here, too, the successes were extraordinary.

If we classify diseases according to their duration, we may say that the last fifty years of the 19th century vanquished mainly infections of short duration and with a very high mortality rate, while the first fifty years of the 20th century vanquished more chronic infections. In either case the battle was against infections whose course could be prognosticated fairly easily, and not against the most frequent causes of death: non-infectious diseases which have far more uncertain prognoses—particularly diseases of the heart. In other words, diseases with simple prognoses have become relatively rare, while chronic diseases with uncertain prognoses have become more common, if only because we have learnt how to keep chronic patients alive. For instance, pernicious anaemia which used to be fatal, is fatal no longer. Now, the longer the duration of a disease, the greater the number of possible complications, and the greater the role of such unpredictable individual characteristics as specific resistance.

This is the reason why physicians, no matter how often they are called upon to make prognoses, usually avoid publishing their prognostic opinions. One of England's leading heart specialists Sir James Mackenzie (1853–1925) used to say that "no doctor lives long enough to write a reliable book on prognosis",[1] and modern doctors would refrain from writing such a book even if they lived to grow as old as Methusaleh. Thus all those medical textbooks which devote a special section to the prognosis of, say, heart diseases, usually preface their remarks with the comment that no fixed rules of prognosis exist.[2]

[1] D. Guthrie, op. cit., p. 56.
[2] R. P. McCombs: *Internal Medicine in General Practice* (Philadelphia and London 1947) p. 94.

Things are a little better with psychiatric prognoses. Most severe mental disorders are chronic, and psychoses, in particular, persist for a very long time—electric shock therapy and the more recent chemo-therapy notwithstanding. Quick cures are very rare indeed, and psycho-analysts, for instance, make a point of warning their patients against them. Permanent cures take years rather than months,[1] and psychiatric prognoses are very long-range predictions, not only about the therapy itself but also about possible relapses after the treatment has been terminated. Relapses are, in fact, the bugbears of psychiatry, and patients can only be pronounced really cured years after the disappearance of all symptoms. But while psychiatric prognoses are apparently the most difficult to make, psychiatrists have the advantage over their other medical colleagues that they can generally follow up their patients' progress. Schizophrenia and manic-depressive states, for instance, are described in thousands of detailed case histories, giving accurate details of relapses, including those which occurred 19 years after termination of treatment.[2] It would appear that though depressive states and schizophrenia—a disorder that is particularly widespread in the U.S.A.—can be cured more readily with recent techniques, the number of relapses, too, have greatly increased. Thus, while 72% of all manic depressives treated, for instance, in the Pennsylvania Hospital in Philadelphia could be discharged as cured, almost 10% of the "cures" had relapses during the subsequent five years—and five years is a very short time when it comes to manic depressives.

Although such statistical data cannot be applied to individual patients, they are nevertheless of great value to doctors who have to decide when, and under what conditions, mental patients whose condition has perceptibly improved, may be released.

Surgery = Foresight

A quite different prognostic situation exists in surgery. No

[1] L. S. Kubie: *Psychoanalyse ohne Geheimnis* (Hamburg 1956), p. 43.
[2] *The Year Book of Neurology, Psychiatry and Neurosurgery* 1945–1955 (Chicago 1955), pp. 285–288.

surgeon worth his name will perform a major operation without weighing up all the risks involved. Now, unlike physicians who seem to have a horror of applying statistical considerations to individual patients, surgeons have long ago realised that only by classifying certain types of operation can they make any surgical decisions at all.

Strictly speaking, surgical prognosis is therefore based on past therapeutic results. True, other branches of medicine also consider therapeutic results, for instance, when using new techniques, but once the technique has been applied, statistics are ignored. Few medical practitioners will be able to tell you in exactly how many cases a new method has worked and in how many cases it has failed. Surgeons on the other hand, keep a strict record of even the simplest routine operations, with the result that they have accumulated a wealth of up-to-date data, which are quite unlike the collection of outdated observations on which most physicians have to rely.

Above all, surgical data contain valuable hints about the prognosis of diseases. Operations are, after all, desperate measures that are only taken when everything else has failed. In many cases, surgical interventions decide the future course of diseases, and even where they do not produce permanent cures, they, at least, get to the bottom of the trouble and lead to better prognoses. However, all this is only a minor aspect of prognostic surgery.

Even before the surgeon is in a position to predict the future course of a disease on the basis of the operation he has performed, he must make two preliminary prognoses. First of all, he must tell the patient how long he must expect to remain bed-ridden if all goes well, and how long he will have to convalesce. Precisely in the the case of relatively minor operations, this part of the prognosis is most important, since frequently it decides the patient one way or another. Thus if the conscientious surgeon tells a patient that he may not be able to go back to work for months, the patient may not be able to spare the time. This type of prognosis is therefore a very delicate matter, not so much for medical as for psychological reasons. Purely technically speaking, however, it is so highly developed today, that surgeons rarely make any mistakes.

The second and more crucial part of surgical prognoses deals with the operational risks. Here statistics are most important, for although quite novel operations are frequently performed— or else surgery would never advance at all—99% of all operations carried out in hospitals throughout the world are based on time-honoured methods. Thus the patient who confides his life to the surgeon's knife is anything but a guinea pig.

However, a surgeon's decision to operate is not based on statistical considerations alone but also on the evaluation of the risks the patient runs if the operation is not performed. In other words, he must balance two independent prognoses: the patient's individual condition and the general surgical risk. In acute appendicitis, for instance, delay may be fatal while the operation itself is relatively simple, whereas in many heart diseases the opposite is often the case.

If the pros and cons are fairly equal, few patients will agree to submit to preventive operations which can be postponed and, for instance, in some cases of cancer in which the dangers of delay and the surgical risks are so nicely balanced that even careful reflection of the pros and cons yields no clear indication, it is the patient's fear or courage which decides the issue. In most cases, however, surgical prognoses have a much more solid foundation than those of medicine because, as we have seen, surgeons have resolutely rejected the extremely individualistic notion that every case is different.

Still, even medicine is beginning to catch up. Where statistics were formerly frowned upon as being unworthy of a true doctor, British attempts,[1] in particular, have led to a new concept in medicine: the Medicine of Probability,[2] whose task it is to classify pathological symptoms so accurately that individual diagnoses and prognoses can be made almost by rote.

Though British doctors are still far from having attained this objective, the Medicine of Probability promises to clear medical prognosis of its present state of utter confusion. The 6000 experimental data that have been compiled for different diseases so far, have already proved their great prognostic worth.

[1] A. Bradford Hill: *Principles of Medical Statistics* (London 1950).
[2] A. Fidler: *Whither Medicine?* Part 2: *The Medicine of Probability* (London 1946), pp. 41–87.

XVIII. Wheel of fortune symbolising man's rise and fall (1541 miniature).

Pregnancy tests

Experienced medical practitioners will assure you that women are much more interested in prognoses than men are. It is perhaps because women plan far less than men do, that they look upon the future as a closed book. But women also consult their doctors for less general reasons, i.e. about specifically feminine problems. Thus many of them will turn to their doctor the moment they suspect that they may be pregnant. All pregnancy tests are diagnoses-cum-prognoses, for once a pregnancy has been diagnosed, we know precisely that —all being well—birth will result 280 days after conception.

Until thirty years ago doctors were generally unable to tell their women patients any more about whether they had conceived or not than the patients knew themselves: they would simply have to wait. Then, in 1927, two Berlin doctors Aschheim and Zondek perfected a method whereby pregnancy could be determined in its early stages. After a great deal of experimental work, they discovered that large amounts of oestrogen were present in the urine of pregnant women, and that if some of that urine is injected into a sexually immature mouse the ovaries of the mouse will show a marked reddening and the presence of corpora lutea. To make quite certain, the experiment has usually to be repeated with a number of mice, and that involves a delay which anxious women find quite unbearable. In the Friedmann test, a speedier variation of the Aschheim-Zondek method, the urine is injected on two successive days into the vein running at the back of the ear of a virgin doe rabbit. Twenty-four hours after the second injection, the animal is killed and its ovaries are investigated. A newly ruptured follicle is a positive sign of pregnancy.

In more recent experiments with frogs, the time lapse has been shortened even further, and, in any case, the tests are kinder to the animals. Female frogs of the South American genus *Xenopus*, when injected with urine from pregnant women, will lay eggs after only eighteen hours. More surprising still is a technique discovered only a few years ago: the urine of male frogs which have had the urine of a pregnant woman injected into them, will be found to contain spermatozoa some 3–6 hours later.[1]

[1] F. W. Roques *et al*: *Diseases of Women* (9th ed. London 1953), p. 64.

The processes involved are not yet fully understood, since the original hormone theories are no longer thought to explain the phenomena. The facts, however, are incontestable, and particularly the older tests are thought to be exceptionally reliable: more than 90% of positive results are borne out by subsequent developments. Even so, the tests are not used as frequently as it was thought they would be: most children still see the light of day without a few small mice or a chaste rabbit having to lay down their lives for them.

Boy or Girl

While early determinations of pregnancy have a medical as well as a curiosity value, another branch of sexual prognosis has curiosity value alone: the prediction of the sex of unborn children.

Interest in this problem is age-old, and in earlier days, when the future existence of a noble line might have hinged on the answer, the problem was, in fact, of great importance. Small wonder then that there have been hundreds of theories about sex determination before birth—most of them sheer myths and old wives' tales. In the course of time these theories have undergone great changes. Aristotle was the father of the fixed notion that a child's sex was determined by the seed, i.e. by the father alone. According to this doctrine (which was in vogue for almost a full 2000 years) young men sired mainly boys, older men produced girls, warm weather led to an increase in boys, and cold winds from the north to more girls. In other words, heat favoured the male sex. In the 17th century, all these theories were challenged by the ovum hypothesis[1] according to which sex was determined by the mother, and, for the next two centuries, opinions were sharply divided. Graduallly it came to be accepted that both parents played a part in the transmission of physiological characters and in the determination of sex. However, at the turn of the last centuries, when the role of chromosomes in the transmission of genetic characters was first appreciated, McChung (1902) was able to show that, while father and mother

[1] Morus: *Eine Weltgeschichte der Sexualität* (2nd ed., Hamburg 1957), pp. 184 ff.

contributed an equal number of chromosomes to their joint offspring, sex was determined exclusively by the father's chromosomes.[1]

Other Aristotelian notions, too, adorned with new biological arguments, have come back into favour. Thus many biologists have taken up his idea of the influence of the climate not only on the number of births—the warmer the weather, the more children are conceived—but also on the distribution of the sexes. Where the climate is "stimulating", i.e. not too cold and not too warm, the number of new-born boys and girls is said to be approximately equal, while boys predominate both in very warm and also in very cold countries.[2]

Such general observations are of little help to expectant parents, who, in the absence of unequivocal answers from the medical profession, have been turning to astrologers and other diviners for thousands of years. There is no pseudo-science that has not tried its hand at this game—none more so than pendulum-divination. As early as 3000 B.C., the Chinese were swinging pendulums to determine the sex of future heirs to the throne, apparently with little success, for the method was subsequently rejected. In the West, however, which is obviously far less daunted by failure, there is still an incredible number of people who believe that boys cause a pendulum to swing right across the stomach of a pregnant woman, while girls induce the pendulum to swing in a circle.

Europeans also attributed pre-natal influences to the moon. This seemed exceedingly plausible when the phases of the moon were seemingly related to the menstrual cycle. Although none of these lunar theories were ever proved to have any factual basis, many people continue to believe that boys will be conceived in the new moon, and girls when the moon is waning.

Still, even believers found this rule a little difficult to live by, for though the moon might govern their children's sex it did not govern their own passions. They therefore ignored the moon when it came to love-making, and resorted to other superstitions. In Italy, for instance, many pregnant women still cut off a lizard's tail, and watch most carefully what happens. If the

[1] L. R. Wharton: *Gynecology* (Philadelphia–London 1947), p. 38.
[2] André Misserand: *A la recherche du temps et du rhythme* (Paris 1940), pp. 146–159.

lizard grows a new and flawless tail, a boy may be expected with complete certainty; girls are associated with stunted growths—not very flattering to the female sex, to be sure.

Cellular sex-differentiation

After centuries of futile attempts to solve this riddle by the most complicated methods—including the Cabbala—biology came to the rescue. The first promising step was taken in 1932, when the American doctors Dorn and Sugermann developed a method that is very similar to the Friedman pregnancy test: the urine of the pregnant woman is injected into the pinna of a male rabbit, though not before five months of pregnancy have passed. If the foetus is male, the rabbit shows no reaction, but with female foetuses there occurs a marked swelling of the rabbit's sexual gland. Unfortunately this simple procedure is not yet conclusive enough to have become very widespread.

Another method is based on the important biological discovery made by the Canadian anatomist, H. G. Barr. In 1949, while examining the brains of cats, Barr discovered the presence of a tiny brown spot in the nerve cells of female cats and its absence in tom-cats. Now, while the existence of such spots in the nerve cells of many animals had been known long before, no one had suspected that they were restricted to the female sex. Here was the first clear evidence that there were sexual distinctions other than the well-known primary and secondary sex characteristics. Further investigations showed that Barr's discovery applied to human beings as well, and not only to their brain but also to their blood and skin.

It seemed reasonable to assume that these microscopic distinctions must already exist in foetuses, and the only problem was how to relate this new knowledge to the practical prediction of an unborn child's sex. After vain attempts to arrive at clear results indirectly by analyses of the mother's blood and urine, three Israeli doctors decided to make direct investigations of the amniotic fluid withdrawn from the uterus of pregnant women. In Jerusalem, twenty women volunteered immediately, and so did forty women in New York. In either case, prognoses were fully confirmed by the sex the children turned out to be at birth.

Despite these successes, only a few doctors have agreed to apply a method that is not entirely without dangers. Still, it seems likely that future improvements will make it possible for every mother to know her child's sex well in advance, thus opening up a new field for medical prognosis.

Infection or Heredity?

While sex prognoses are largely based on curiosity, genetic prognoses would be of far-reaching individual and social importance. Unfortunately, the theory of heredity is still too young to be applied prognostically to all genetic phenomena. Genetics is barely 100 years old and many of its beginnings, viz. the theories of Mendel, Darwin, and of his cousin Galton— the founder of eugenics—were too general to be applied in individual cases. The only practical prognostic results which we owe to that early stage are largely based on the large-scale anthropological investigations of physical structure, profile, hair and eye colour, made particularly by Rudolf Virchow working with German school-children. However, it quickly emerged that such external characters were less valuable prognostic criteria than biochemical traits, too small to have been determined with the technical equipment of the time.

Things only changed at the turn of the century, and the year 1902 became a milestone in genetic history. For it was in that year that Mendel's hundred-year-old laws governing the appearance of hybrid peas were rediscovered by Prof. Bateson. Two years earlier, Karl Landsteiner, a Viennese pathologist, had managed to classify human blood groups and shown the physiological basis of blood relationships.

Some of the genetic consequences of these discoveries could be applied at once, while others emerged very much later. Thus, in 1940, a substance first discovered in the red blood cells of the Rhesus monkey, the so-called Rhesus factor, was shown to be present in 85% of humans who are said to be Rh+. Now, while the absence of the Rhesus factor has no ill effects in itself, a Rh−

mother whose embryo has Rh + blood from the father, is likely to
unleash an intra-uterine blood struggle that frequently ends with
the death of the foetus, or may cause the child's health to be
severely impaired. All women ought therefore to have a blood test
before marriage or at least at the beginning of pregnancy, since
suitable treatment and preventive measures may greatly
reduce the danger to the child's life. This is one of the most
important prognostic achievements of eugenics so far.

In other respects, too, it has become clear that the mother's
pre- and post-natal condition is of far greater importance than
that of the father. Today it is generally held that there are much
fewer directly hereditary diseases than was formerly believed
and that, for instance, tubercular or syphilitic fathers do not
transmit the infective organism with their spermatozoa. If the
child is nevertheless born with such infections, we can say with
certainty that it became infected inside the mother's womb or
during birth—which naturally does not mean that the mother
herself may not have been infected by the child's father. Prognoses of the child's health and protective measures to safeguard
it—i.e. possible separation from the mother immediately after
birth—are therefore mainly based on the mother's condition.

However, the father, even if he has not infected the mother,
is not without any influence on his children's health. Thus non-
infectious congenital defects, for instance diabetes, may be
transmitted by parents of either sex. Arterio-sclerosis is claimed
by some to be based on hereditary factors, and there has also been
some talk about an hereditary predisposition towards cancer,
but, by and large, the number of established hereditary illnesses
has shrunk with the years. Even such classical examples as
haemophilia and colour blindness have not really been proved
to be hereditary by *direct* biological demonstrations. Better
knowledge of chromosomes and genes—the specifically hereditary factors within the chromosomes—may well lead to more
plausible explanations, but explanations and proofs are not the
same thing.

The secret of family resemblance

Though our knowledge of hereditary diseases is still full of gaps, it is nevertheless more advanced than our knowledge of the transmission of other hereditary characters. By these we do not so much mean the inheritance of genius or of special artistic talents, of which science knows little more than any layman can read from the family histories of famous men, but the transmission of physiological characters such as size, figure, eye and hair colour, etc., in short everything on which parent-child resemblance is commonly based. Now, all these questions are completely unsolved, for when we are told that genes producing blue eyes, i.e. eyes with little pigment, are not invariably transmitted, we cannot very well predict a child's eye colour from that of its parents. Nor do Mendelian principles with their dominant and recessive characters prove very helpful, for to apply them one would have to go many generations back— and which one of us can remember the colour of our great-grandfather's eyes?

Nonetheless, Americans in particular have compiled long lists from which parents may glean the probable appearance of their future children. Thus a popular scientific book[1] tells us that if some members of the family of one of the parents have blue, grey, or green eyes, while brown is the predominant colour in the other parent's family, the children will probably but not necessarily, have brown eyes. Similarly with hair colour: if the family of one of the parents has predominantly dark and the family of the other predominantly fair hair, the children will probably have dark hair, but they may also have fair and more rarely red hair. If the family of one of the parents have prominent noses, the child is likely to have a prominent nose, if one of the parents is tall and the other small, the child will probably be small, and so on. Generally speaking, the more striking characteristics of the parents will be passed on to their children.

Now, if this general prognosis were true, one would expect mankind to become progressively more dark-eyed and dark-haired, more hook-nosed, and much shorter of stature. In actual fact, the Roman nose has become the exception rather than the rule, there is no marked dwindling in the number of fair people, and there is no doubt that Europeans have, in fact, grown much taller, probably because of better nutrition and better general

[1] A. Scheinfeld: *The New You and Heredity* (Philadelphia–New York 1951), pp. 118–123.

conditions. Thus students in Western Europe and North America are 2–4″ taller than students two generations ago, and a mediaeval coat of armour would only just fit a modern adolescent. In 1956, when the Paris Museum of Costumes held an historical exhibition, special dummies had to be built to wear Rococo clothes which barely fitted modern twelve to fourteen year old girls. Only when it came to 20th century dress could living models be fitted into them.[1]

None of these developments can be explained genetically, and sceptics might well conclude that the achievements of genetics are extremely slight. In fact, they would be quite wrong, for genetics must be credited with considerable achievements during the last fifty years. It is true, however that much work still remains to be done before genetic knowledge can be applied to prediction with any degree of certainty.

[1] Report by Mme. Delpierre, Assistant Curator of the *Musée Carnavalet* and the *Musée du Costume* in Paris (December 1956).

CHAPTER 8

Quantity and Quality

*M*EDICAL FINDINGS ABOUT BIRTH, SEX, DISEASE, AND death form one of the main bases for demographic predictions, though demographers usually treat all this information far less carefully than the doctors who supply it. The data are simply fed into giant calculating machines from which they emerge as vital statistics. In addition to these, demography also investigates economic, social, political, legal and religious data —in short a huge and complex conglomeration of most varied phenomena. But rather than sort them out, demographers prefer to apply their ill-assorted facts to the future. While doctors as a whole may be said to be reluctant prophets, demographers are prophets for the sheer joy of it. True, some of them are a little shy in this respect and prefer to consider demography as a purely historical science, but they are a very small minority. Thus, leading demographers have drawn up most elegant graphs about population increases in Europe during the next fifty years, and claim they can tell you precisely how many men will people the earth in A.D. 2000. Unfortunately the magnitude of their audacity is equalled only by that of their errors.

Pastor Süssmilch's "divine" order

This love of far-reaching prophecies has good historical reasons, for the first demographic successes did, in fact, border on the miraculous. While other sciences had to undergo a long period of trial and error, demographers made their greatest and most momentous discovery right from the start: an examination of church records at the beginning of the 17th century convinced them that the number of annual baptisms, marriages and deaths was as regular as the motion of the planets. Where they had expected chaos, they found what one of the past masters of demography, the German clergymen Johann Peter Süssmilch (1707 to 1767) described as "divine order."[1]

Life and death, marriage and birth, and all other apparently unpredictable events of family life, became as predictable as the calendar when they were considered not as family matters but, say, as affecting a large town like London. Here one man might have been married three times and have sired fourteen children of which eight had survived, another might have contracted only one marriage to father ten children of which only four had survived; a third man might have no children at all, and a fourth might have been a confirmed bachelor, but all the same the number of marriages and births followed a regular pattern over the years, and so did the death rate, except during epidemics, of course. Even the causes of death or the sex ratio remained surprisingly regular.

It did not need the first British census in 1801[2] to tell most people that the population had been increasing ever since the Great Plague, though the fact that this increase followed a regular rhythm was an unsuspected discovery. For the first time, future population figures could be estimated accurately, and those concerned could make exact provision for, say, an adequate number of cribs and hearses, for grain imports to feed the growing population and, last but not least, for tax assessments. In short, ethnography, which one of its founders, Sir William Petty (1623–1687), had called political arithmetic, proved a very useful science, and its exponents earned great honours.

According to governments and economists alike, the bigger the population the better off a given country was, not so much for military reasons (foreign mercenaries were ten a penny at the time), as for economic. The greater the population, the greater the number of workers, the cheaper their labour power, and hence the cheaper the manufactured articles and the greater the revenue from exports. Densely populated countries like Holland were rich, while sparsely populated countries like Russia were poor. Clever statesmen naturally based their policies

---

[1] J. P. Süssmilch: *Die göttliche Ordnung in den Verhältnissen des menschlichen Geschlechts* (Berlin 1741).

[2] General Register Office: *Matters of Life and Death* (London 1951), p. 3.

on the example of the rich countries and tried to persuade their compatriots to have as many children as possible. They also encouraged immigration.

Malthus' forebodings

As time went on, however, at least some economists began to realise that something had gone wrong with this calculation, for while countries as a whole certainly grew wealthier with increases of population, the majority of their inhabitants grew poorer the while. The French Revolution was to show that such large-scale poverty was a direct threat to the luxury of the rich, and that population increases were no unqualified blessings.

The man who formulated this new attitude most uncompromisingly was Robert Thomas Malthus, an English curate. In a small anonymous essay (1798)[1] and later in his famous *Principles* (1820)[2], a work full of statistical data, he put forward the thesis that poverty, disease and war were all the direct results of man's concupiscence, which led him to produce more children than he could feed. Higher wages would do little to alter man's misery, for the better off they were the more children the workers would be able to support, and the more vicious the circle would become. According to Malthus, it was a natural law that if men were allowed to follow their sexual inclinations without let or hindrance, mankind would multiply much more quickly than would the natural resources needed to support it. While the former increased in geometric progression the latter could, at best, be stepped up in arithmetic progression. Malthus's thesis was at first considered downright scandalous, since the idea of enforced sexual abstinence for the poorer classes seemed to run counter to all the tenets of morality and decency. With time, however, Malthus became a household name even outside England—not with the masses, of course, but with the upper classes who now had every reason to underpay their

[1] T. R. Malthus: *Essay on the Principle of Population as it affects the Future Improvement of Society.*
[2] T. R. Malthus: *Principles of Political Economy with a view to their Practical Application.*

workers even further. But Malthus made his greatest hit with the economists who discuss his theories to this day, even though his ideas of mathematical progressions have clearly been shown to be false, and his statistical approach to be based on false premises. Thus his investigations had convinced him that the population of Europe would double every 25 years unless there were plagues or particularly bloody wars. Had he been right, there would have been 12,000 million Europeans in 1950, when, in fact, Europe, including the Soviet Union, has a total population of just under 600 million. Thus in the 150 years which have passed since Malthus wrote his gloomy prophecies, the population has only just more than trebled instead of increasing by 60 times, and this despite the fact that plagues and war casualties took a far smaller toll of human lives than they did before.

But we do not have to look at modern times to prove Malthus wrong. His mathematical notions did not even apply to the 18th century, from which he took most of his statistics. As far as we can tell from the sparse and unreliable statistical data of that period, the population of Europe barely doubled from 1700 to 1800.[1] In fact, only very young immigrant countries ever double their population in 25 years, and not even the United States managed to maintain this rate of increase after 1880.

Depopulation by prosperity

Still, all these arithmetical arguments do not weaken Malthus's crucial point, viz. that for purely economic and agricultural reasons men can never maintain as many children as they could produce. It is an incontestable fact that mankind is more prolific than Mother Earth who, despite all advances in agronomy still fails to feed all her children properly. Nor have chemists managed to synthesise sufficient quantities of digestible proteins to alter the picture to any large extent, and what talk there is of supplying mankind with all the calories it needs from coal, water, and air is meanwhile purely utopian.

[1] Article on *Population* in *Encyclopaedia of the Social Sciences* (N.Y. 1948).

On the other hand, our propagative capacity is such that mankind could, in fact, double its numbers in much less than 25 years. The male of our species whose every ejaculation liberates some hundreds of millions of sperms has an almost unlimited reproductive capacity, and only the female places some restriction on the rate of propagation. But during the 30 years of her sexual maturity, every healthy woman can produce up to fifteen children, and even more if she does not breast-feed them. Because of the great decrease in the incidence of venereal diseases which contributed so greatly to sterility in the past, and also because of advances in pre-natal care, man's potential reproductive capacity has become far greater than it was in Malthus's day. Fortunately, men use this capacity to only a limited extent: in the richest and most civilised countries they have only a third or a quarter the number of children they could have. Reproducion has largely become a voluntary act.

This is precisely what Malthus could not have predicted, nor could he have had the slightest inkling of how voluntary parenthood would affect the social composition of modern societies. In his day, the upper classes produced roughly as many children as the poorer classes, though many more of the rich children survived. But by the second half of the 19th century a reverse trend set in, first in France, then in England and finally in the rest of Europe: birth control was increasingly being practised by the upper classes, i.e. precisely those people, who according to Malthus, had least reason to do so.

Somewhat overzealous ethnographers immediately turned this new trend into a principle: poverty led to higher, and wealth to lower birth-rates. And since poor countries with the most appalling hygienic conditions still had a higher birth than death-rate, they concluded further that poverty led to increased populations, while growing wealth led to smaller populations or at best to a state of equilibrium. This theory[1] which was extremely popular in the first third of the 20th century became the basis of the most daring prophecies, so much so that some pessimists predicted that the whole of Europe would be turned into one large cemetery, while others were convinced that the black and yellow races, who had not yet fallen victim to the

[1] Julius Wolf: *Die Theorie der sozialen Entwicklung* in *Grundlagen und Kritik des Sozialismus* (Berlin 1919), Vol. II, pp. 299–319.

degenerate doctrine of birth control, would soon drive the white man out of his every preserve.

When the 1929 crisis made its sudden and untoward appearance, demographers everywhere waited with bated breath for its expected repercussions on the birth-rate. If the new theory was correct, a steep increase in the birth-rate had to be expected in all great industrial countries, now that sex was the only pleasure left to millions of unemployed men. Clearly these millions could not afford to pay for contraceptives, let alone for abortions. As it turned out, however, all demographic speculation proved to be fallacious—poverty failed to go hand in hand with complete irresponsibility. Even the poorest men seemed to take the necessary precautions, realising as they did that the cupboard was bare enough already.

Thus the birth-rate in Europe, America and even in Japan declined during the thirties. The one exception was Germany, where the Hitler regime drove the birth-rate up by government incentives and propaganda. While the number of births in Germany had fallen from 1,810,000 in 1901 to 971,000 in 1933, it was up to 1,277,000 in 1936. The democracies looked on in astonishment, but refused to make equally far-reaching inroads into the private lives of their citizens.

Hence things looked very black for them on the eve of the Second World War. The gradual depopulation of Europe seemed inevitable, for no matter whether things became better or worse, people refused to have enough children. The only consolation was the "discovery" of a birth-rate cycle—periodic increases and decreases in population, alternating with periods of stability. While the evidence for the existence of such a cycle was regrettably sparse, demographers could point to a great 19th century precedent, and precedents are always grist to the prophetic mills. It appeared that, though the North and West European birth-rate had dropped for some 20 years after the Napoleonic wars, it had subsequently picked up to increase again about 1880.[1] Now, if this development were to be repeated after the First World War, a long period of growth could be expected from 1945 onwards. Other observations and reflections led to the conclusion that, if only because of existing age

[1] R. R. Kuczinski: *The International Decline of Fertility in Political Arithmetic* trans. Lancelot Hogben (London 1935), p. 50 f.

distributions, the long decline in the birth-rate was bound to be followed by a period of stability. Shrewd ethnographers were quick to apply these considerations to the next three centuries.[1]

Those who remained pessimistic even in the face of such brilliant statistical prognoses, were consoled by being told that, in any case, a gradual decline in the birth-rate was far better than a steep rise. For instance, at the time of the Holy Roman Empire, Europe counted only about thirty million inhabitants.[2] Had the population increased as rapidly as it did in the 19th century, Europe alone would count ten trillion inhabitants, and every spot on earth would be as densely populated as the City of London. This kind of argument is reminiscent of the story about the provident sailor who two thousand years ago put by a penny and whose modern descendants could turn the accumulated compound interest into a nugget of gold the size of the earth. In other words, mankind was much better off, whichever way you looked at it.

Europe, 1970

Still, people continued to worry about the depopulation of Europe so much, that, in January 1939, the League of Nations felt impelled to investigate the problem fully. Though the war had started a few months later, the organisers of this laudable enterprise did not permit this trifling incident to interfere with their monumental task. After almost five years of arduous work, which was largely carried out by a group of Princeton ethnographers, the task was completed and the results were published while the war was still going on. The very title—*The Future Population of Europe and the Soviet Union*[3] showed that it was a truly prophetic work. In fact, it predicted the future for 30 years ahead though, if the truth be told, no errors of such magnitude had ever been committed in any "objective" international

[1] R. R. Kuczinski, op. cit., p. 101 f.
[2] Article on Population in *Handwörterbuch der Staatswissenschaften* (4th ed. Jena 1924).
[3] League of Nations, Geneva 1944.

survey before or since. What the experts had done was simply to apply yesterday's yardstick to tomorrow's cloth. It was taken for granted that, since the birth-rate in some Western countries had barely kept up with the death-rate before the war, the war itself would produce sufficient casualties to decrease the ratio further still. This trend would continue until 1970, by which time Britain would have a population of only 46·8 million inhabitants—7% less than in 1940—while the population of France would drop by as much as 10% to 37 million inhabitants. Things looked somewhat brighter for Germany, and, although by 1944 it must have been plain in Geneva and in Princeton that the Hitler regime and the Nazi birth drive were unlikely to survive for long, the experts nevertheless assumed that the population of Germany would increase to 72·2 million by 1955, and drop to 69·8 million by 1970.

The population of Southern and Eastern Europe, too, would take a leap upwards: that of belligerent Italy by 10%, and that of neutral Spain by a similar amount which, however, would drop off slightly by 1960. Greater increases still would occur in Poland, Rumania and Yugoslavia (20%) and in the U.S.S.R. which would hold the record with an increase of 44% (from 174 million to 251 million).

To-day, it has already become quite obvious that the prophecies for the year 1970 have very little chance of being confirmed by events: they are far too low for Northern, Western and Southern Europe, and far too high for Eastern Europe. While this double error balanced things out to some extent, the total population of Europe was nevertheless over-estimated by some 15,000,000.

Most striking of all was the miscalculation of the figures for the Soviet Union, and this despite the fact that the "prophets" could have had no illusions about Russia's tremendous war losses. Thus the League of Nations and later the United Nations experts calculated that the Soviet population would increase by 15 million from 1940 to 1945, and this, together with misconceptions about the subsequent birth-rate, led them to over-estimate the annual population increase by 2–3 million, so much so that by 1955 the Soviet Union was expected to have 216 million inhabitants.[1] Then came the great surprise: in June

[1] United Nations: *Monthly Bulletin of Statistics* (N.Y.) March 1956.

1956 the Soviet Union lifted the veil over her own census figures and it appeared that the Soviet Union including Soviet Asia had a mere 200·2 million inhabitants—60 million less than the experts had calculated. In fact, the total population had grown by only 8·5 million since 1940, and while the increase had been most marked in Soviet Asia, White Russia and the Ukraine had fewer inhabitants than sixteen years before. In the table that follows we have contrasted League of Nations and United Nations predictions with actual developments in the leading European countries (with the exception of those whose territories have been so drastically revised as to make direct comparisons impossible).

Population of Europe 1940—1955
(in millions)

Country	1940 Actual	1945 Predicted	1945 Actual	1955 Predicted	1955 Actual
Gt. Britain	50·2	50·6	48·2	50·2	51·0
France	40·2	40·8	39·8	39·7	43·3
Belgium	8·3	8·3	8·3	8·3	8·8
Holland	8·8	9·2	9·2	9·8	10·7
Switzerland	4·2	4·3	4·4	4·2	5·0
Denmark	3·8	3·9	4·0	4·0	4·5
Sweden	6·3	6·4	6·6	6·3	7·3
Norway	2·9	3·0	3·1	3·0	3·4
Spain	25·6	26·4	26·8	27·5	29·0
Portugal	7·6	8·0	8·0	8·5	8·8

Clearly, the estimates for 1945, i.e. for 1–2 years ahead, were relatively correct for most countries, and this despite unpredictable war losses. All the more surprising, therefore, are the discrepancies in the post-war figures, which are partly due to an unforeseen recession in the death-rate but must be mainly attributed to increases in the birth-rate. While an increase in births had been expected for the immediate post-war period, no one suspected that this trend would continue. Precisely sixty years after the decline in the European birth-rate first began, the pendulum had begun to swing in the opposite direction. Was this, after all, the proof that the birth-rate was, in fact, a cyclic phenomenon?

True, in some countries the change had not come about quite naturally, and, particularly in France, the state helped to accelerate the process by generous family allowances: workers with four children were paid about twice the wages of bachelors. But even in countries that were not so open-handed, the birth-rate raced ahead by leaps and bounds. This trend was most marked in the United States where people had begun to speak of a baby boom,[1] and where the annual birth rate between 1946 and 1954 was 60% up on the corresponding figures during the pre-war recession, and this despite the fact that the number of potential mothers had increased by only $33\frac{1}{3}$%. Since this increase coincided with a period of extraordinary prosperity, the old notion gave way to a new demographic theory: economic boom—many children, economic crisis—few children.

Europe, 2000

Convinced of this truth, the prophets could set to work with renewed vigour. The table below lists three leading ethnographers' forecasts for A.D. 2000, the first dated 1945 when the post-war trend was still uncertain, and the others dated 1953 and 1956 respectively, by which time the new trend in the Western world had been appreciated.

The increase in world population during the second half of our century is therefore expected to be 35%, 40% or 47% respectively—a little less than the increase during the first half of the century (50%). All in all, it would appear that the world population will have doubled from 1900 to 2000, just as happened in Europe during the 18th and 19th centuries, though, in future, Europe will apparently lag behind the rest of the world. Even the most optimistic modern estimates do not consider that Europe (excluding the Soviet Union) can count on a population increase of more than 55% by A.D. 2000.

The population of Asia, on the other hand, which only a few decades ago was periodically stricken by plagues and famine to such an extent that the average increases were often smaller

[1] Metropolitan Life Insurance Co. Statistical Bulletin (N.Y.) May 1955.

than they were in Europe—and this despite the far higher Asian birth-rate—is expected to increase by leaps and bounds in the future. The mortality rate is declining in even the most hygienically and economically backward countries, and while it still exceeds the European rate by far, the gap is being narrowed year by year. In China, for instance, the annual mortality rate is said to be 0·08% as against the annual birth-rate of 0·45%,[1] so that there is an annual population increase of 22 million inhabitants. Admittedly this enormous increase will not continue for ever, since a declining mortality rate usually brings a declining birth-rate in its wake.

World Population in A.D. 2000[2]

(in millions)

Area	Actual Population in 1950	Estimate for A.D. 2000		
		Notestein (1945)	Woytinsky 1953	Fourastié and Vimont 1956
World	2400	3345	3250	3550
N. America	166	176	220	220
S. America	162	283	280	280
Europe (excldg. U.S.S.R.)	396	417	440	450
U.S.S.R.	193	298	260	275
Asia (excldg. U.S.S.R.)	1272	1900	1750	2000
Africa	198	250	280	300
Oceania	13	21	20	20

Moreover, this development is being encouraged by the governments themselves. Japan and India, and more recently China, are actively propagating birth control and rational family planning. Everyone may have as many children as he wants but no more. While birth control has not so far managed to capture the imagination of the illiterate Chinese masses, modern means of mass communication are sure to sway them in the end.

[1] United Nations *Monthly Bulletin of Statistics* (N.Y.) August 1957.
[2] Jean Fourastié and Claude Vimont: *Histoire de demain* (Paris 1956), p. 17.

This influence must, in any case, not be ignored in population forecasts, for it has already played a large, if not decisive, role in the decline of the Western birth-rate. When, as seems possible, 19th century birth-control techniques are superseded by harmless chemical preparations, the repercussions may be such that all demographic predictions may once again go by the board.

The weaker sex

Demographic predictions come up against another major obstacle as well: the sex ratio. Everywhere in the Western world, women outnumber men, and not only in countries whose male population has been decimated by wars. Thus, in Western Germany, there is a surplus of women over men of three million, i.e. of 12% and in Britain of two million (8%). In many large cities, this surplus is such that a woman's chances of marriage are appreciably reduced, and, in Vienna for instance, women outnumber men by almost 30%.

This phenomenon is particularly strange, since, in the West at least, the number of new-born boys always exceeds that of new-born girls. This fact has long been appreciated and was first mentioned in John Graunt's *Natural and Political Observation upon the Bills of Mortality* (1662). The common belief that an excess of boys is born exclusively during wars, when nature, as it were, makes up for her losses, is a fallacy. In peace time, too, the sex ratio remains fairly constant, 104 boys being born for every 100 girls, though with marked regional, and apparently even greater social differences.

Previously it was believed that racial factors, too, were involved, because the Negro sex ratio in the United States is smaller than that of the whites. However, it has since appeared that whenever hygienic conditions were improved the Negro sex ratio approaches that of the rest of the population. The upper classes in the United States have a particularly high male to female ratio (125 : 100),[1] and the ratio is therefore a

[1] M. E. Bernstein: *Changes in sex ratio, upper social strata* in *Human Biology*, December 1948.

kind of economic index, explaining, for instance, why more girls than boys are born in poor countries like India and China.

The embryonic male to female ratio is far greater still. Miscarriages have shown that it is about 3 : 2, and that it can be as much as 4 : 1 during the first months of pregnancy.[1] Thus the male death-rate begins to exceed the female death-rate in the womb, and this process is continued after birth when the infantile mortality rate of boys is universally greater than that of girls.

Thus, though more boys are conceived, more girls survive, so much so that during the 19th and early 20th centuries the number of five-year-old boys and girls was approximately equal in Western Europe. In much higher age-groups, puerperal fever tended to kill off the mothers so that males often predominated, but since both puerperal fever and also births (and hence their danger to the mother's life) have declined, and since men, moreover, tend to die earlier than women, women have begun to gain the (numerical) upper hand.

A surfeit of women

The future consequences of this tendency have been the subject of keen speculation among demographers, some of whom have held that, since male survival depends on environmental factors (which are constantly being ameliorated) the present excess of women over men is only a passing phenomenon.

The facts, however, do not seem to bear out this hypothesis. Better conditions of life, and particularly social health measures have tended to weight the balance even further in favour of women. Thus among teenagers, who were not affected directly by the last World War, women exceed men by 3–5%, and the time when a large number of men will be relegated to enforced bachelordom seems very far off indeed, if it will ever come at all.

Geneticists, too, have had their say on this subject, and their

[1] C. Stern: *Grundlage der menschlichen Erblehre* (Göttingen–Berlin–Frankfort 1955), p. 351.

pronouncements go a long way towards reassuring womankind. According to them, the sex ratio can be controlled within the predictable future by direct medical intervention.

Though these hopes, which are based on successful animal experiments some 30 years ago, have not yet shown any signs of being fulfilled, biologists have not allowed themselves to become discouraged. Thus Curt Stern, a German-born geneticist working at Berkeley University (California), is convinced that sex determinations of human beings will be voluntarily controlled one day,[1] and another leading expert, the American biologist Laurence H. Snyder feels that, though none of the present methods have been tested sufficiently, voluntary sex determination in human beings is a theoretical possibility, at least.[2]

Opinions about successful methods are largely divided, though two procedures seem to be the most promising. In the first, electrical or chemical techniques are used to isolate "male" from "female" sperms, and the desired sperm is introduced into the uterus by artificial insemination. This procedure involves practising the strictest birth control since a single careless slip might upset it.

The second procedure involves conditioning the uterus in such a way that it becomes receptive either to male or to female sperms alone. In other words, the sperms would not have to be isolated at all, but one type would be "sterilised" *in utero*, probably by hormone treatment. There would therefore be no need for artificial insemination. For that reason alone, this method is preferable in practice. In any case, it is now realised that sex can only be fixed before, and not, as was previously thought, after conception.

However, as we have seen, the whole subject is still in its theoretical stages and no one can say with certainty whether either method will lead to practical results. Should it do so, the social repercussions would be tremendous, though, unless family life as such were to disappear completely, there is little chance of an Amazonian super-state, or an all-male race of warriors, being set up.

[1] C. Stern, op. cit., p. 367.
[2] Laurence H. Snyder: *Grundlagen der Vererbung* (Frankfort–Berlin) p. 323.

Comparing I.Q.s

So far we have discussed populations quantitatively, and we shall now look at their qualitative aspects. Clearly mere numbers are not enough, and parents and governments alike are concerned with producing the best possible human material. However, qualitative predictions prove even more difficult to make than those dealing with quantity.

In 1883, Sir Francis Galton coined the term "eugenics" for the science which deals with scientific breeding to determine the quality of the offspring. Galton himself was much too rational and liberal a man to have looked upon human beings as mere breeding animals but unfortunately many of his disciples turned his doctrine into just that—even during his own lifetime. The American sterilisation laws—under which fifty thousand Americans were compulsorily sterilised for eugenic reasons from 1911–1950—and the excesses of the Hitler regime have given eugenics so bad a reputation that it will have to wage a long battle to wipe out the blot on its name.

Eugenics is a prophetic science by definition, for its aims are to control the future. This is perhaps one of the reasons why its disciples have made so many promises unsupported by any known genetic facts. While European eugenics stresses the physical development of the offspring, in America and also in Scandinavia the emphasis is placed on mental health, and eugenic measures are here (and particularly in 28 of the United States) directed at eradicating congenital mental deficiencies and criminal lunacy. The strictest laws exist in California, where thirty thousand "inferior" men have been sterilised, though strict proof that this measure has appreciably increased the mental health of Californians is still wanting.

In America there is also a more "positive" form of eugenics. Many American psychologists and teachers have made it their chosen task to determine intelligence, to classify human beings accordingly, and to encourage particularly promising children, who are sent out into the world not only with school certificates but with an I.Q. (intelligence quotient) certificate as well. I.Q.s are established on the basis of answers to a long questionnaire and are graded according to a fixed scale. Thus a ten-year-old boy of average intelligence is given an I.Q. of 100; if his intelligence is that of an eight-year-old boy he is given an I.Q. of 80, and if he is as bright as a normal twelve-year-old boy he is given an I.Q. of 120. Modern Americans carry their I.Q.s with them as other people carry Identity cards, unless of course the I.Q. is low, in which case they often lose it.

This inherently dangerous game with numbers, which may lead to arrogance on the one hand and feelings of inferiority on the other, is now put to large-scale prognostic uses. Even though I.Q. tests have revealed little else that is remarkable, they have shown that intelligence expresses itself rather early and remains almost constant for decades. In school-children below the age of ten the tests are admittedly of small prognostic value, but thereafter they are taken as criteria of suitability for given jobs, and general suitability. And, in fact, in a large control experiment with 1500 formerly gifted school-children, it appeared that their I.Q. had not changed greatly after 25 years. Men who had been found to have a high I.Q. at school, continued to show their prowess in professional life and usually managed to obtain good positions[1] not only in intellectual spheres but also as businessmen and technicians.

In other countries, people are inclined to be a little more sceptical about using particularly pre-adolescent I.Q. tests as prognostic criteria, though few would deny that general intelligence tests are better standards of judging subsequent professional performance than the old-fashioned system of examinations and reports which tell us more about what knowledge a given pupil has attained than about his ability to gain and to apply new knowledge—the very things that matter in professional life.

Much more debatable is the relevance of I.Q. tests to eugenic prognoses, i.e. it is by no means certain that parents with high I.Q.s will necessarily have more intelligent children than parents with low I.Q.s. Though a great deal of research has been done to determine to what extent intelligence is inherited, and to what extent it is modified by environmental factors,[2] the results are far from conclusive.

The only thing that seems certain is that, since the children of

[1] L. M. Terman and M. A. Merrill: *Measuring Intelligence* (Boston–New York–Chicago 1937).
[2] Anne Anastasi and J. P. Foley: *Differential Psychology* (N. Y. 1949).

intellectual parents generally have higher I.Q.s than children of unskilled workers, general eugenic prognoses can be made for one generation ahead, but not for subsequent generations. The fact that children of mentally undistinguished parents may nevertheless be geniuses must, in the present state of eugenics, be considered the happy exception rather than the rule.

CHAPTER 9

Gambling and Safe Play

*A*LL MAN'S ECONOMIC STRIVINGS MOVE BETWEEN TWO apparently opposite poles: the urge to attain easy riches by gambling, and the need for security. Adventurers and stolid business men seem to represent two very distinct types, two philosophies, and two methods of fashioning the future, for while the former are gamblers by nature, or at best successful speculators, the latter not only avoid gambling and speculation but despise them as utterly immoral.

But between these two apparently irreconcilable attitudes, there is a close inner connection: gambling and certainty obey the same laws of probability—without these laws the most respectable Insurance Society and the most lurid casino alike would collapse. Gamblers are usually unaware of this fact; they expect to be paid their winnings, and rarely ask themselves where the money comes from.

Nor do people with insurance policies usually worry about being mere pawns in a very big and most complicated game, or about the fact that the security they are offered, no matter with what guarantees, is only safe within the bounds of probability, or, in this case, actuarial calculations. By paying their premiums, they "purchase" security from the "vendor"—the insurance company,[1] which, in order to fulfil its obligations, has to run great risks itself. These risks are in many respects much more difficult to foresee than the risks of the gaming table. Insurance companies have to play with life and death, with catastrophies of all kinds, with accidents—in short with events whose frequency and gravity can only be estimated very approximately.

Insurance companies usually emphasise that they are merely trustees of wealth and thus clearly distinguished from gambling houses. This claim, too, is only true to some extent, for gambling houses must also keep large funds "in trust" if they are not to become insolvent during the first heavy setback.

[1] Maurice Fauque: *Les Assurances* (3rd ed. Paris 1954), p. 14.

The essential difference between these two institutions is that insurance companies contract to pay for certain accidents (or at fixed dates) while the gaming tables pay for sheer luck.

The gambler's mentality

It would seem that gamblers worry far less about the future than anyone else. However their outward fatalism rarely gives a true picture of their real mental attitude. The vast majority of gamblers, far from being fatalistic, believe that they can persuade fate to be particularly kind to them—which is the main reason why they gamble at all. Not a few feel like great conquerors who challenge fate in order to vanquish it. Fate must be forced to submit to them. A gambler who gets up from the table with neither a scoop nor with empty pockets, is no real gambler at all, but only a looker-on. Gambling means winning or losing to the limit, and not just staking for fun.

Many big-time gamblers have therefore tried to turn gambling into an art. Such men do not just stake on any number at roulette, but choose their numbers in accordance with a simple plan. Thus they will stake on red only after black has turned up a given number of times, or vice versa, on the assumption that, in the long run, both colours turn up an equal number of times.

Other players try to win by "doubling up". Having lost the first round, they double their original stake in the second round and so on. If the odds are even (as they are when staking on red or black in roulette) they will have staked $1 + 2$ units in the second round in order to win back 2×2 units, and $1 + 2 + 4$ units in the third round to win back 2×4 units, etc.—i.e. they will never win back more than double their *original* stake. Unfortunately, if they have a long run of bad luck, the stakes have to be so great, that all but the richest gamblers usually run out of cash. No wonder then that "doubling up" has ruined so many roulette players.

Almost all games of chance—except such very simple ones as tossing coins and throwing dice—allow of combinations that apparently increase the chances of winning. Many so-called "scientific" gambling systems are based on the belief that certain lucky numbers which have turned up in the past, are likely to turn up again in the future. What happened once is bound to happen again, remains the motto of most gamblers—hence their preoccupation with cataloguing past results. In practice, however, probablitity is not as straightforward as it appears in mathematical books, since in order to apply its laws successfully, a continuous record of a vast number of games at a particular table must be kept. Now, not even the most indefatigable gamblers spend 24 hours a day observing and recording games at one table, and they must therefore rely on the special sheets published by the big casinos, or organise an intelligence service of their own.

But even when they have all the information they need, gamblers are not usually strong-minded enough to follow a monotonous system, particularly when they are losing. Thus they may decide not to stake when the system decrees that they should, or go to another table to try their luck there. Since they have no records about what has just been happening at the new table, they are forced to gamble like the other punters whom they despise as amateurs.

Gamblers par excellence

The question therefore remains whether the systematic gambler has greater chances of success than his happy-go-lucky counterpart. What we know of famous gamblers and great coups at the gaming tables leads us to suspect that the question must be answered in the negative. The biggest of coups, in which gamblers won vast fortunes within a few hours and "broke the bank", were made by gamblers in the true sense of the word, and not by followers of systems. Theirs was the victory of discontinuity over continuity, of chance over calculation, of the improbable over the probable.

To give but a few of the most famous cases: in the middle of the 19th century, casinos throughout Europe dreaded the name of the Prince of Canino—the pseudonym of Charles-Lucien Bonaparte, a cousin of the then President of the French Republic

who later became Napoleon III. His great connections alone
procured the Prince the necessary credits to play with unheard-
of stakes. He would never stake less than the permitted maximum—which was much higher than it is today—and always
accompanied his main bet with a side bet on one of the two
colours. In this way he could make his money last longer, but
not cover the losses from his main bets, had these been persistent. He was therefore a pure rather than a systematic gambler,
and this despite his being well-versed in the mathematics of his
day.

But though Charles Lucien Bonaparte often lost consistently
for a few hours on end, his tremendous reserves always enabled
him to recoup his losses and to leave the table as the winner. His
greatest trump was, in fact, his ability to get up when he had
won enough, and not to strain his luck, as most gamblers in his
place would have done. He would also allow some time to elapse
after his last victory, and then begin anew in another casino. He
might therefore be called the discontinuous gambler *par
excellence*.

His most sensational coup was made in Bad Homburg where
he won 560,000 gold francs—the equivalent of £185,000
today—within one week and broke the bank. The directors of
the casino, the famous brothers Blanc who subsequently became
the directors of the Monte Carlo casino, were forced to borrow
money from Rothschild's Bank and to reduce their maximum
stakes.[1] However, this emergency measure proved of small
avail, for in 1860, eight years after the Bonaparte episode, a
Spaniard by the name of Thomas Garcia managed to relieve the
Homburg casino of 800,000 gold francs (£270,000) by working
with a number of accomplices all of whom staked on the same
number, thus exceeding the permitted maximum stake. Once
again the casino was in serious trouble, but Garcia was too much
of a gambler to be satisfied. Instead, he returned time and again
to the tables, until he had lost every penny of his winnings.

Monte Carlo, too, which became the world's leading casino
in the 1860's and remained so until 1914, when Latin American
and Asian casinos raised their maximum stakes, was the scene of

---

[1] E. Caesar Conte Corti: *Der Zauberer von Homburg und Monte Carlo*
(Berlin 1955), pp. 66–71.

many a desperate struggle to break the bank. Those legendary Russian Grand Dukes and Princesses—like the Princess Suvorov who during one afternoon lost 300,000 francs, won 700,000 francs, and finally got up with a net loss of 300,000 francs—were not the bank's real enemies. With or without a system, they would usually stay at the table until their stake-money had run out, to return again after an interval. Much more dangerous, were such reckless gamblers as Vincenzo Bugeja, a Maltese merchant, who entered into the battle with a million gold francs and forced the management to send to Paris for additional funds—despite the fact that the casino had a cash reserve of over two million francs.

"The man who broke the bank of Monte Carlo", however, was, in fact, a myth put out by the casino to lure new customers to its tables. In actual fact, casinos became more and more careful, restricting maximum stakes and always keeping large enough reserves to match up to even the richest and most obstinate gamblers. "Breaking the bank" came to mean no more than that a given table had to interrupt the game until sufficient cash was fetched from the office. Continuity, therefore, always scored over discontinuity.

Gaming systems

Nevertheless the organisation of gambling houses involves a most complex and difficult application of probability laws, for while these laws are the same for all games of chance, their operation differs from case to case.

By and large, gambling falls into one of three categories. The simplest is common gaming in which all the stakes go into a common bank, and where the total amount—usually after deduction of a commission—is distributed among the participants according to a fixed scale. This is the principle of the football pool in which the total investment and the odds vary from week to week, but in which the directors run no risks, provided only that their overheads are covered.

The second type is the lottery, in which the total number of tickets, and hence the total stake are fixed in advance. Here, too, the total stake is redistributed to the participants, after the organisers have deducted their own share to cover costs, etc. In most countries, lotteries are run by the state, whose institutions benefit from the additional revenue obtained. Thus only the gamblers and not the organisers are thrown at fate's mercy, and if they fully appreciated the odds against them, they would be bound to give up buying lottery tickets altogether. True, the government does not conceal any figures, and gamblers might argue that, if only they lived long enough and never missed a single draw, they would be bound to win in the end.

The third way, the gaming table, seems to involve greater risks for the organisers and to be fairer to gamblers, for here either party is liable to lose. In fact, the organisers run even greater risks, for while the gamblers can restrict their stakes, the organisers cannot restrict the number of players. While the gambler has to contend with only one unknown: the winning number, the bank must contend with two unknowns: the winning number and the unpredictable total stake on this number.

The fact that popular casinos nevertheless make good profits is, as we have seen, due to probability laws. To the individual gambler, the chances of acting according to these laws are small and rather unattractive. Thus, during 1000 million games of roulette, the chances of black (or red) turning up on 30 successive occasions are only 1 : 1,000,000,000 and even if the gambler were to play 1000 games a day—which would take him sixteen hours at the rate of one game per minute—he might have to wait 2700 years before such an event occurred. Casino records do, in fact, show that the maximum run on a given colour is 24,[1] though probability considerations show that two runs of 25 may be expected every week, if 1000 games a day are played.

Time and probability

Such contradictions between theory and practice are clearly perturbing to mathematicians. Hence many of them have always

[1] Emile Borel: *Les probabilités et la vie* (Paris 1950), p. 21.

dismissed probability theory as too vague to be anything but a perversion of true and precise mathematics, and this despite the fact that some of the greatest mathematicians of all time— Bernouilli, Laplace, and Gauss—played a leading part in its formulation. Some mathematicians have even questioned the validity of the fundamental theorem of probability, i.e. Bernouilli's Theorem (which states that the probability of an event is a function of its occurrence in the past), calling it a mere tautology which throws no fresh light on anything. Others again, have called probability theory "unrealistic", and its applications too full of practical errors to be worth anyone's while.

Yet others—and this is perhaps the most telling reproach— maintain that, after three centuries, probability theory is just where it was when it began. This, for instance, is the contention of the Rumanian mathematician Pius Servien, according to whom probability theory is bad science and bad mathematics, and relevant exclusively to the throw of dice, without, even in that field, being able to predict anything precise about any one throw.[1] Probability theory tells us nothing about the nature of chance, or about any possible laws governing it. In other words, we are no further than Voltaire was when he said that what we call chance may well be the unknown cause of a known effect.[2]

What astounds non-mathematicians most, is the cavalier manner with which probability theoreticians treat the concept of time, and the way in which they effect a complete separation of time from number. For probability it makes no difference whether a long series of events occurs during one hour or during one century. Thus if we play roulette once a year or once a minute, our chances of success are the same, since only the *frequency* of a given number turning up, and not the interval between two successive throws, affects our luck. For this very reason, probability calculations, unlike predictions based on periodic phenomena, seem completely irrelevant to human action and thought, which must be time-bound or else stray into fantasy. Instead of telling us that it will be our turn tomorrow, the theory merely promises us that our turn will come some day.

[1] Pius Servien: *Science et hasard* (Paris 1952) pp. 59 and 185.
[2] Voltaire: Article on Atheism in the *Dictionnaire philosophique* (1764).

State draws

All these objections notwithstanding, probability theory has maintained and proved itself in the most diverse fields. From the gaming table it has advanced into public and private finance, both as an incentive and also as a great leveller.

Gambling which seems so disreputable in the casinos, takes on a respectable guise in high finance, so much so that only the most uncompromising of moralists object when the state pays off its loans by public draws, thus favouring some of its creditors at the expense of others. Even non-speculative investors bear this injustice gladly, for it combines security with a small flutter.

Governments may also cash in on the gambling urge in other ways. Thus Premium Bonds, which bear no interest at all, are safe investments with enticing one-way risks. The investor can lose nothing (except interest) and stands to gain a (tax free) bonus, which may be vastly greater than his original investment. In this way, the government has brilliantly balanced the gambler's with the stolid business man's instincts—two instincts that are apparently poles apart. Many respectable citizens, who hate gambling like the plague and have never set foot on a racecourse, seem to have no scruples of conscience about speculating in this way.

Oddly enough, Premium Bonds are most popular of all in the Soviet Union where public gambling is most strictly forbidden, but where those who contribute to their country's welfare by subscribing to these bonds, may become wealthy overnight—at least by Soviet standards.

In April 1957, however, economic difficulties forced the Soviet Government to suspend repayment of the Bonds, together with draws, until 1983. By that distant date, which only a few of the old creditors will live to see, the government hopes to have repaid all previous loans. As far as her lotteries are concerned, therefore, Russia plans far longer ahead than in the economic sphere. In the Soviet Union, the smile of fortune is apparently eternal, and gratification can therefore be postponed *ad lib*.

The speculative element of lottery loans is quite distinct from that of Stock Exchange transactions which are generally bound up far more closely with complex economic processes. All attempts so far to apply probability theory to market fluctuations have ended in abysmal failure, precisely because the stock market is governed by such dynamic factors as economic developments, political and psychological trends, and not by the simple situations characteristic of lotteries, roulette, and card games played for money (baccarrat, vingt-et-un, etc.).

Mathematical forecasts are most reliable where the facts are clearly circumscribed, but fail wherever subjective factors and fluctuations play a large part, and where moods and whims may be more important than sober logic—in short wherever psychological factors are decisive. In America, two European scholars, a Hungarian mathematician and a Viennese economist have tried to establish a theory of games from purely logical considerations,[1] but though their profound book penetrated into the mentality and strategy of gamblers like none before or since, it contributed little to the art of predicting the actual results of speculative acts.

Shipwreck and conflagration

The greatest and most important field of mathematical forecasting is insurance. In gambling, probability theory may prove of practical help here and there, but not even the biggest casinos bother to employ a full-time mathematician. They know that probability will work in their favour even without such help. In Insurance Companies, on the other hand, mathematicians play an essential role, so much so that there is a special branch of actuarial statistics which deals with mortality tables, premium rates, etc. Probability is the heart of insurance, and though Insurance Companies must gamble on the future, they do their utmost to reduce their own risks and thus to protect their policy holders. So successful are they, that insurance companies rarely if ever go bankrupt.

Though modern insurance is unthinkable without probability estimates, insurance was born independently of, and long before, probability theory. If we ignore the very ancient practice

[1] O. Morgenstern and J. Von Neumann: *Theory of games and economic behaviour* (Princeton 1944).

of covering funeral costs by public subscription, insurance proper may be said to date back to the late Middle Ages, when the first insurance contracts were signed.

These first covers were extended to ships and shipping, which were then exposed to the double danger of natural catastrophes and piracy. While such large maritime associations as the German *Hansa* and the English *Company of Merchant Adventurers* could readily bear the occasional loss of a few ships, smaller companies were easily ruined by such disasters, and though no prophet was needed to point this out, it took a long time before appropriate action was taken. Mediterranean shippers and merchant-sailors were far too individualistic and too envious of one another to make common cause. True, they would occasionally sail out on common trading expeditions and found new colonies, but to make themselves responsible for one another's losses went against their sense of business propriety.

As insurance against maritime losses involved major financial risks, it is not surprising that the only people who were initially prepared and able to take it up were wealthy Italian bankers—the great Florentine houses of the Bardi, the Peruzzi and the Frescobaldi. The first policies were restricted to one sea-voyage or to a limited period of time, but as insurance expanded, as losses could more easily be recouped from current profits, and as experience increasingly showed what risks were the most serious, policies became more and more elastic. Meanwhile, all maritime insurance had been placed under public supervision, for the protection of all the parties concerned. In the great ports of Genoa, Barcelona, Bruges, Antwerp, and London special assurance offices saw to it that all business was conducted properly, so that fraudulent claims on the one hand, and delay in payment on the other, became increasingly rarer. By the 16th century, maritime insurance was an established branch of big business, with rigid laws and customs. The oceans were as stormy as they ever had been and piracy was still rife, but the financial risks were fast diminishing.

The second great branch of insurance, fire insurance, only came into its own during the 17th century, particularly in England. The Great Fire of London in September 1666, in which 13,000 houses were destroyed, was the signal that something had to be done about a possible repetition of such a disaster. True, no insurance company could have made good that damage—as no modern insurance company could rebuild a bombed-out city from its own funds—but the Fire of London drove home the point that it was better to have some restitution than none at all.

Since the Great Fire remained a unique event, insurance companies did well out of this new demand, and fire insurance became another rewarding field for private enterprise.

Wagers with death

The third branch of insurance, life insurance, was born later and had a much greater struggle to see the light of day. Here was an entirely novel idea, for while shipwreck and fire, however frequent, were exceptional events, death was anything but that. Life Insurance was therefore looked upon by many as direct interference with the will of God.

Still, the idea caught on, particularly when the probability experts pointed out that death, though inevitable, could strike some earlier than others, and was therefore an excellent object of insurance, and provision against it a commendable way of ensuring the welfare of bereaved families. Those who lived longer, and paid in more money therefore helped their fellow-men—a proposition to which not even the staunchest puritan could object. True, life insurance is a gamble with death, but the odds can easily be worked out from mortality tables, so that no one loses in the end.

Actually, the first beginnings of life insurance go back to the 17th century, long before mortality tables were known. It was then that a number of Italian cities asked their citizens to subscribe to life annuities, the returns from which varied with the subscriber's age. Young people who had a long life-expectancy were repaid at the rate of 5% per annum, while old people were paid up to $12\frac{1}{2}\%$ per annum. In 1663, an Italian banker, Lorenzo Tonti introduced this system to France, where so-called *tontines*, i.e. loans by public subscriptions, the last survivor obtaining all the remaining funds, exist to this day. Tontines were, however, a rather crude way of assessing life risks, and at bottom, merely a variation of the common mediaeval custom of providing for the future. Thus well-to-do and considerate fathers would deposit money in their children's name, often at birth, so assuring their descendants of a life-long annuity. A young gentleman with so provident a father was made for life, while his sister was sure to be a good match for anyone. True, if the original capital fell by the wayside for one reason or another, so did the annuity, but a father who had made such provision was judged by one and all to have done everything in his power to safeguard his descendants. His was the peak of financial foresight.

Only in the second half of the 17th century, could life insurance proper make its debut, for it was then that research into English church registers led to the compilation of the first mortality tables from which the average life expectancy of a man in his thirties, forties or fifties could be calculated. While no individual prognoses could be based on these tables, predictions for large groups proved uncannily correct. Shrewd financiers realised at once that this newly acquired knowledge could be put to profitable use, since all people, irrespective of age, could now be insured against death. Naturally old and ailing people had to pay higher premiums, but even if they died the day after a policy was issued to them, their dependents would be paid the full amount.

It was a lucky coincidence that at the very time when the first mortality tables were being computed, England learnt of probability theory from Holland and France.[1] Fifty years later when she first became acquainted with Bernouilli's *Ars conjecturandi* (The Art of Conjecture)—the result of twenty years of work—she had all the elements needed for putting Life Insurance on firm ground.

In England, Life Insurance soon developed into a flourishing business, but on the continent it ran into unexpected difficulties. The authorities, while recognising that life insurance policies in favour of one's dependents were praiseworthy indeed, felt that the benefits might encourage unscrupulous persons to despatch their benefactors to an untimely grave. One of the results of fire insurance had been an increase in arson, and no government

[1] De Witt: *De vardye van de lif-renten na proportie van de los-renten* (Den Haag 1671)

wanted to see such avarice being directed at life itself.

These fears, and the religious objections we mentioned earlier, caused the governments of France, Prussia, and Genoa to prohibit all forms of life insurance[1] for a whole century. France gave way after the Napoleonic wars, and Germany followed in 1827.

From then on vast amounts of money poured into insurance offices. Life insurance companies built up tremendous reserves which they invested in all sorts of sound enterprises, gradually becoming the financial empires they are today. In the United States, where more than half the adult population is insured, the total value of life insurance policies was 450,000 million dollars in 1956, and insurance companies had assets to the tune of 100,000 million dollars. In Switzerland 170 people in every 100 households carry life insurance, and in other West European countries, too, life insurance figures run into millions of pounds.

If some disaster were ever to kill off a large proportion of the population, no insurance company could possibly meet its obligation. But the probability of such a disaster is small enough for insurance companies to be able to say with good consciences that they offer mankind as much security as is within the bounds of reason.

From the cradle to the grave

Nevertheless, some countries have thought it best to make doubly sure. Since wars and other catastrophies invariably require the government to intervene, and since, moreover, the West, at least, has come to realise its responsibility to those who are too poor to provide for their own future, social insurance against accidents, disease, and unemployment have become matters of state in most European countries.

It was in England that the most comprehensive plan ever to offer some measure of security from the cradle to the grave was first put into practice. While the Second World War was still in full swing and while bombs were pouring down on London, an Oxford don, Sir William Beveridge, worked out a plan for insuring the entire population against occupational and economic

[1] H. E. Raynes: *A History of British Insurance* (London 1950), p. 119.

hazards. The price was to be a relatively small weekly contribution to a National Insurance Fund, which would not only pay compensation for accidents, illness, and unemployment, but also contribute to such happy, if expensive, events as birth and marriage. In addition, the Fund would also pay family allowances and provide a pension for all men over 65 and all women over 60 years of age. According to Beveridge's somewhat optimistic estimate, the total cost of this scheme would have been no more than 697 million pounds in 1945, and 858 million pounds in 1965, when the plan was expected to be in full operation.[1]

The Beveridge plan aroused tremendous excitement not only in England but also in all the allied countries. For some months, the name of Beveridge was better known than that of even the most famous generals. But then the government had second thoughts and refused to implement the plan, and it was not until after the war that some of its main suggestions were carried into effect.

England is also a pioneer in another field of insurance: the all-risks policy. Thus Lloyd's, for instance, will underwrite almost any kind of risk imaginable. Film stars can insure their eyes or their lovely legs, acrobats can insure their biceps, peace-lovers can insure against a world war, and neurotics against artificial satellites dropping on their back gardens. In short, as long as men are willing to pay the appropriate premium, Lloyd's is willing to give them almost any kind of cover. But what does the word "appropriate" really mean in such cases? There is, in fact, no objective standard for judging many risks, since probability theory can only be applied to large-scale phenomena susceptible to statistical analysis. The weirder the risk, therefore, the more an insurance policy becomes a straight bet, much as mediaeval maritime policies were, in which the insurers said to themselves that if the captain can brave a voyage, the risks cannot be all that great.

Subjective and objective chances

We have just touched upon a crucial question which concerns

[1] Sir William Beveridge: *Report on Social Insurance and Allied Services*, 17 Nov. 1942—*The Pillars of Security* (London 1943), p. 73.

not only insurance but science also, and particularly theoretical physics in which statistical phenomena play an ever-increasing role: where is the dividing line between subjective and objective probability estimates, where does mere speculation end and calculable probability begin?

Philosophers who have delved into this question and who have given all sorts of answers to it, fall into two groups: those who contend that the future is based on too many chance factors to be assessed in anything but degrees of probability, and those who maintain that, since all nature (and all human actions) follow fixed laws, the future is *in principle*, fully predictable, and that so-called probability or chance is only the measure of our own subjective ignorance.[1] This attitude which was characteristic of 18th century rationalism and of 19th century natural philosophy, continues to hold sway to this day, particularly through the influence of the great English economist John Maynard Keynes. According to Keynes "objective chance" is always derived from "subjective chance", for whenever we attribute a coincidence to objective chance we simply state our ignorance of the law of connection between the two.[2]

However, when we climb down from the pedestal of philosophy, we find that the distinction between subjective and objective chance is not as great as philosophers would have us believe. Thus no one in his right senses will bother to say that the objective chance of next summer being warmer than last winter, is merely a reflection of the degree of our subjective ignorance. Predictions of this kind are admittedly based on past (subjective) observations, but that does not in the least affect their practical (objective) validity.

It is on such observations that most of what we call probability is based. Probability statements are merely projections of the past into the future, on the assumption that the causes— no matter whether they are known precisely or not—will remain the same and will continue to have the same effects. Nor are quantitive predictions, characterised by degrees of probability, any more subjective than purely qualitative predictions. Thus, the statement that the probable deaths from heart and vascular

[1] Henri Poincaré: *Calcul des probabilités* (2nd ed. Paris 1912), p. 2.
[2] John Maynard Keynes: *A Treatise of Probability* (London 1921), p. 288.

diseases will account for 25% of all deaths in the ensuing year, is no less objective than the statement that these diseases will be frequent causes of deaths. The only difference is that the quantitative statement makes the additional assumption that deaths from other causes will also remain stable.

Probability only becomes truly subjective in the absence of sufficient empirical evidence. Thus whenever scientists, economists, or politicians have made generalisations from inadequate data, they have been subjective—and almost invariably wrong. The fault lies not with probability theory, but with those who forget that probability theory applies to aggregates and to aggregates alone.

Predicting the improbable

Unfortunately language itself lets us down in this respect, for when we say an event is probable, we assume that it is likely to happen, and never realise that the probability of its occurrence may be anything from 0 to 1.

Mediaeval philosophy took over from Aristotle the distinction of probability into four fixed categories, the highest of which was complete certainty, and the lowest, in which assertion and negation were equally balanced, was doubt (*dubitatio, aporia*). The second degree was suspicion (*suspicio, hypolepsis*), in which the assertion just outweighed the negation, the third was belief (*opinio, doxa*), in which the assertion seemed much more probable than the negation but was not completely proven. We, too, could do with a similar non-mathematical classification of degrees of probability.

Another thing that confuses the layman is the absence of any connection between aggregate predictions and their consequences for the individual. If health statistics show that 25 out of every 100 people die of heart or vascular diseases, or that the average life-expectancy in the United States is 77 years, this does not tell the individual anything about the possible causes of his own death or about his own life expectancy. Men being what they are, they are far more concerned with their own fate than with that of mankind as a whole, and are inclined to apply statistical predictions to themselves and to act accordingly.

If the predictions fail to oblige, the whole of probability theory is dismissed as worthless, even though it has fulfilled its own promise: to forecast aggregate phenomena.

Wherever such aggregate predictions have been applied by governments or large institutions, they have shown their extreme usefulness, and have helped to turn mere chance into serious prognosis. Only when statistics are put to uses for which they were never intended, do they prove to be a useless—and sometimes a dangerous—toy.

CHAPTER 10

The Mystery of the Business Cycle

*P*ROBABILITY THEORY GIVES US A GREAT MANY GLIMPSES into the future, and is therefore an excellent method of forecasting—particularly for people who do not live by the clock. While probability can tell us little about the temporal sequence of events, it teaches us much about their juxtaposition, so that we can see a host of like individual processes as a recognisable pattern rather than a kaleidoscope.

Admittedly, probability can also be applied to fixed sequences of events, as for instance in genetics, where fathers invariably precede their sons. But, by and large, time sequences play no more than a secondary role in probability theory, which is static rather than dynamic, and considers constantly recurring, rather than constantly changing, events.

It is for this very reason that probability theory, despite its doubtful antecedents, enjoys the favours of conservative economists and sociologists, while radicals reject or simply ignore it. According to probability theory, all human aggregates follow a definite pattern: only the fewest of men can be rich, can reach very old age, or attain great fame, nor will this distribution be altered by revolutionary changes in economics, geriatrics, or politics.

The law of income distribution

In economics, this doctrine is associated with the name of Vilfredo Pareto (1848–1923), who was convinced that the existing distribution of incomes was the soundest possible basis of economic and social equilibrium. But even if it was not, little could be done about it, since the distribution was governed by an immutable mathematical and mechanical law, as incontestable as any law of physics.

Pareto[1] did not derive his conclusions from observations of the largest group, i.e. people with small incomes, for this might have been embarrassing. Instead, he divided society into an uneven number of equal groups—a very small number of groups representing very high incomes, and a very large number representing very small incomes. Graphically, this distribution could be represented by a splendid curve, and—on the logarithmic scale—by the straightest of straight lines.

The elegant result, on paper, was taken for proof positive that national incomes were not distributed by mere chance, but that they were governed by a universally valid natural law. In these circumstances it was deemed unethical, not to say unnatural, to suggest reducing very high incomes. Moreover, Pareto had clearly shown that any such attempts to upset the "natural" economic order would simply lead to a few groups moving up, at the expense of others, but would not affect the total picture to any appreciable extent.

This remarkable "discovery" made its appearance in economic textbooks throughout the world, and came to be known as Pareto's Law. Though it is still upheld by some economists today, it was long ago shown to be, and always to have been, statistically inaccurate.[2] Had it been true, all attempts to improve the economic lot of the poor at the expense of the rich, would have been doomed to failure from the start.

According to Pareto, not even social revolutions could change the economic order, for all economics were said to have an inherent and permanent mechanism which, being greater than any one social system, inevitably led back to the *status quo ante*. All coercive re-allocations of the national income were therefore deplorable interruptions of an otherwise harmonious state of equilibrium.

Unreal and psychologically fallacious though Pareto's theory was, it nevertheless contained a grain of truth, for redistributions of incomes are generally nothing else than re-allocations of the national cake between different, though numerically equal groups, and have little effect on the population as a whole. It is simply a case of Peter paying Paul.

Another factor militating against successful social demands

[1] V. Pareto: *Cours d'Economie Politique* (1897).
[2] Eric Roll: *A History of Economic Thought* (London 1945), p. 414.

for a higher share in the national economy, is inflation. Very significantly, most people simply ignore the fact that wage increases can be offset by lower profits, and take it for granted that, as wages go up, so prices must rise. Inflation has therefore become an orthodox method of maintaining social equilibrium— Paul robs Peter to pay Peter a generous increase, and Peter is delighted. Monetary "reforms" of this kind are a cheap way of keeping people contented. Thus when Franklin D. Roosevelt launched his New Deal, which involved far-reaching social and economic reforms, the proportion of the U.S. national income represented by wages and salaries went up by barely one per cent.

Pareto was therefore not quite so silly as he sounds to many modern economists. Even in the Soviet Union, where economic distinctions are admittedly smaller than they are in capitalist countries, there is a marked tendency to widen the gap. While maximum differences in real wages were 10 : 1 (apart from very exceptional cases) in the first 20 years after the Revolution, differences of 50 : 1 are fairly common today. No one seems to mind that leading scientists earn fifty times as much money as unskilled workers, and, in fact, the ratio seems to be growing greater still.

The discovery of business cycles

Pareto's Law was one of the last great attempts to set up a universally valid social and economic law based on statistics. Since all such attempts have generally proved to be utter failures, economists have increasingly turned away from them. John Maynard Keynes and his disciples make a point of shunning all general prognoses and look upon economic processes, not so much as tending towards equilibrium, but as being characterised by marked deviations, particularly right at the top and right at the bottom of the social scale.

These deviations can be modified and even avoided, if the consequences of unemployment, investment, inflation and deflation are appreciated in time. All these processes are inter-related, and economists, like physicians, must occasionally prescribe antidotes. Naturally, it would be even better to prevent the illness from starting in the first place, but economists are not primarily prophets, and all they can do is to tell mankind that certain causes have certain effects, and how the worst effects can be prevented.

The real prophets among economists are the believers in cycles who, having observed that certain economic phenomena—and particularly crises—recur with great regularity, conclude that these phenomena are periodic. Thus, they confidently assume that the economic picture of the future will be a repetition of the past.

When periodic theory made its first appearance at the beginning of the 19th century, economics was still a young science and, like all young sciences, it was very self-conscious. Ever since Adam Smith in his *Wealth of Nations*[1] had extolled the advantages of free trade, it was a general axiom that, if only reason and freedom were allowed to replace all economic restrictions, things were bound to become better and better. Since then it has appeared that free trade is not quite the good fairy Adam Smith had made it out to be; it leads not only to merciless competition—which was deemed most desirable—but also to most undesirable crises from which all the contestants emerge as losers.

Cycle research

Not even the most orthodox economists could afford to ignore this incontestable fact, though they continued to hold fast for as long as they could to the French economist Bastiat's contention that free trade must needs lead to complete harmony.[2] As crises multiplied, however, even the most die-hard conservatives realised that the combined acts of human volition which governed free trade, were in turn governed by what appears to be a superhuman force that played havoc with man's plans at periodic intervals.

Economists now faced an entirely new task. Even if they could not tell precisely how to avoid the next economic crisis,

[1] Adam Smith: *Inquiry into the nature and causes of wealth of nations* (1776).
[2] C.-F. Bastiat: *Harmonies économiques* (1849).

they could at least observe and record these periodic upsets, and use their records for predictive purposes. A new branch of economics was born—Business Cycle Research—whose main task it was to determine which way the economic wind was blowing.

But before this task could be tackled effectively, an untold amount of theoretical and statistical spade work had first to be done. Though papers and records on business cycles had reached mountainous proportions, no individual theory had proved its absolute worth. So, statistical research proceeded apace and economists vied with one another to collect better and bigger data. Business cycle research, being largely historical and retrospective, can only foretell the future once it has probed the past as fully as possible.

Today, hundreds of public, semi-public, and private institutions all over the world devote themselves exclusively or predominantly to business cycle research. In addition, many banks, industrial companies, and other businesses have special offices devoted to the same task. If we counted all the statisticians and other staff who are directly or indirectly involved in this work, we should find that they far outnumber the staff of meteorological institutes.

As so often happens, quality has not kept up with quantity. Though cycle research in general has become mere routine, some of its offshoots are extremely unsalubrious. Particularly in America, there is a regular Stock Exchange branch whose practices are very reminiscent of those of soothsayers. Then again, cycle theory has often degenerated into mere scholastic hair splitting, whose practical results are in no relationship to the amount of work that has gone into it. But, all in all, the achievements of this young branch of predictive science are far from insignificant, and it would be wrong to dismiss it, simply because of such false prophecies as those made on the eve of the 1929 crisis, or immediately after the Second World War.

Crises

The fact that modern cycle research began in the 19th century, does not mean that the idea of cycles in nature is of relatively recent origin. Since time immemorial, farmers have been keenly interested in cyclical phenomena and in arranging their work accordingly. Planetary orbits, the weather, the seasons—in short everything sent by the heavens, has a more or less cyclical character, and human beings working out of doors could not fail to notice it.

In other respects, too, cycles have always played a large role in agriculture. Thus arable land had to be left fallow from time to time (which later gave rise to the practice of the rotation of crops) for, just like men or beasts, the soil needed time to recuperate from strenuous labours. The fact that reckless avarice does not pay dividends on the land, was known to every farmer.

In industry, however, everything seemed to be different. The only rhythmical interruptions here, were a minimum of time for sleeping and a day off for observing the Sabbath. Otherwise, work went on continuously, particularly after the invention of the steam engine when interruptions of work meant letting the boilers go out. Continuity of production became an economic principle, and since machines were becoming better and better, there seemed to be no limit to what man could produce. But then, quite suddenly, the limit was nevertheless reached, not admittedly on the productive, but on the distributive side. The greater the quantity of goods which poured from the factory, the more difficult it became to dispose of them. The first such great interruptions of the productive process were significantly called "trade crises" to show that trade, rather than over-production, was to blame. Clearly the fault lay with the customers, who refused to buy what was being offered them. Only a few impertinent outsiders, like the Swiss economist de Sismondi (1773–1842)[1] blamed over-production and low wages, but public opinion and more orthodox economists paid no heed to him.

The question when the first of these crises occurred is still very hotly contested. While it was formerly thought that the great distributive slump of 1816, on which de Sismondi based his theory of crises, was the first economic crisis in the modern

[1] Simonde de Sismondi: *Nouveaux principes de l'Economie politique* (1819).

sense, more recent investigations have shown that crises had occurred as early as the 18th century. Still, these very early crises could not as yet have been periodic and were certainly local affairs. Thus the years 1787–1793, i.e. the time of the French Revolution, were years of great prosperity in England. In what follows, we shall therefore concentrate on more recent crises, and begin with the general depression which followed immediately after the Napoleonic wars. This crisis, although apparently due to extraordinary causes, was followed by a similar upheaval in 1825, i.e. after ten years of peace, by another in 1836, and by a third, affecting the whole of Europe in 1847. Crises therefore seemed to recur every nine to eleven years, each lasting for two to three years, each followed by gradual improvements, and some by exceptional prosperity. But crises rather than prosperity were in the public's eye, since crises caused bankruptcies, public scandals, dumping of goods, mass-immigration, suicides, political disorders, etc. Thus the idea of business cycles was not yet born, and people spoke of periodic crises instead, in much the same way that they had previously spoken of epidemics.

The Juglar-cycle

The first man to mention business cycles as such was the French economist Clément Juglar who, turning from his studies of periodic population phenomena—marriages, births and deaths—to an investigation of fluctuations in the rate of interest of the Banks of France and England, discovered a surprising rhythm in them.

In 1860, after ten years of further study, Juglar published the results of his observations and calculations in a book that said far more than its title, *Des crises commerciales et leur retour périodique en France, en Angleterre et aux Etats-Unis* (Of commercial crises and their periodic return in France, England, and the United States), would have led one to suspect. The book propounded the revolutionary doctrine that, far from being isolated events, crises were mere phases in long business cycles, whose purpose it was to slough off the dead tissue accumulated during the previous period of prosperity. In other words, crises were mere trials by fate (the original Greek meaning of the word) during which the wheat was separated from the chaff. While individuals might suffer, the economy as a whole was purified and strengthened by this somewhat painful, but altogether wholesome, purgative.

Like so many other important discoveries, Juglar's business cycle remained unnoticed for quite some time. Even so well-read a man as Karl Marx ignored it completely when, seven years later, he developed his own revolutionary theory of crises in his *Das Kapital*. True, there were basic differences between the two economists, for while Juglar's theory was bourgeois— he had no wish to destroy the capitalist system simply because it led to periodic crises—Marx looked upon crises as proofs positive of the degeneracy of that system. Where Juglar saw the economy moving forward in cycles of equal duration, Marx saw one gigantic downward spiral with crises recurring more and more frequently, and becoming more and more violent until rock bottom, and the end of capitalism, were reached simultaneously and inevitably. Then the workers would usher in the new age of socialism, and the spiral would finally come to an end.

The next hundred years were to prove Juglar right and Marx wrong. While some crises were admittedly much more violent than the terrible crisis of 1857 on which both economists had largely based their theories, others were not. Only in one respect was Marx proved right. Crises in the second half of the 19th century and the early 20th century occurred more frequently than they had during the first half of the 19th century, but even then the spiral did not narrow a great deal: the interval between crises was reduced from 9–11 years to 7–9 years.

Moreover, each crisis now seemed to have a different cause. In 1866 the cause was a financial miscalculation, in 1873 a property speculation, in 1907 a credit squeeze, and in 1929 wild stock exchange speculation. Each crisis looked different, with the result that a host of theories was put forward, only to be disproved on the next occasion.

Only one point seemed to be generally accepted: crises were a regular symptom of the economy. True, in times of prosperity this fact was glossed over and many people deluded themselves with the hope that periodic crises were gone forever, particularly during the 1920s when Americans were convinced that the golden age was here to stay. From now on, depressions could be met with reduced profit-takings, and all was well in the best possible of worlds. And so it was until—1929.

Although many European economists were also deceived by the American "economic miracle", not all were equally credulous. It was precisely in the 1920s that Business Cycle Research came into its own, and began to carry out detailed investigations of even the smallest market and interest fluctuations, in order to derive generally valid laws from them. When the 1929 crisis finally came, even the greatest American "miracle" economists had to admit that their European colleagues had been right and that the old doctrine of business cycles was as valid as ever it had been. Thus, on the eve of the Second World War, economists on both sides of the Atlantic were agreed that every boom was invariably followed by a slump. The only question was whether the next slump might not be so severe as to put an end to prosperity for ever. Perhaps Marx rather than Juglar had been right after all.

Kitchins and Kondratieffs

Meanwhile, business cycle theoreticians had come up against yet another difficulty. Although 7–9 year Juglar cycles existed beyond all doubt, these cycles alone could no longer explain the total economic picture. Perhaps there were other cycles in addition to Juglar's, interfering with it in much the same way that sound waves interfere with one another—producing higher crests here, and lower troughs there. The first positive discovery of this kind was made in the 1920s, when Joseph Kitchin[1] managed to isolate independent cycles, each lasting about 40 months, in the economy of Britain and the U.S. from 1890–1922. A parallel investigation by the American W. L. Crum, which went back as far as 1866, came to much the same result.

These shorter cycles followed similar courses to their big brothers'. Here too, long periods of prosperity were followed by sudden reversals in which the stock market slumped, consumption fell off and unemployment increased for a number of months,

[1] *Review of Economic Statistics*, January 1923.

until the pendulum gradually swung back again. The existence of such miniature cycles could be demonstrated in all phases of the Juglar cycle, on whose basic rhythm, however, they had no effect. Thus even during the prosperous 1920s the Kitchin cycle caused small depressions in 1924 and again in 1927 which, though no real crises, led to temporary economic set-backs, for which the term *recession* was coined. From then on, business-cycle theoreticians would be at odds in deciding whether business set-backs were the beginnings of a new crisis or merely of a new recession.

In addition to these shorter cycles, economists also discovered very long, historical, cycles, the so-called "great waves", each lasting 40–50 years, and each characterised by an upward and a subsequent downward trend lasting from 20–25 years. For instance, in Germany there was an upward swing lasting from 1843 to 1873, and again from 1895 to 1913, while there was a depression from 1874 to 1894. The first man to analyse these long periods systematically was N. D. Kondratieff,[1] after whom the cycles came to be known as Kondratieffs, to distinguish them from the shorter Juglars and Kitchins.[2] According to Kondratieff a "long wave" lasts for almost forty-five years, though other economists think that they may last fifty or even fifty-four years.[3]

Nor are economists agreed on the historical beginnings of these long cycles. While the first long wave reconstructed from reliable statistical material is said by some to have begun at the end of the 18th century and to have lasted into the 1840s, the second to have lasted into the 1890s, and the third up to the end of the Second World War or until a few years later,[4] others claim that the two world wars must be ignored since they merely interfered with the smooth functioning of the cycles.

Some modern historians, and Toynbee[5] in particular, have tried to relate long business cycles to political history and

[1] N. D. Kondratieff: *Die langen Wellen der Konjunktur* in Archiv der Sozialwissenschaft, December 1926.
[2] J. A. Schumpeter: *Business Cycles* (New York 1939), p. 169.
[3] Simon Kuznets: *Economic Change* (N.Y. 1953), p. 109.
[4] E. R. Dewey and E. F. Dakin: *Cycles, the Science of Prediction* (N.Y. 1947).
[5] Arnold Toynbee: *A Study of History*, Vol. IX, p. 322.

especially to war-and-peace cycles. Unfortunately, none of these efforts have led to tangible results. At most, we can agree that long wars—e.g. the Napoleonic wars, the wars of national liberation in the 1850s and 1860s, and the First World War— coincided with upward trends of the three corresponding Kondratieff's cycles, while the Second World War did not (unless the third long wave is allowed to end in 1940 rather than in 1945).

Many leading economists rightly object that two or three parallel events occurring at intervals of 45 or 50 years are no proper basis for a cycle theory, or for economic predictions. In any case, long waves are of small practical use, for neither governments nor private enterprise can generally afford to plan for so many years ahead.

Of pigs and rubber plants

Far more important for practical purposes are the cycles governing individual branches of the economy. Thus United States economists have discovered an eighteen-year cycle for the building trade, though Dewey and Dakin's prediction that this cycle would reach a low in 1952 has not been fulfilled. Building construction in 1952 was not only very much more intense than before the war, but 20% higher than in 1947, when the prediction was made. 14·8 year cycles are said to govern cattle and black pepper, 23 months cycles to govern the American textile industry, 34 months cycles to govern the sugar market, etc. Almost every important industry has at one time or another been said to have a cycle, though few such cycles have ever proved reliable prognostic criteria.

There is much better evidence in favour of cycles in which two independent economic phenomena follow each other at regular intervals, and in which one phenomenon can be predicted from the occurrence of another.

One of the most famous cases is the pork-price cycle discovered by the German Institute of Business Cycle Research in the 1920s. Statisticians had noticed for many years that the price of pork underwent marked periodic fluctuations, not, however, all of the same intensity. As a rule, prices, within a cycle, fluctuated by from 30–50%, quite independently of the general state of the market. Since the demand for pork was fairly constant, these fluctuations were clearly the result of changes in the conditions of supply.

In fact, every 40 months or so, farmers would either flood the market with pork or else cause an acute shortage. The reasons are quite simple: farmers are usually adaptable people, and if pigs fetch high prices they switch to pig rearing. Now it takes about 15 months to rear a pig for market, and a prior few months to reorganise a farm. Thus roughly 18 months after the market began to boom, a glut of pigs starts to pour into the butchers' shops. Butchers, in turn, realising that pork is becoming more and more plentiful, reduce their prices until pork rearing is no longer a profitable business. The farmers devote their attention to other livestock or crops instead, until there is a new scarcity of pigs, and so *ad infinitum*.

Although most pig breeders ought to have learned their lesson, they could never resist the lure of high prices. Even when business cycle experts explained to them the error of their ways in detail,[1] they took little notice and continued to breed pigs as they always had done—too much or too little. The Institute itself, however, had scored a great hit, and for many years the German Institute for Cycle Research was able to predict pork prices very accurately, 12 months in advance. Only in 1933, at the peak of the general economic crisis, did their predictions fail, because millions of people could no longer afford to buy pork, i.e. the cycle collapsed for an entirely different set of reasons.

The history of the pork cycle is one of the more impressive pages in the annals of serious economic prognosis. Even so, it would be wrong to base general economic laws on it. The cycle only worked because pig breeders acted according to classical *laissez-faire* axioms: high prices—many pigs, low prices—few pigs. Now, this axiom cannot be applied universally, even to completely free agricultural economies since the peasants of many primitive countries would never dream of increasing production when prices rise. If they manage to obtain more

[1] A. Hanau: *Die Prognose der Schweinepreise.* Special edition of Vierteljahrshefte zur Konjunkturforschung (Berlin 1928).

money for their products than they require for their immediate needs, they much prefer to take things easy for a bit.

This is precisely what happens in Malaya: if rubber prices rise, the Malay native taps fewer trees, but when the market falls, he is forced to exploit his plantation to the full, since otherwise he and his family would go hungry.[1] On the other hand, in parts of Indonesia where the main crop is rice, and rubber is only a secondary industry, the natives are extremely hard-working and respond quite differently to market fluctuations. The moment the rubber prices rise, they tap the trees very heavily to get the best of the boom. Thus, in the case of rubber whose price depends on the international market and a great many regional factors, it is very much more difficult to predict price fluctuations than in the case of German pork.

Trading hopes

The world's most important raw materials are usually offered for sale in Commodity Markets, ostensibly to safeguard the producers against sudden price fluctuations. In fact, actual sales represent only a fraction—and often an insignificant fraction—of the exchange transactions, the vast majority being dealings in futures. Thus American commodity exchanges will sell you coffee and cocoa beans, wheat, cotton, and 1001 other articles, that have not even been planted.

A great many of these articles are, in fact, never delivered at all. When the agreed delivery date is reached, the vendor simply pays the purchaser the difference between the agreed price and the ruling market price, or, if the market has dropped, he collects the difference himself. Thus commodity transactions are, in fact, speculations with future markets rather than with tangible articles. The actual risk to the individual is smaller than it might appear, for, whenever the market seems to be going against them, speculators can usually sell their risks to somebody else.

Thus dealing in "futures" are not, in reality, what their name implies—anyone can contract out of this kind of future at any time. In this way "futures" become short-term transactions, and

[1] J. W. F. Rowe: *Markets and Men* (Cambridge 1936), p. 129.

speculators can always try to sail with the wind. On the exchange floor the distant future contracts into hours or minutes—a newly acquired "future" can be disposed of at any moment.

However, since such transactions are somewhat costly and not entirely without risk, even professional speculators prefer to stick to their "futures" for at least a few weeks, and are therefore keenly interested in predictions.

Psychology plays a greater role in stock exchange predictions than it does in most other business spheres. Prices are not so much dictated by urgent requirements of vendors or purchasers, as by assessments of the public mind. Thus, buyers always believe that public demand for certain shares will rise, while the vendors always think the precise opposite. If this were not the case, there would be no need for stock exchanges at all, since straightforward investments could be handled very efficiently by banks and other public institutions.

The stock exchange is therefore a market for hopes and expectations, in which the future is bought or sold at a discount. Needless to say, this involves attempts to look into the future, and the stock exchange is fully conscious of this prophetic task. Each working day, a consort of prophets assembles on its floor in order to determine what quotations will result from their joint efforts. Their ability to do so seems—to them, at least— beyond any doubt, for jobbers rarely look upon themselves as mere gamblers.

Speculators, unlike gamblers, believe that they act with due consideration and foresight. Speculation is a kind of planning, even though the speculator himself rarely influences the success or failure of his plan, but rather participates in somebody else's —a company chairman's, nature's, an engineer's, or a government's. These, and a host of other factors, are the subjects of his speculations, and since their outcome is rarely known in advance, the successful speculator must in some way become a prophet.

Before he can do so, he must know as much as possible about the shares he proposes to deal in and also about the general economic outlook—it is unusual for individual shares to run counter to the general trend. They may rise steeply while the market itself rises slowly, or drop steeply in a weak market, but only exceptionally will they fall during a boom or rise during a slump. General economic trends are therefore the most important subject of all stock exchange predictions.

Wall Street Prophets

Particularly in America, there are a number of special offices and publications exclusively concerned with predictions of stock exchange, as distinct from general economic, trends. While the two are obviously related, the stock exchange may react badly where the economy as a whole reacts well. Thus while the economy needs large reserves for future expansion or building, the stock exchange usually prefers large dividends. Tax reforms, too, can be an incentive to production, and at the same time have a depressing effect on the market.

Above all, political news and rumours influence the stock exchange much more strongly than they do the rest of the economy. The stock exchange is a most sensitive barometer of current trends, and responds to the slightest change. A day on which the market does not change is most unpromising, and if this tendency persists the market usually turns dull—prices begin to fall. Some speculators invariably contract out of a dull market, and it is therefore important to keep the exchange seething with excitement. Politics supply the most excellent stimulus.

Professional experts vie with one another in dishing up political sensations, and particularly "inside" information not known to the editors of daily newspapers. Thus the most sought-after stock exchange bulletins are usually headed "strictly confidential", and the source of their information is often the editor's own fertile brain.

Some stock exchange prophets prefer to consult the spirits, instead, and one of the most famous Wall Street forecasters of recent times, Frederick N. Goldsmith, was wont to consult a comic strip published by one of the American dailies. Other readers might merely laugh at the strips, but Goldsmith knew better—the spirit of a deceased Wall Street speculator had given him the key to their hidden meaning. Nor were these strips the sum total of his inspiration, for, thanks to a gifted medium, he was in daily contact with the spirit of the late John Pierpont Morgan—no wonder that 90–95% of his tips were said to be correct and that subscribers to his circular letter paid him 25 dollars for the privilege of sharing his inspirations. His annual income from these activities was 39,000 dollars, and he was allowed to continue his beneficent activities for 50 years. Only when he had reached the ripe old age of 83, did the authorities begin to take note and to put a stop to his remarkable performance.[1]

Now, secret information from the spiritual realm is the exception rather than the rule, even in Wall Street. Most speculators prefer more down-to-earth information and, because nowadays so much depends on the decisions of governments, Washington has become an important centre of tips even for the New York Stock Exchange. No dealer can afford to ignore rumours with an authentic Washington stamp, and rumours, true or false, have become part of their stock-in-trade.

Most conscientious experts have begun to classify all rumours according to their degree of credibility, and one of the most prominent American sheets dealing with this kind of information which, by the way, is not exclusively addressed to stock exchange speculators, classifies its information by means of ticks. Thus, a doubtful and unverifiable story is given one tick, one that seems less doubtful, two ticks, and one that has been authenticated by the editor, three ticks.[2] Even so, the rumour that Eisenhower would not seek re-election was given three ticks just before he stood for nomination, and so was the story that France, after the electoral successes of the Communists and Poujadists in Spring 1956, was closer to a revolution than she had been at any time during the past eight years. Another three-tick story was that Israel and Egypt would go to war—seven months earlier than they did.

As one can see, such predictions are anything but reliable, and often look ridiculous in the light of subsequent events. Nevertheless, it is a fact that not only on the stock exchange but also in normal business, men often base important decisions on assump-

[1] *Time*, 27th October 1948.
[2] *Personal from Pearson. A weekly interpretative Washington News Letter* edited by Drew Pearson (Washington 1956).

tions and rumours that are subsequently proved to have been utterly false. Luckily, in stock exchange speculations at least, it does not so much matter whether a rumour is true or false—the only thing that counts is how many people believe in it. For this very reason, diplomats and statesmen who try to use private information for playing the market, often lose their shirts. True, they have advance knowledge of political events, but they know little about the psychology of the stock exchange and therefore derive false conclusions from the correct premises. A classical example was that of Friedrich von Holstein—one of Bismarck's closest confidants—who played the market so unsuccessfully, that despite all his private information, he eventually owed his bank 300,000 marks.[1]

The postman always knocks twice

Since private information, however reliable, is a very inadequate a key to success in the stock exchange, American forecasters, in particular, have tried to use more "reliable"criteria. Illogical though price fluctuations may appear to be to the layman, they must surely have a logic of their own. Thus if one ignores individual ups and downs and investigates over-all fluctuations instead, clear periodic patterns are said to emerge.

For instance, if a dull market suddenly becomes cheerful, a slight reversal may be expected three days afterwards. This is called a "technical reaction" in stock exchange circles, though it is really a psychological reaction: investors who have had to wait a long time to sell their shares at a profit take the first opportunity to do so. Conversely, a sudden fall in the market is often followed by a slight improvement within a few days, when those who have waited to buy shares at a lower price suddenly step in. However, these small and transitory reactions have no bearing on the main trend or on the general economic situation, nor are they regular enough to be relied upon. Sometimes, the

[1] F. von Holstein: *Stock Exchange Correspondence* edited by Ernst Feder (Berlin 1925)—R. Lewinsohn and F. Pick: *Sinn und Unsinn der Börse* (Berlin 1933).

main trend may continue for up to a fortnight without any reaction, but, by and large, jobbers have done well by taking this factor into account.

Far more questionable is the problem of more persistent stock exchange patterns. Before the war, many Wall Street experts thought they could detect a 40-day cycle of slight reversals in the general trend. This cycle offered the skilled manipulator excellent and repeated chances of profit-taking. Of late, the 40-day cycle seems to have been discarded by many in favour of a 24-day cycle.

A more persistent American belief is based on the so-called Dow-theory, propounded by Charles Dow and S. A. Nelson at the turn of the century. According to this theory, successful stock exchange speculators have only to watch the movements of industrial and railway shares very carefully. If both groups of shares begin to rise simultaneously, a boom is imminent, if both drop simultaneously, a lasting depression may be expected, and if both move in opposite directions, the future is altogether unpredictable.

The predictions made for many years by Dow's pupil, William Hamilton, the editor of the *Wall Street Journal*, on the basis of Dow's theory, have been right 50% of the time and wrong just as often,[1] but the prophecies of most other Wall Street prophets fall far short of even this sparse result. In other words, stock exchange speculation might just as well (or better) be based on the toss of a coin. An investigation of 7500 predictions by 16 well-known "forecast bureaus" has shown that the vast majority was wrong.[2]

The Dow theory in its "classical" form is, at best, a tautology. Far more interesting is a variation on the same theme, based on the well-known fact that the postman always knocks twice. In America, stock exchange fluctuations have always been looked upon as the struggle between optimistic bulls and pessimistic bears. Whenever the bulls fail to drive prices beyond the level that held before the last downward reaction, the time of the bears has clearly come, i.e. the market will drop. Conversely, if after a small upward reaction, prices do not drop below the former

[1] G. Leffler: *The Stock Market* (N.Y. 1951), p. 522.
[2] A. Cowles: *Can Stock Market Forecasters Forecast?* in *Econometria* Vol. I, No. 3 (July 1933).

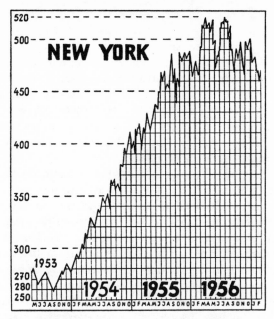

30. Wall Street quotations of industrial shares.
A long upward trend ends with a "double top".

level, the bears are out of office, and the bulls are about to take over.

On stock exchange graphs, these trends are quite clear to see. Thus if, at intervals of a few weeks or even a few months, there appear two crests or troughs of equal intensity, it is usually safe to say that the boom or slump is over. But like all such rules, this one, too, fails from time to time—some postmen leave after only one knock. Booms may turn into slumps without any prior warning, and vice versa. In that case, stock exchange graphs, instead of showing two highs or two lows, will show anything else you like. But, within certain limits, postmen generally persevere, and double knocks—"double bottoms" or "double tops" as American experts call them—are, in fact, tested means of predicting not only stock exchange fluctuations, but also of predicting such mass-psychological phenomena as politics or even fashions: if a trend reaches two successive peaks, it is often the beginning of the end.

The cycle-barometer

Significant though the specific psychological trends of stock exchange fluctuations are, the market as such is also influenced by the general economic situation, and market trends opposed to general trends can never be of anything but the shortest duration. To assess general trends, however, is extremely difficult. A century ago, when the first attempts were being made to tackle this problem systematically, all that people had to go by were crises—sudden drops in prices, frequent bankruptcies and set-backs in external trade. When things went more smoothly, it seemed impossible to say anything at all about future trends or to evaluate small fluctuations. True, some experts studied bank rates, or kept records of the prices of the most important raw materials such as coal and iron, but little was known about imports and exports, about the labour market, and about unemployment, since no statistics on these subjects had been compiled. Nor was anything known about turnover, bank credits, stocks, and profits and losses, which were kept strict secrets, unless insolvency or legal proceedings brought some of the facts to the notice of the public.

Private enterprise was far more private and unrestricted than it is today, and this meant that every business shrouded its own activities in a thick veil of mystery. The less the competitors knew about one, the better it was for all concerned. Even the national economy was nothing but a legal, philosophic and political abstraction, for bureaucratic officials were as reluctant to reveal what they knew as were private entrepreneurs.

Oddly enough, the history of economic analysis followed a parallel course to the history of painting. Having tried to depict nature as realistically as possible and producing a host of quite unnaturally posed pictures as a result, economists like painters turned to impressionism in the 1880s. The economic impressionist *par excellence* was Alfred de Foville who, taking 32 apparently unrelated economic and social phenomena on which statistics had been compiled, viz. post office revenue, legacies, coal output, tobacco sales, inland revenue, box-office receipts, suicides, births, etc., compiled a "barometer" (see Fig. 31) on which socially favourable trends were marked in white, bad trends in black, and intermediate trends in different shades of

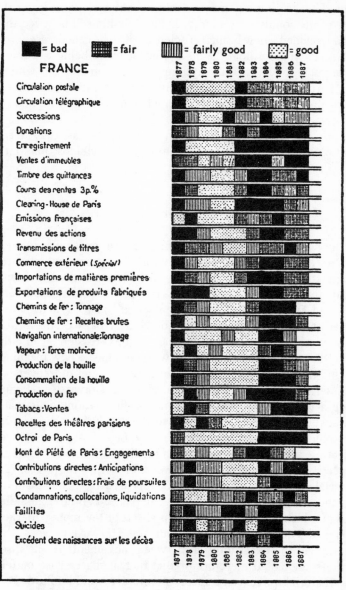

31. De Foville's General Barometer, one of the first attempts to present a pictorial analysis of economic phenomena.

grey. Thus, a single glance would give anyone a fair idea of the state of the country's economy. De Foville himself believed that he had founded a new branch of science which he called "economic and social meteorology",[1] his colourful chart being a General Barometer. In fact, it was anything but a barometer, for while a real barometer measures a specific phenomenon, viz. atmospheric pressure, De Foville's barometer measured phenomena of all sorts. Nevertheless, the term "barometer" was to become part of the vocabulary of many economists, as they made frantic attempts to predict the future from kaleidoscopic data.

Harvard knows no crisis

At the beginning of the 20th century, the impressionist method was at last found wanting, both for diagnostic and also for prognostic purposes. People began to realise that economic trends had to be evaluated far more realistically than any colourful impressionist schemes allowed. Just as artists discarded subtle touches in favour of bold strokes of the brush, economists, too, looked for new means of expression. While the term "barometer" had stuck, the word assumed a new meaning.

This time, the light came out of America, and moreover out of America's Mecca of knowledge: Harvard University. Having made a very careful study of economic fluctuations over many years, the Harvard experts came to the conclusion that general economic trends can be expressed by means of three curves reflecting trends in the stock, commodity, and money markets respectively. Their main guides were, in fact, share prices, raw materials and rates of interest. It appeared from these curves that the stock market was always a jump ahead of the commodity market which, in turn, was a jump ahead of the money market. This had been known before, but the Harvard experts also determined the exact interval between movements in the three markets, and could therefore predict that, if shares rose or fell, raw material prices and rates of interest would follow at a certain date.

Immediately after the First World War, the Harvard

[1] A. de Foville: *Essai de météorologie économique et sociale* (Paris 1888).

Committee for Economic Research began to publish its three curves and to make regular predictions based on them. These predictions caused a great sensation, not only because they were more accurate than any prior estimates of this kind, but chiefly because eminent men were now using the stock exchange for making general economic predictions, when all previous forecasters had done the precise opposite. Moreover, the Harvard economists were respected as disinterested scientists—no one following their advice ran the danger of being taken for a ride to some swindler's direct advantage.

For a time all went well. From 1919 to 1925, the stock exchange curve fulfilled its promise admirably, but in 1925 the spell was broken. Shares kept rising but commodity prices refused to follow. Rates of interest, on the other hand, followed with a vengeance, not least because wild stock exchange speculation drove them up so high that they became usurious. Havard tried its best to repair the barometer, but the mercury seemed to have run out of it.

Thus the Harvard team, like all great experts, failed to predict the great depression of 1929. What was even worse, it betrayed its own theory, by proclaiming that the stock exchange slump was only a transitory phenomenon which could have no lasting effects on the commodity and money markets, i.e. on the general economy. In short, there was no real crisis, and no cause for concern. When the public learned better, the Harvard barometer became one more victim of the depression, and with it ended one of the most interesting and fruitful attempts to make regular economic prognoses.

The German barometer

All the same, Harvard had set an example, and some of its disciples fared far better than their teacher. One of the most successful was the *Institut für Konjunkturforschung* (Institute for Business Cycle Research) founded in Berlin in 1925. Under the brilliant leadership of Ernst Wagemann, this Institute quickly gained international recognition. Its triple barometer system was a variation of the Harvard barometer. In Germany, the stock exchange played a very much smaller role than it did in America and, for that reason alone, share prices had to step into the background. Again, on the commodity market, the German economists investigated turnover rather than price fluctuations, arguing quite logically that prices were largely reflections of supply and demand.

While the first or monetary barometer registered prices, wages, and rates of interest,[1] the second or productive baro-meter registered industrial output, employment, orders, imports of raw material and semi-finished goods, bank credits, the circulation of money, and bank reserves of gold and foreign exchange. The fact that money, credit, and production, were all treated under one heading was not so much a question of prin-ciple as of expediency. Since production and business figures took some time to prepare, bank credits were a fair indication of future production, and bank reserves reflected the possible volume of future imports.

The third or trading barometer registered everything con-cerned with internal and external trade: the turnover of indivi-dual sectors of the economy, the production of consumer goods, total imports and exports, and also wage incomes. The three barometers therefore overlapped to some extent, while some factors, e.g. building and estate transactions were completely ignored. Many other objections, too, could have been raised against the German barometer system, which nevertheless proved its practical, if limited, usefulness.

In fact, the Berlin Institute for Business Cycle Research rarely tried to make predictions for more than three months ahead, and, by and large, it made few mistakes. True, much of its success was due to the fact that a number of leading industrial concerns gave the Institute full access to their order books, and once the future orders of leading businesses are known it is not too difficult to predict if production will rise or fall, or if the level of employment will be maintained. The rest of the work was a mere compilation of graphs which expressed the known facts in impressive ways.

A frequent mistake of national business cycle research institutes is that they look upon their own country as the hub

[1] Ernst Wagemann: *Struktur und Rhythmus der Weltwirtschaft* (Berlin 1931), p. 177 ff.

of the world and ignore the rest of mankind. Although the German institute was less guilty in this respect than its counterparts in other countries, it, too, allowed itself to be carried away by the "economic miracle" and by ideas of eternal prosperity. Thus it failed to predict the great collapse of autumn 1929, or even to appreciate the seriousness and persistence of the subsequent depression. However, in 1932, it was one of the first to recognise that the worst was over, and that things were about to improve again.

The post-war crisis fails to materialise

During the war, Business Cycle Institutes were put out of independent business altogether, since government decisions put a stop to all market fluctuations. Economic research institutes became government departments, and were supplied with large sums of money to carry out comprehensive investigations. Still, many economists must have longed for the good old times of the free economy, for only extreme dissatisfaction can explain the excessively gloomy prophecies they made at that time.

They had an unprecedented opportunity, and once again they failed bitterly; more bitterly, in fact, than just before the 1929 crisis, for this time no one expected them to predict the great turning point—the end of the war. All that people wanted to know from them was what things would be like once all the horror was over. Particularly in America, on which no bombs had fallen, an extra year of war was not nearly as great a worry as the question how the over-inflated war economy could be switched to peacetime conditions.

The vast majority of economic experts were convinced that this transition would involve a violent crisis, and even Colin Clark, an Australian economist and statistician, whose (1942) predictions about the economics of 1960 came closest to the truth, expressed the fear that the anticipated post-war boom would be followed by a fairly severe and prolonged depression, the last of its kind. Subsequent depressions would also occur but be short-lived, and from the late 1940s onward there would be a prolonged upward trend.[1] Americans were much more pessimistic, still. Post-war unemployment figures of 12–15 million—or, counting women engaged in war work, of up to 20 million—were commonly predicted, on the assumption that, the First World War having led to a short but extraordinarily heavy readjustment crisis, there was no reason for believing that things would be different after the Second World War.

Then there occurred the *real* American economic miracle— the demobilisation of ten million people was effected without any upheavals, the transition to a peacetime economy proceeded extremely smoothly and unemployment figures rose to less than four million—half as much as before the war. Undaunted, the prophets of gloom now proclaimed that the worst had merely been postponed. Demobilisation had simply coincided with a favourable phase of the Kitchin-cycle, but the crisis was bound to come sooner or later. Like mediaeval astrologers who proclaimed volcanoes and earthquakes whenever unfavourable planets threatened to combine under one sign of the Zodiac, so modern economists threatened mankind with terrible disasters on the occasion of the impending coincidence of the three most important cycles: the Kondratieff, the Juglar, and the Kitchin. All three would reach their nadir in 1948, when a world-shaking depression would begin, to last until 1952.

This prophecy, too, was wholly false—as mankind was to learn with great relief. True, America had a marked recession in 1949, but nothing resembling a real crisis, while Europe continued to make uninterrupted economic progress. Cycle theory has not yet recovered from this last body blow, and its exponents have rightly been reproached with confusing the past with the future.

Models to order

The failure of the generally expected post-war crisis to materialise and the prolonged prosperity which, apart from relatively mild recessions (1946, 1949, 1954), has been so characteristic of recent trends, have revived America's faith in

[1] Colin Clark: *The Economics of* 1960 (London 1942), p. 108.

eternal bliss on earth. The spectre of 1929 is slowly but steadily receding.

Is this faith really justified? Optimists adduce three weighty arguments in its favour: firstly the American economy has become far less speculative, as post-war stock exchange transactions show. Moreover speculation is far more strictly controlled today than it was in 1929, when reckless gamblers could use unlimited credit to drive quotations to giddy heights. Secondly, Keynesian principles can be applied: if there is a downward trend the economy can be helped back on its legs by an injection of a measured dose of inflation, while unhealthy expansion can be counteracted by such deflationary measures as a credit squeeze. These prophylactic and therapeutic financial measures have helped to avoid excesses, or to nip them in the bud, and there is no reason to believe that they will be less successful in the future.

The third and most convincing argument (which economists usually keep under their hats) is rearmament. The United States spends twenty times as much money on its armed forces and military aid abroad as she did before the war. Roughly twelve per cent, and in some years as much as fifteen per cent of the national income is directly or indirectly devoted to military expenditure, giving full employment to 10–12 million people at the state's expense—to as many people, in fact, as were unemployed before the war. While the miserable pre-war unemployment benefits hardly kept the wolf from the door, military expenditure now helps to maintain a general state of boom. A rich country can easily afford to spend an eighth of its income on armaments, and then turn the expenditure into good business, as well. If the enormous military budget—45,000 million dollars in 1957—were suddenly to be drastically reduced, there is no doubt that a very serious crisis would ensue. In practice, this is unlikely to happen and so, the economists argue, the future looks rosy, indeed. At worst, there may be minor recessions.

European economists, too, generally subscribe to this new optimism, and though many of them have not abjured cycle theories, they no longer worry about determining what phase in a given cycle the present stage represents. They continue to rely on statistics, and general indexes, but they no longer look upon "barometers" as omens. After all, economic developments are men-made, and men can fashion them to their will. This is precisely the task of modern cycle research. True, economic institutes cannot dictate economic developments—certainly not in a free economy—but they can advise those in whose hands the decisions lie. Economic institutes are therefore increasingly turning therapist and refurbishing their theoretical basis. Now that cycle theories have been discarded, new theories must take their place, and these are only in the process of being constructed. While certain pathological symptoms of the economy are well-known, others are not, and economists still find it difficult to say what curative methods must be applied to individual cases, and above all what dosage must be administered.

The better to deal with all contingencies, economists have recently started constructing "econometric" models of specific economic situations. On the basis of the simple statistical (stochistic) models, actual developments can be compared with theoretical expectations, while the complex models show, for instance, what repercussions on the rest of the economy can be expected from wage increases.

Models of this kind may be called conditional predictions, since, while certain basic assumptions are made, variable factors must also be taken into account, and of these there is an almost unlimited number, particularly when, like most econometrists, we consider political factors as well. Still econometrists appear to be undaunted, and the Dutch econometrist Jan Tinbergen, investigating the American trade cycle, thought nothing of constructing his model with 30–40 variable factors.[1]

True, the results of these gigantic labours are somewhat frightening to the layman, who may easily throw his hands up in despair when he reads the following formula:

$$(1 + \tau') \, \xi_0 = - \tau' \, (1 \cdot 04 - c) - \delta'_1 \, (\sigma - 1 - \Lambda - \Lambda\sigma)$$
$$- \delta'_2 \, (\Lambda - \sigma\Lambda) + \delta'\Lambda - \sigma + c + \Lambda\sigma - 0 \cdot 04$$

which simply expresses the expected effects of a modest tax reform on purchasing power. But those who are used to mathematical symbols will not be discouraged. The only thing that matters, in econometry as in anything else, is not the scientific façade or the splendour of the tools, but the actual results. So

[1] Jan Tinbergen: *Einführung in die Ökonometrie* (Zurich 1952), p. 252.

far, econometry has been unable to tell us much about the economic picture of tomorrow—nor is that its purpose. What econometry can do and has done is to predict with great accuracy what effects will result from what economic changes—and that is great progress, indeed.

CHAPTER 11

Forging the Future

*I*T IS ONLY A STEP FROM SPECULATION TO PLANNING—BUT A
very big one. For while the speculator is a small-time
planner without any influence on the objects of his speculation,
the real planner tries to bring these objects into existence by
his own actions—to realise the conditions which will make his
predictions come true.

Every language has often confused the two concepts, mis-
taking the "planner" for the mere "schemer". Thus, in ancient
Rome, *planus* meant adventurer, vagabond, juggler, or charlatan,
and in the 17th and 18th centuries, people who travelled about
propagating a plan were derogatorily called "project-makers",
though it was due to them that such important institutions as the
Bank of England were born, and though the world would have
been very much poorer without them.

Nevertheless, there are good reasons why planners have
always been disliked. Not only did so many of their plans prove
so many expensive illusions, but they have always taken the
future much too much for granted. Ordinary people much prefer
to plan the future in small doses, while most planners want to
take it by storm. All plans must therefore overcome the initial
inertia of the masses, which explains why they are most
popular when the masses are most unsettled, for instance
during the great depression.

Rearmament plans

Inertia can only be overcome by force, and not surprisingly,
therefore, the first great plans were plans of war. Before
declaring war, a country had to be armed and, at a time when
there were no standing armies, military campaigns involved
making far more radical inroads into the nation's economy and

way of life than they do today. Building and equipping a navy, for instance, had far greater economic repercussions than the building of atom bombs in our time. Entire forests had to be cut down, thousands of people were press-ganged into arms production, produce was requisitioned—in short, the whole economy was stood on its head according to an official master plan.

The feudal system lent itself most readily to the speedy execution of such plans, since serfs were used to doing what they were told. However, since it fell to different feudal lords to supply fully equipped contingents of troops, it was never quite certain how big the total striking force would be. Even the first standing armies, which were formed during the Renaissance, were too weak to deal with external foes and had to be supplemented by auxiliaries during emergencies. As the state was unable to solve this problem by itself, individuals took over the task of recruiting. Such men were known as condottieri, professional military captains, and they raised troops for princes-at-war right up to the 17th century. Their most famous German representative was Wallenstein, a great general but an even greater businessman and planner.

When governments began to fear the political dangers involved, they introduced a slight change: henceforth they would make the recruitment and equipment plan themselves, and leave only its execution in the hands of private entrepreneurs, of *munitionnaires generaux*, as the first big-business men of all time were called. Only after the Napoleonic wars was a stop put to even this form of activity. Governments now did their own recruiting and equipping and gave their orders direct to the arms industry.

The state could only do this, after it had subjected its own finances to a very strict plan. No longer was it possible to tax the people only when the coffers were empty. Large-scale military expenditure—the greatest drain on the state's resources—forced governments to estimate next year's military programme in advance, even in peacetime. Thus, in England, the Chancellor of the Exchequer has presented Parliament with an annual budget ever since 1799, though his early budgets were more in the nature of a review of past events than of a plan for the future.

Planning the nation's economy

The original idea of a budget of next year's revenue and expenditure came from France. Its originator was the Baron Joseph-Dominique Louis (1755–1837) who managed to cure France's financial troubles after the Napoleonic wars. Like his protector Talleyrand, Louis was a former priest. Though a convinced liberal, Baron Louis felt that the state had a right to tax the people according to its future needs. Since France had an annual expenditure of nearly 1000 million gold francs—an astronomical amount in those days—his was a gigantic task.

The Baron's first problem was to find a method of assessing the nation—a very ticklish business, particularly when the effects of changes in taxation were not known, and all the experts were at loggerheads. In the end, President Villèle decreed that the known figures from the year before were to be the basis for next year's budget. Despite the fact that, in the intervening year the entire economic position might have changed radically, Villèle's rather primitive "penultimate year method" proved so successful—and not in France alone—that it remained common practice for a hundred years.

The secret of its success was due to its inherent error, for, as it turned out, the national revenue increased from year to year, except during severe crises. Revenue was therefore under-estimated, and expenditure kept correspondingly low, with the result that the coffers grew fuller and fuller. No wonder then that the French method was considered to be a sign of great political wisdom. When one of France's most brilliant Ministers of Finance, Léon Say, tried to change this system in the 1880s by taking into account annual increases in revenue based on average increases during the past five years, the only result was that Parliament voted more generous sums for various projects. After Say's retirement, France quickly returned to her old and tested principle of deliberate self-deception.

It was only during the inflation which followed in the wake of the First World War that the orthodox penultimate year method, together with the Say system and its variations, suffered serious shipwreck throughout the world. Inflation had made nonsense of all estimates based on previous revenue and expenditure. The value of money changed from day to day and whatever estimates government statisticians produced, were always one step behind the times. Although this appeared at first sight to benefit the taxpayers, the resulting deficit merely produced ever greater inflation—and the vicious circle continued.

The bitter lesson of that confused period is that all provisions for the future involve the existence of a stable standard. In financial terms, this standard is the purchasing value of money, and once that value fluctuates too violently, objective predictions are no longer possible and wild speculation takes their place.

Budgeting

The great crisis of the 1930s also showed that government economic plans cannot be made outside the context of the general economic situation. On that occasion, though the value of money rose, the expected revenue nevertheless fell off because industry and commerce had become paralysed. It became clear that it was not enough merely to plan government revenue and expenditure and that comprehensive national estimates, of which government budget was only a part, had also to be prepared from year to year. The national economy was, as it were, the vascular system, while the government economy was only the lymph system of the body politic. This, in any event, is how financial experts imagined things to be, and their diagrams showed from which sectors of the economy and through which channels the state obtained its finances, how state finance was ploughed back into the national economy, and how individual enterprises used this finance. These diagrams looked very impressive, since, with a few strokes of the pen, they presented a comprehensive anatomical and physiological analysis of the national economy as a whole.

The only question was whether the analysis did, in fact, foot the bill. Difficult enough as it was to anticipate next year's state income and expenditure correctly, how could one anticipate the much more complex changes in the national income, depending as they do on wage levels, raw material deliveries, and a host of other variables? And, as it turned out, the general economic estimates presented simultaneously with the national budgets in the United States, Britain, France, the Scandinavian countries, and in Holland (where they were worked out extremely skilfully) were generally full of flaws. Thus errors of 3–5% were thought to be most reasonable, despite the fact that total changes in the annual national income rarely exceed 10%.

On the other hand, modern techniques of economic analysis have made the budget itself a fairly reliable instrument. Moreover, the state, unlike private industry, can always take steps to fit the facts to the figures, by increasing or relaxing controls, so much so that, particularly in Britain and France, errors have been reduced to less than 1%.[1] In hardly any other sphere has the art of prediction reached so high a degree of perfection.

The classical annual budget of most countries does, however, produce its own problems. Most government expenditure is earmarked for such long-term projects as harbour installations, road construction, irrigation, and drainage. In young countries, the state must also set aside funds for establishing new industries, and while total costs are distributed over the requisite number of years, the longer the plans, the greater the number of annual revisions. For one thing, prices are more likely to fluctuate in the long run, and the experts are therefore forced to look further ahead than they can reasonably be expected to do.

To get over this difficulty, governments usually budget an annual sum towards these long-term projects. However, this procedure has serious drawbacks, since the suppliers and executors of these long-term plans cannot invest money in plans that are subject to annual revision. They therefore insist on long-term contracts, and governments have often been forced to comply, and thus to enter the ranks of long-term planners.

Planning by persuasion

So far we have spoken of special government plans and not of wholly planned economies. In capitalist countries, private property is respected, and the authority of entrepreneurs only restricted when it clashes with the interests of the state. Under

[1] Maurice Duverger: *Institutions financières* (Paris 1956), p. 323.

socialism, on the other hand, private enterprise is not only subordinated to the state, but abolished.

Modern economic plans usually aim at increasing production, though some plans, e.g. some American farm schemes and some international trust agreements, aim at preventing gluts.

The success of any economic plan depends primarily on its financial and practical feasibility. Not even governments can work miracles. It also depends on a less obvious factor: political agreement. Many a recent economic plan has been so thwarted or deformed by political opposition, that all its predictions were upset.

A good example is the famous French Monnet plan, or as it was officially known: *Le premier plan de modernisation et equipement*. This plan which was worked out immediately after the war by Jean Monnet, an American-trained industrial expert, with the blessings of the Socialist statesman Léon Blum, was one of the most far-reaching plans ever presented in Europe. It was meant to cover the entire French economy, private and nationalised sectors—coal, electricity, and transport—alike, and to increase total production by modernising equipment and efficiency.

It was estimated that the implementation of the plan would take four years, but in 1947, by the time preparations and discussions had delayed it for years, political conditions had changed so radically, that all the French government could do was to set a productive norm instead, and to persuade private enterprise to act according to its general directives. Mixed committees consisting of government officials and private employers were meant to determine the details of the plan for their particular industry, but there was no coercion to see that their suggestions were adopted. The Monnet plan, as far as it affected private industry was, therefore, no more than a means of information and propaganda.

Nor were its effects on the public sector very much more drastic. The big government construction programme that had been suggested by the planners, was never officially approved by Parliament. All the government could therefore do was to make annual and piecemeal budget concessions to the planners. The plan as such had no legal standing which, in a country like France, did little to enhance it or the status of the planners. No wonder that so many things kept going wrong with it. The original plan, which was meant to run until the end of 1950, was replaced by a new four-year plan as early as 1st January 1949. The four-year plan thus became a five-year plan, and, when it was extended further in 1953, it turned into a seven-year plan.

It would have needed a miracle for the plan to be implemented in these circumstances. True, the plan contributed to France's modernisation, but that modernisation would have come about in any event. Discrepancies of 10–20% from the planned norms were the rule, and while some industries increased their output, others did the precise opposite.

Though there was little public interest left by the time the Monnet plan had run its full term, a new four-year "modernisation and equipment plan" was launched in 1954. The new plan had fairly modest aims, and its annual target of a 4% increase in industrial output was, in fact, surpassed by far. In order to synchronise the second plan with the new Parliament's term of office, it was precipitately cut short, and a new plan began in 1957. France's third plan is now in operation and is meant to run on until 1961.

Planning will by then have become a venerable French institution. In 1956, the French planning authorities published a memorandum in which, using impressive arguments and figures, they painted a glowing picture of the French economy in A.D. 1965. Industrial production would be 77% and agricultural production 25% above the 1954 level. Possibly, the memorandum argued, these increases will be no more than 59% and 18% respectively, for progress is sometimes slower than expected. If neither norm is fulfilled, it will not be the planners' fault for: "If men must submit to the future it is only because thay have failed to prepare it. The future can only be fashioned if we tackle it with full awareness of the advances to be made, the resistances which have to be overcome, and the aims which have to be reached."[1]

Water and land

One of the main errors of the French planners was clearly their

[1] Commissariat Général au Plan: Perspectives de l'Economie française 1965 (Paris 1956), p. 6.

failure to offer private enterprise adequate incentives. American planners rely far less on the art of persuasion than on tangible rewards.

True, United States planners have to face far greater opposition than their European colleagues, since the American Constitution, suffused as it is with the spirit of 18th century liberalism, is in principle opposed to every limitation of individual freedom and hence to every kind of centralisation. All plans run the risk of being condemned as unconstitutional by the Supreme Court, and many have in fact fallen by the wayside for this very reason.

One of the few economic plans to meet with the Supreme Court's approval was that of the Tennessee Valley Authority (T.V.A.).

The Tennessee valley was an impoverished region in the south, where periodic floods added to the people's other misfortunes. To improve the lot of two-and-a-half million people living there, Franklin D. Roosevelt established the T.V.A. in 1933, and instructed it to rehabilitate the area. Even so, many Democrats and Republicans questioned the government's right to produce electricity, to set up farms, and to do many other things that had always been the preserves of private enterprise. What was even worse, the director was to be paid a fixed annual salary of 10,000 dollars, intead of being offered a share in the profits.[1] This step was not only unheard of but outraged common sense—no one could be expected to do his best if he had no direct financial stake in the outcome.

But the miracle happened. The T.V.A. proved so excellent a planner that in the course of one year, 14,000 farmers were set up in business and $2\frac{1}{2}$ million acres were reclaimed for agricultural use. Hundreds of thousands of people were offered cheap electricity, and private businesses in seven States derived direct benefits from the plan.

Roosevelt was less successful in his efforts to take the entire U.S. economy out of the doldrums. It was his basic intention to adapt production to consumption, using radical legislation that practically amounted to complete state control of industrial output. It is difficult to say how far Roosevelt might not have gone with his plans, had not his National Industrial Recovery Act (N.I.R.A.) been declared unconstitutional in May 1935, and

[1] F. Zweig: *The Planning of Free Societies* (London 1942), p. 114.

his Agricultural Adjustment Act (A.A.A.) in January 1936, the latter after a petition to the Supreme Court by a poultry dealer.

Nevertheless, government legislation managed to salvage essential agricultural measures, and these remnants from the Roosevelt area continue to be the most important and effective plans ever laid in the western world. Five of the staple crops whose cultivation takes up roughly 50% of the arable area of the United States: wheat, maize, rice, tobacco, and cotton, are produced according to government plan. The moment the crops have been harvested, the Department of Agriculture, after careful consideration of available supplies and the international market conditions, suggests what crops are to be planted next year. The suggestions are then submitted to the farmers, and if more than one-third of them object, the Department must revise its plans. The revised plan is, however, final and binding.

This does not mean that farmers are fined if they do not comply, but simply that they are not allowed to market their surpluses. Compliance, on the other hand, is rewarded by guaranteed government subsidies of from 75–90% of the market price, in the form of government purchases and credits. These subsidies cost the U.S.A. more than 2000 million dollars a year.

Although the details of the plan are formally adjusted from year to year, the American plan for agriculture is nevertheless a permanent institution. While it has not so far managed to keep prices absolutely stable or to adapt production fully to consumption, the gaps have been greatly reduced and severe agricultural crises avoided.

In any case, a complete solution to this problem will not be possible until harvests as such can be controlled, and harvests, even from the same soil worked with the same equipment, still fluctuate by an annual 20–30%, and occasionally by as much as 50%. Until we manage to make very precise weather forecasts for a whole year in advance, or else cultivate crops that are completely insensitive to the weather, there is no possibility of stabilising farm prices by other than restrictive economic practices.

The only slight advance in harvest forecasts is that we now have more accurate means of estimating harvests while the crops are growing. Unfortunately random sampling, as used in Gallup polls, have proved inadequate, for there is no such thing as a typical field—weather conditions change from place to place. On the other hand, aerial surveys can give one a fair idea of the state of the crops over wide regions, and an aerial check is, in fact, kept over 25% of America's growing crops. Still, no survey of this or any other kind can foresee weather changes, so that estimates have constantly to be revised. Differences of 10% within a few weeks are by no means unusual, and often frustrate the entire purpose of the survey.

Recalcitrant coffee

Plans for annual crops were not, however, the first agricultural plans. Every afforestation scheme is a planned economic operation in which the time of felling can be predicted with great accuracy, and in which new trees are planted years before their timber is used. Since the big forests of most countries are government property, planning usually proceeds smoothly, and even where private property is in control, the state generally claims the right of preventing the excesses of greedy profiteers.

Since the beginning of the 20th century, governments have also begun to take an interest in fruit-bearing trees and plants. In Brazil, in particular, a leading industrialist from São Paulo, one Alexandre Siciliano, led a movement to relieve individual coffee planters of their marketing problems and to fix international prices by strict control of production.

This was the beginning of the notorious coffee valorisation scheme, which was meant to keep rigid control of the world's coffee supplies by stockpiling, vast financial transactions, and above all by keeping a check on over-production. At first a tax was levied on all new trees, and later, as stocks piled up, the planting of new trees was forbidden altogether, a practice observed to this day by many coffee-producing countries. Since a coffee tree takes from four to six years to bear fruit, the effects are not felt immediately, though the market begins to rise the moment shortages are anticipated. Conversely, the world market begins to drop the moment news gets abroad that coffee trees are being planted in Brazil. Now, all these fluctuations are based on the assumption that the harvests will otherwise be normal, whereas, in fact, coffee is the most contrary of all crops. Not uncommonly, the same plot will produce twice as much coffee as it did the year before, and one exceptional harvest, is, of course, sufficient to invalidate the whole scheme. In 1929, when a bumper crop went hand in hand with an international economic crisis, Brazil was left holding enough coffee to supply the entire world for three years, and 78 million sacks of coffee were burnt, in order to prevent prices from hitting rock bottom. Thus ended another badly devised economic plan.

"Projections"

Planning seems much easier in industry. Any manufacturer with sufficient financial and technical resources can work out on paper the precise industrial capacity of a new plant. Unfortunately there is often a great discrepancy between capacity and actual output, for output depends largely on demand, and demand is very much more difficult to predict.

Nevertheless every industrialist wishing to extend or to modernise his factory, is forced to plan, not so much his new buildings and plant (that he usually leaves to his architects and engineers) as his finances. To obtain credit for his building projects, he must be able to convince his bankers or the public whom he invites to take up his shares of the profitability of his enterprise.

But even companies which can finance new projects from their own reserves, usually make these projects known to the public, if only for propaganda reasons. The secretiveness of former times has given way to the prestige publicity of today. In America all big enterprises and even some that are not so big will gladly show you their development plans. These plans often look so far into the future and involve so many billions of dollars that they would make even a multi-millionaire stagger. Lesser people only marvel at the shrewdness and confidence of their revered industrial leaders, and put aside all thoughts of impending crises. How can there be crises in the face of so much foresight, and what, after all, were crises if not the result of lack of confidence, lack of investments, and lack of planning?

However, neither the economic experts who design these development plans, nor the company directors who approve them and publish them, are pledged to complete them. After all, no one demands or even expects that they should swim against the tide. If the economic situation should deteriorate, or if other reasons should persuade the directors to drop or to change a given development plan, no one could reproach them on that account, or claim damages because they had failed to predict the future correctly. Development plans are admittedly predictions and, beyond that, declared intentions, but intentions often lead to unexpected results. While any plan is admittedly better than no plan at all, bad plans which turn out to be unworkable must clearly be abandoned.

A new American—and to a lesser extent European— favourite goes by the name of "projection", a kind of forecast that can be changed *ad lib.*

Very shrewd industrialists will "project" not only the future of their own enterprise but of an entire industry. Thus the President of General Motors "projected" on the eve of 1957 that the United States would produce 6,400,000 new cars that year—considerably more than in 1956. In May, 1957, he informed his company and the public that his projection would have to be revised, and that a mere 5,880,000 cars were to be expected in 1957—a difference of 8% compared with his previous projection. This meant a large drop in earnings not only for the motor industry, but for countless workers as well.

It seems obvious that this new method, while not improving prognostic techniques, makes them very much simpler. Hence a spate of projections has lately been assailing the public ear. Civil servants and other leading lights, who were previously afraid to express anything to which even the least doubt might have clung, will now pour out figures at you at the slightest provocation. A prediction in the old sense of the word can be wrong, a plan can fail, but a projection is always as safe as the Bank of England. It is a non-predictive prediction, an unplanned plan. Unfortunately errors in projection may often be very costly. For instance, projections for the motor industry usually involve adjusting factories to certain production levels, and if the projection was false, much money, time, and labour is wasted. Moreover, raw materials may have been ordered in too large or too small quantities, with additional losses, or at the wrong price.

Planless planning

The plans we have discussed so far differ characteristically from the economic plans of the Soviet Union and other Communist countries. While the capitalist and communist systems have many factors in common, e.g. the West is increasingly adopting government controls, and Russia has learnt to make individual factories balance their accounts, Russia's planned economy nevertheless represents a very special system, in which predictions have a different and much greater significance than they have in the West.

Oddly enough, the moment the practical problem of socialisation first arose in Russia after the October Revolution, no practical means of solving it had been worked out. During the fifty years that had passed since Karl Marx wrote his *Das Kapital*, no one had bothered to supply a blue print of the new economic society, or to make any specific proposals.

This was no accident, for Karl Marx, the founder of modern socialism, had warned time after time that detailed plans for a future socialist society were futile and dangerous. All that was known with certainty was that the capitalist system would collapse one day and, while socialists ought to do their utmost to hasten its demise, any plans beyond that would simply compromise the socialist idea. For that reason, Marx was violently opposed to those socialists who drew up detailed political and economic blue prints of the future society. All such men were nothing but utopian cranks whose practical contribution was nil.

Marx's disciples took their master's advice very much to heart. Those who, like August Bebel, felt impelled to mention man's happy lot in the socialist society for propaganda purposes, generally restricted themselves to vague promises of a shorter working day, or to such topical issues as the redistribution of landed estates among smallholders.

The resulting confusion can best be appreciated from the first measures which the Bolsheviks were forced to take after they seized power. The Supreme Economic Council, founded in December 1917, could think of nothing better than to give urgent instructions to the Academy of Science to set up a number of expert commissions for suggesting preliminary "laws" of industrial reorganisation and economic development. Thus the Academy of Science became the organiser of the great socialist plan—which to the reader may seem more utopian an idea than any of Thomas More's. In fact, the activities of the Academy were strictly circumscribed, and few of the sub-committee's suggestions were applied in practice. The only tangible result was the emergence of an institute whose task it was to predict future economic developments.

It was only in February 1920, that Lenin instructed the economic institute to turn planner. No longer were the experts merely expected to make predictions or to point out short-comings in various sectors of industry—they were instructed to formulate programmes instead. During the next congress of the Communist Party, Lenin's instructions were endorsed and elaborated: "The basis of economic rehabilitation is undeviating adherence to a consolidated economic plan for the next historical epoch."[1].

Marx would have shuddered at the thought of a total economic plan for an entire historical epoch, and, in fact, the grandiose plan became a restricted plan for electrification rather than for total reorganisation. However, the "Goelro Plan", as it became known, was said to be only a beginning, the handle for cranking the entire economic machine. Or, as Lenin put it: "Soviets+electrification=socialism."

A more ambitious scheme was started in February 1921, when the civil war had ended. It was the so-called "Gosplan", which was not so much a plan as a series of government commit-tees entrusted with planning. Two years were to pass before some partial plans for the metal and transport industry emerged from that body. Meanwhile, taking "two steps forward and one step back", Lenin had ushered in the age of the NEP (New Economic Policy) which made concessions to peasants, private enterprise, and consumers, and re-introduced a small measure of capitalism.

[1] A. Kurski: *Die Planung der Volkswirtschaft in der UdSSR* (Moscow 1949), p. 35.

Critics of the Five-year Plan

But even when the NEP phase was over and the state once more resumed strict control, planning techniques were still not perfected. One innovation—which was, in fact, a return to capitalist budget methods—was the introduction in 1925–1926 of annual plans for individual industries within the framework of a larger plan. Every industry was expected to reach a fixed norm of production, often on pain of death to those in charge, many of whom were, in fact, shot as saboteurs.

Stalin, who had meanwhile come to power, was anything but an enthusiastic planner. On the occasion of a debate on wheat shortage (1928), he declared that, though it would be wrong to underestimate the role and importance of planning, it would be even more mistaken to exaggerate its importance and to assume that the Soviet Union had reached a stage of development where it is possible to plan and control every last detail of every process.[1]

Two years later, when the first five-year plan was already on its way, Stalin still felt doubtful about the possibilities of a carefully planned economy: "The five-year plan is neither final nor immutable. For us, the five-year plan, like any other plan, is only a first approximation that must be adapted, re-modelled, and improved on the basis of practical experience. No five-year plan can foresee all the potentialities of our society, as they are unfolded in the course of our work, during the implementation of the plan in the factory, in the workshop, in the collective farm, in the district, etc."[2]

Still, the five-year plan proved more effective than Stalin had believed. While the original plan was slightly modified from time to time and from place to place, it was implemented much in the way the commission had envisaged it would be. In 1931 the annual norms were significantly renamed "economic plans", and while non-fulfilment of norms had been a crime, non-fulfilment of economic plans was rank treason.

All in all, it took Russia 10 years to prepare her first plan or, if we consider 1931 as the beginning of planning proper, even 13 years. From makeshift and often mistaken improvisations,

[1] J. Stalin: *Problems of Leninism* (Moscow 1947).
[2] Jean Romeuf: *L'Economie planifiée* (Paris 1955), pp. 17–18.

Russia progressed first to partial plans and finally to a total plan. Actually, the total plan—if we use plan to mean correct foresight—was a "failure", for its target was exceeded by far. (93·7% of the total target and 108% of the heavy industrial target were reached by the end of the fourth year of the first five-year plan.) Still, the planners did not mind. By her plans, Russia had raised her stricken economy to incredible heights. Within a few years, an agrarian country had been transformed into an industrial giant—albeit with threats and persecutions. Industry now accounted for 78% of total production. There is no doubt that the plan was a great practical success, despite the fact that it was a predictive failure.

The correct proportions

However, the most difficult problem of a planned economy, viz. the adaptation of production to demand, had not been solved. Now, socialists had always reproached capitalists with being too greedy for profits to bother about the people's real needs. Socialists, unlike capitalists, would strive single-mindedly to provide mankind with all its necessities. But now it appeared that things were not quite as straightforward as that—at least not in practice. Though the profit motive had been abolished in the Soviet Union, there seemed to be no way of assessing, let alone of fulfilling, popular demand.

Sometimes miscalculations assumed grotesque forms. Thus, on a trip through the Soviet Union, I came across a Ukrainian lemon-squeezer factory that had fulfilled its norm admirably. Unfortunately there was no demand for its products since, as a result of a bad harvest, there were no lemons to be squeezed for love or money. True, lemon squeezers are not perishable, and can be stored for future use, but, during a time of acute shortages, material and labour could surely have been employed more usefully elsewhere. While statistics reflected a great upsurge of production, the nation continued to go about in rags and tatters. Targets might be fulfilled, but until they bore some relation to actual needs, the people tended to remember the failures rather than the triumphs.

By the second five-year-old plan (1933–1937) the planners had learned from experience to gauge the balance of supply and demand more accurately. Moreover, at a time when capitalism was in the throes of its worst crisis and production in the West completely paralysed, Russia had made up her mind to double industrial production. Incredible though it sounded, this aim was, in fact, realised, or rather exceeded, for industrial production rose by 17·1% annually instead of the planned 16·5%.

This welcome discrepancy between predictions and actual results increased with the years. Thus, during the fourth five-year plan (1947–1950) industrial production was said to have risen by 73% and not by the planned 48%. Once again, the result was a triumph for industry, but a failure of planning as such. Russia's plans might be minimum targets, but they were never plans in the literal sense of the word.

Errors were also committed in assessing the relative rate of expansion of the main pillars of Russia's economy—heavy industry, light industry, and agriculture. Heavy industry always made greater advances than the two other sectors, possibly because of rearmament, but in any case much to the consumers' distress. During the fifth five-year plan (1951–1955) an attempt was made to remedy this, as well. As a result, the targets for heavy industry were fixed below the level of leading capital countries, and industry as a whole was planned to have an annual expansion of only 12%.

This time, the results were more in accordance with the predictions. After all, Russia's giant strides were not entirely the results of planning alone: young countries, like young men, always grow very quickly, to consolidate rather than grow further when maturity is reached.

Planning ahead—for how long?

One of the fundamental questions of rational planning is how far one can hope to look into the future. In such partial plans as the construction of power stations, the time involved can easily be computed from the availability of materials and manpower, and all the planner need do is to gauge the demand for electricity correctly and to build accordingly.

Large economic plans pose entirely different problems. Even if there is no shortage of materials and manpower, long-range plans introduce so many uncertainty factors, that an arbitrary time limit has to be imposed upon them. Russia has made the five-year term so popular that it has assumed an almost magical quality. In fact, five years was determined neither by the stars, nor yet by Marx, Lenin or Stalin. It was simply the result of a compromise between the opinions of planners, some of whom preferred 10–15 year plans—the intended duration of the Goelro Plan—while others, usually more conservative party members, preferred to plan for a maximum of two years.

The main argument of the conservative group was that it was unreasonable to expect a permanent expansion of production. In industrialisation, as in agriculture, there was a law of diminishing returns—once the optimum had been reached, further expansion would lead to increasing costs and wasteful investment. A planned economy was said to move in ellipses rather than straight lines—a decreasing rate of expansion and investment were inevitable. And, in the long run, these staid economists were, in fact, proved right, for the original industrial expansion of 22% per annum has now dropped to less than half that figure. On the other hand, had they had their will, and had timid two-year plans in fact been allowed to replace the five-year plans, Russia's economy might well have made far shorter strides than it did.

In April 1929, when the XVIth congress of the Communist party finally sanctioned the first five-year plan, five years became a sacrosanct period, and anyone challenging it was branded as a Trotskyist or capitalist saboteur. Within the given five years, original plans might well be refashioned, but the time-span of the plan was unassailable. There was no law against completing the plan in, say, four years—as happened during the first plan—but the plan had to run its full term, not least because a new plan took a long time to prepare, and because the sooner the target was fulfilled the greater the propaganda triumph.

Still, many Soviet planners continued to hanker after an even longer plan, of which the individual five-year plans were mere sub-divisions. Thus the idea of the fifteen-year plan was born, and once again the choice of 15 years was purely arbitrary—there were no specific projects that lasted for precisely that period. Still $15 = 3 \times 5$, and if 5 was a magic number, 15 was triply so.

Thus, at the beginning of 1941, a few months before German troops invaded Russia, a Party Congress demanded that the Soviet Union outstrip the industrial production and the standard of living of the United States within—15 years. When the government gave its blessing to the project, the planners set to work, ignoring the fact that half of Europe was already in flames, and blissfully oblivious of Hitler's next move.

Though the plan died a premature death, a new 15-year "perspective" plan was initiated the moment the war was won. Its details were never published, for the plan was looked upon as an internal programme that could be changed at any moment, and that would merely help to tell the planners what to aim for when each five-year plan was over.

The revolt of the body

As it turned out, the "perspective" was blurred by an entirely unsuspected event: the revolt of the body against its head. Centralisation and Moscow's leading role in the Soviet economy had apparently been pushed too far. In the spring of 1957, Nikita Khrushchev, all-powerful secretary of the all-powerful Central Committee of the Communist Party, proclaimed to the world that centralised planning had led to a plague of useless bureaucrats, to national dissatisfaction, and to industrial break-downs. From now on, things were going to be quite different: decentralisation, and regional plans would replace Moscow's autocracy once and for all. True, even before Khrushchev, Moscow had left many problems in the hands of local authorities. Side by side with the federal Gosplan there had always been regional Gosplans, regional planning commissions (Oblplans), area planning commissions (Raiplans) and urban planning commissions (Gorplans) all with a certain measure of independence. Still, the last word and above all the final control had always been with Moscow.

While centralisation had never been pleasant for the people, it had seemed logical and unavoidable. If every local authority had been allowed to plan in its own way, there would have been no plan at all. Planning must always proceed from the centre outwards and not the other way round. If planning were as simple as building a house, if stresses and strains could be looked up in tables, decentralised planning might be feasible, but no such tables have as yet been set up. Thus, if thousands of independent authorities develop their own plans, a large proportion of these plans will either overlap or clash. While this may not be a disadvantage to the population, this type of "planning" would have all the disadvantages of private enterprise and of bureaucracy. And Khrushchev's decentralisation did, in fact, lead to immediate difficulties. Regional authorities failed to surrender their surpluses, thus impeding the plans not only of neighbouring regions but of the country as a whole. The rate of total industrial expansion fell for the first time, and by as much as 7%.

In view of this failure, Khrushchev changed the party line in September 1957. Since political considerations alone made it inadvisable to return to full-scale centralisation, he simply called a halt to the sixth five-year plan, which had another three years to run. Until the end of 1958, the current work would be continued provisionally, and in 1959 a new great seven-year plan would be initiated, with a radically different approach.

Nor had orthodox Soviet planning run into hot water in Russia alone. Long before Khrushchev launched his bombshell attack on Stalin, it had become quite plain that Moscow's planning system was not a ready-made export article. In satellite countries, the planning authorities, assisted by experts from Moscow, realised to their horror that what was meat for the Soviet Union was poison for their own socialist system. There was a lack of statistical information, of an efficient state machinery, and of industrial leaders—in short many of the essential cogs of the great wheel were missing.

Above all, the people seemed more opposed to planning than their Soviet neighbours ever had been. When planning was first begun, private capital had not yet been completely liquidated nor war-damage made good. Adding a new economic system to all their other troubles was more than most men were prepared to shoulder.

No wonder then, that the first satellite plans, despite their sonorous words and impressive programmes, were concerned with simple reconstruction rather than with the building of the new society. They were most successful in Czechoslovakia, which had suffered relatively little war damage and which had a fairly large number of skilled technicians. Moreover Prague stepped far more gingerly than other satellite capitals, and even drew freely on the French Monnet Plan. The total plan was confided to a committee of 15 economists, supported by 14 technical sub-committees. The politicians wisely sat back and left the job to those best qualified to tackle it.

However, as the satellite countries became more and more dependent on Moscow, their plans had to be increasingly geared to Russia's economy. It seemed pointless to draw up independent plans, and to work towards great increases in production, when it was uncertain whether Russia would be able to supply the required machinery and raw materials. At the beginning of 1949, a first attempt was therefore made to co-ordinate the economic plans of the entire Communist bloc under the C.O.M.E.C.O.N. (Council for Mutual Economic Aid) but that attempt proved premature and abortive.

A fresh start was made in 1955, when it was resolved that the beginning of the sixth Russian five-year plan in 1956 would coincide with the start of co-ordinated five-year plans in all the People's Democracies—which meant that 300 million people in eight countries would henceforth collaborate in forging a common destiny. Alas, Russia's internal economic difficulties, Poland's economic crisis which forced her to call for American help, the events in Hungary, and other set-backs thwarted the implementation of this stupendous plan. Once again, Stalin's words seem to have been confirmed: "Even the five-year plan is only a first approximation".

Dictating and planning

It would be quite wrong to conclude, however, that Communist planning is a mere hit and miss affair. Russia, for one, has benefited greatly from it. But benefits apart, to what extent is it possible to make plans agree precisely with the predictions on which they are based?

Soviet plans do not help us to answer this question. During their implementation, too many of the original ideas were changed too radically for much of the original plans to have remained. The aims of the plan, i.e. increases of industrial potential, improvements in the standard of living, may have been fulfilled, but not the original predictions on which these plans were made.

To a certain extent this may be due to political factors. The West has always argued that totalitarian planning depends on the whims of dictators, and such whims are singularly unpredictable. Thus Caesar, Napoleon, and Hitler believed in destiny or in the stars and left many of their plans to "fate". Stalin, who seemed less cranky in this respect, was content to be proclaimed the spiritual father and patron saint of the five-year plan, without worrying overmuch about its details.

This attitude is easily explained. A dictator whose only task it is to initiate a plan every five years, thereafter to let the experts take over, would be surrendering most of his power. A real dictator must be free to impose his will at any time, to revoke decisions, or to change his mind whenever he so chooses. Economic plans under an absolute dictator are therefore variable plans, not so much as a result of changes in external conditions as of the dictator's unpredictable whims.

It is quite possible that under a less autocratic regime, economic plans would keep more closely to the original targets. But even in that case, the planners will not simply be able to fold their hands and, confident in their own infallible foresight, leave the rest to a well-oiled machine. They will have to watch very carefully for necessary changes, though they will never make changes simply to assert their will. On the contrary, it would be their primary concern to see that the original plan is implemented as closely as possible, thus confirming their predictions. Moreover, democratic plans have no need to be minimum plans whose targets must be exceeded to prove the excellence of the regime. Though democratic plans may therefore lose much of the momentum so characteristic of Stalin's plans, they are far more likely to fulfil their promise precisely.

Self-regulation

While Communists are convinced that men must be coerced into fulfilling or outstripping their own targets, the West has recently developed a theory for correlating intentions and results very precisely. Cybernetics, though not literally a science of planning, is closely linked to it. Like econometrics, it is a mathematical technique developed by engineers. Though its present applications are restricted to the construction of computers and other machines, its real scope is very much wider. According to its founder, the American mathematician Norbert Wiener, cybernetics is the study of "control and communication in the animal and the machine".[1] That definition, too, is not wide enough. Cybernetics is derived from the Greek Kybernetes —steersman—from which our own word "governor" was originally coined, and cybernetics is, in fact, the science of steering a straight course.

According to cyberneticists, all organic units tend towards automatic self-regulation, and hence towards equilibrium. The task of the new discipline is to study this phenomenon, and to apply the results not only to technology but also to the social life.

Now, what has been lacking in all economic plans so far is precisely what cybernetics is trying to establish, viz. a sensitive apparatus that would automatically react to outside disturbances and correct them without stopping the whole machinery. Planning, both the Eastern and the Western variety, has been far too eclectic, and has always lacked a proper theory of its own. For that very reason the execution of all plans has always been far too greatly governed by the personal qualities of the individual planners.

This does not mean that cybernetics intends to demote men to mere cogs in a machine. After all, electrical engineers have not surrendered one iota of their human dignity by working according to the laws of Ampère, Maxwell and Hertz. No matter how sweeping a theory, men will always be able to prove their worth within it.

A better theory simply means better planning, i.e. more

---

[1] Norbert Wiener: *Cybernetics or Control and Communication in the Animal and the Machine* (N.Y.—Paris, 1949), p. 19. (See also: L. de Broglie: *Cybernetics* in *New Perspectives in Microphysics* (N.Y. 1960).

accurate predictions. Only when we know what we *can* achieve, can we decide what we *should* achieve. Now, our capacity for achievement depends largely on conditions that we can create at will, and on others that we can take into account. The more we allow for such variables, the greater the chances of our plans' success.

True, not even the best-laid plan can be like a machine that runs automatically, and in which everything is self-regulated. Economic plans involve millions of heads and hands who use tools for the purpose for which they were designed. Only by assuming that men will act reasonably, can we rely on their automatic insight and foresight. In that way, even the word "automatism" loses its horror. Automatic reactions, be they acquired or instinctive, are matters of pride rather than shame —as any good driver will tell you. They are part and parcel of self-regulation, and hence a basic element of all human plans worth making.

The Future of Prediction

*T*HIS BOOK BEGAN WITH A FANFARE AND ENDS WITH the muffled beat of a drum. The introductory remark that every man must constantly look into the future or perish is true beyond all doubt. But can men ever hope to prophesy correctly? How often do they err? Have they become better prophets or worse?

The reader, as he has followed our quest, must surely have decided that, in some respects at least, man's skill in probing the future is no greater than it was in ancient Babylon, whose prophets consulted the liver. Unless a man is already in the throes of death, no one can tell how long he will live and whether he will die of natural causes or in an accident. To this day, no one can predict where and when the next flood will strike, or even whether it will be raining in eight days' time. The further we delve into the even more complex problems of our cultural, economic, and political future, the more uncertain our grounds of prophecy become. The best laid plans of the best-intentioned men have always had a tendency to gang agley.

Such is the truth, but fortunately it is not the whole truth. As scientific knowledge has grown, so have the possibilities of applying that knowledge to technological problems, and hence to technological predictions. Only this process has not been uninterrupted for, at times, the entire framework had to be demolished to make way for an entirely new edifice. But such is the nature of progress in all fields—only by scrapping the old can the new be born at all. What is decisive is not the number of changes that have to be made, but the durable residue, and of that the art of prediction has its full measure.

In at least three respects, we can look more fully and clearly into the future than our ancestors did. We know more about causal connections, about the prediction of aggregate phenomena, and about eliminating chance by deliberate planning.

Specialisation without "specialists"

The first of these three advances is the direct result of specialisation. Ancient prophets believed that the entire future could be
predicted from a single prophetic source: the stars, the intestines
of animals, or dreams. Modern prognosis, on the other hand,
assumes that only the specific effects of specific causes can
reasonably be predicted, and has made the connection between
cause and effect the subject of specialist study. While a country
doctor may well be a great amateur meteorologist, and while he
may forecast weather changes from some of his patients'
symptoms, he would be a fool to conclude that all diseases are
caused by barometric fluctuations.

Modern predictions rightly abhor all precipitate generalisations, and are based on empiricial proof instead. Only experiments which can be repeated under equal conditions are considered
to be reliable evidence—all the rest is doubtful. In practice, these
standards are often found to be a little too strict. Thus some
large scale phenomena cannot be tested in the laboratory for fear of
blowing it up, and similarly, while vast mountainous areas could
perhaps be levelled by atomic explosion, no reasonable man or
conscientious government will allow itself to put this contention
to the test. Predictions about the effects of atomic destruction are
not based on full-scale experiments but rather on mathematical
considerations which assume that an increase in fissionable
material will cause a proportionate increase in destructive effect.

Such purely arithmetical deductions are characteristic of our
mathematical age, but may not be entirely legitimate. The
assumption that large-scale processes do not differ qualitatively
from analogous small-scale processes is just another impermissible generalisation. Thus scientists have become commend-
ably reluctant to establish general laws from an inadequate
number of particular instances, with the result that, in medicine
for instance, prediction has become much more difficult but—
much more certain. On the other hand, there is a great need that
scientists shed their reluctance to say anything at all about the
future, for they, more than anyone else, are trained prognosti-
cians. Their modesty merely opens the back door to all sorts of
charlatans, and there is no reason why scholars should withhold
from the world what prognoses they can legitimately make.

Collective predictions

The second field in which great advances have been made is the field of aggregate predictions of such phenomena as, for instance, the mortality rate of a given country. Aggregate predictions are usually the projections of statistical averages into the future, on the basis of probability theory. If external factors suddenly change conditions so radically, that past statistical averages no longer apply, then the whole basis of statistical predictions is of course undermined. We have seen that this is precisely what happened with predictions about declining birth and mortality rates.

Only a few decades ago, it seemed that methods of aggregate prediction were as perfect as they could be. Life insurance and later social insurance had helped to turn this method of prediction into one of the basic pillars of all mathematical prognoses, and governments used it to predict, for instance, how many schools and how many hospitals had to be built to absorb future generations, how many recruits would be available for conscription, and so on. Since then, the revolution in physics has opened up even greater statistical horizons and provided even more efficient mathematical tools. Simultaneously the old notion of historical and economic cycles has increasingly been challenged.

Cycle theories failed so badly in the post-war age, that many economists have foresworn them once and for all. Perhaps their disappointments have made them a little too rash, for all cycle theories are merely tentative, and few people ever claimed that they were indicative of anything but a given age or condition. There is no reason to suppose that future phenomena will not follow a certain, predictable, rhythm, or that we ought to desist from trying to look for it. Rhythmical phenomena do, after all, exist in many spheres, and remain the basis of many useful predictions, particularly in biology.

Restricting chance

Planning is the third great advance in the field of prediction. The reader may wonder how we can say this after the many critical remarks we have made about it. However, planning is still in its infancy, and was, moreover, born under exceptionally difficult conditions. Nevertheless, the idea that a large country should be able to predict its future even half-way correctly five years in advance, would have struck 19th century capitalists and socialists alike as utterly fantastic, as an idle play with figures.

Today no one can doubt that some of even the most far-reaching economic plans can be implemented, and that production, in particular, can be regulated years in advance. Whether one must accept the restrictions of individual liberty which were associated with the Russian plan is quite a different matter. The practical success of planning as such is beyond any doubt, the only thing that is doubtful is the degree of accuracy with which the original plans correspond with the final outcome, i.e. whether plans must constantly be revised as they were in Russia or whether, under different political conditions, they would require fewer modifications and thus lead to more predictable results.

There is a great deal of evidence that discrepancies of 10% or even of 20% can be avoided with better techniques. But even if this were not the case, we need only reverse the percentage errors of the Russian predictions to realise that errors of 10 or 20% mean a degree of accuracy of 80–90%.

The reader might object that no matter which way we look at the figures, errors of 10 or 20% are considerable and must have tremendous economic repercussions, particularly when we consider that changes, let alone errors, of that magnitude are rare in any economic system. Still this objection hardly applies to such revolutionary changes as were wrought by the first Russian five-year plans, and do not, in any case, alter the fact that Russia's plans are proof positive that men can largely if not completely fashion their future when they put their minds to it.

The crux of planning is not so much the accurate fulfilment of a given target as the frontal attack on the age-old oppressive fear that men are the helpless victims of pure chance and fate. While the element of chance cannot be completely eradicated from even the best-laid plans, it can at least be drastically reduced. Planning means reducing pure chance to its minimum, and its results have shown to what great extent this can be done. Much of what was previously considered chance has since proved to be nothing but lack of reasonable human foresight. The moment our minds are made up and we have the will to implement our decision, chance begins to prove a mere illusion.

The limits between chance and choice are not drawn for all time—with the help of reason and goodwill, the field of choice can for ever be widened. It would be wider still, if men ceased being as secretive as they are. Much that we consider unpredictable is nothing but the veil of mystery men have drawn over their plans and intentions. In some fields—national finances, foreign policy—the veil is slowly being lifted, but in other fields, particularly in technology, it is being pulled tighter all the while.

However, where there are no such restrictions, wherever men have had a common interest in the future, they have been able to fashion it beyond their wildest expectations. Despite their relapses into magic and divination, human beings have at last developed effective methods of prediction. Fantastic prophecies have given way to serious prognoses, vague hopes receded before considered plans, and probability has ceased to be mere speculation and has become a respectable scientific term instead.

This, by and large, is the state of prediction today. Much remains to be done, but one thing is beyond all doubt: the sphere of unpredictable events is rapidly contracting. That much, at least, we can predict with absolute certainty.

Index

Roman numerals denote Plates and figs. in italics denote Figures in text.

Abu-Maaschar (Albumazar), 76-7
Academy: Moral & Pol. Sci. (Paris), 148
  Mysteries of Naples, 84
  New Athenian, 73
  Science (Moscow), 293
Adad, 51, 58, *8*
Agricultural Adjustment Act (A.A.A.), 288
Akkad, *53*, 59-60
Albategnius (Al-Battan), 77
Alea (Dice), 20, 22-3, 29, I, *1*
Alexander the Great, 67, 178
Alexander Severus, 75
Alexandria, 67
Almanachs, 179-80, 184
Amandry, P., 70fn
American Inst. Pub. Opinion, 170
American Soc. Psych. Research, 114
Ammonius, 81
Amon-Râ, 67
Ampère, A-M., 303
Anastasie, A. & J. P. Filey, 232fn

Anticyclones, 191
Apollo, 70-1
Arabs, 73, 76-8, 80, 200
Archontes, 69
Aristotle, 72, 139, 146, 152, 211, 249
Arlington (U.S.A.), 188
Arnoux, A., 84fn
Ascheim-Zondek Test, 209
Assurbanipal, 52
Assyria, *52-3*, 55-7
Astres, Journal French Order of Astrologers, 106, 109
Astrology, 38, 49, 51-2, 57-62, 67-8, 73-4, 81, 83-6, 92, 96-118, 143, 158, 177-82, 193, 211, 276, 305
Astronomy, 19, 39, 58-9, 62, 68, 73, 80-3, 96-8, 144-6
  German Astronomical Soc., 114
Athens, 69, 72-4, 145-6
Atom Bomb, 27, 94, 120
Attila, 149
Augustine, St., 76, 147
Augustus, 75
Austria, 107, 120-2, 129, 149, 162, 199

Babson, R. W., 35
Babylonia, 51-7, 58, 60-5, 74-5, 145, 147, 149, 178, 314
Balaclava, 185-6
Barometer, 181-2: Business, 270-3, *31*
Barr, H. G., 212
Bastiat, C-F., 254
Bateman, F., 130fn, 137fn, 138fn
Bateson, Prof., 213
Bebel, A., 292
Bellamy, E., 43-4
Bergen, 186-7
Bergson, Henri, 126, 140
Bernoulli, Jakob, 89, 240, 245
Bernstein, M. E., 228fn
Bessel, 39
Bethe, 194
Beveridge, Sir W., 246-8
Bjerknes, V. & J., 186-7
Blanc Bros., 237
Blenkenship, A. B., 168fn
Blum, Léon, 286
Bohr, Niels, 128
Boll, M., 89fn, 90fn.
Boltzmann, L., 56-7
Bonaparte, Ch-L, 'Prince of Canino', 236-7
Bonaparte, Napoleon I, 85, 160-2, 244, 246, 281, 301, XV
Borel, Emile, 28, 239fn
Borneo, 53
Box, Bart J., 114
Bradford Hill, A., 208fn
Brahe, Tycho, 83
Brahmism, 143-4
Brazil 116, 289-90

Breasted, J. H., 67fn
Brit. Inst. Public Opinion, 171-3
Broad, C. D., 141
Broglie, L. de, 140, 302fn
Brooks, C. E. P., 197fn
Brugsch, T., 199fn
Brückner, E., 195
Brunswig (1547), *18*
Budget, National, 281-6
Bugeja, V., 238
Burma, 53
Business Cycle Research, 235, 255, 259, 261, 273-5
    German Inst. for, 261-3, 273-5
Buys-Ballot (Ballot Laws), 187

Cabbala, 145, 148-50, 212
Caesar, J., 75, 301
Cagliostro (G. Balsamo), 90
Calendars, 58, 120, 143-4
Capitalism, 43, 154, 253, 258, 284, 292, 294, 307
Caraffa, Cardinal, 96
Cardano, G., 83-5, 88, *19, 20*
Carneades, 73
Cards, 50, 91, 139, 242, XIV, XV
Catherine de Medici, 45-7
Cazotte, J., 91
Chaldeans, 57-60, 63, 73-5
Challis, 39
Chance, 23, 26-7, 87-9, 108-10, 238-9, 248, 250, 252
Charles IV, 149

China, 52, 60-2, 146, 149, 194, 197, 211, 227, 229
Chiromancy, 91, 113
Christianity, 36-7
Choice, 41, 164-9
Chromosomes, 210-1, 213-4
Cicero, 76
Clairvoyance, 91, 128-42
Clark, Colin, 275-6
Cleanthes, 57-8
Cleromancy, 69
Cocco d'Ascoti, 81
Collingwood, R. G., 155fn
Commodity Markets, 261-5, 267-9, 274
Company of Merchant Adventurers, 243
Comte, A., 152-3, 158
Confucius (Kung-tse), 60-1
Conteneau, G., 53fn, 59fn, 66fn, 70fn
Continuity, 155, 238, 256-7
Copernicus, N., 68, 83
Cornelius, Hispalus, 75
Couderc, P., 52fn, 81fn, 98fn, 111fn
Cowles, A., 268fn
Croesus, 71
Crum, W. L., 259
Curschmann, H., 199fn
Cybernetics, 302
Cycle Theories, 23, 34-5
  see also Business &
    Rhythms,
Cyclones, 191

Dakin & Dewey, E. R., 261
Darwin, Charles, Darwinism, 33, 39-40, 92, 154, 213

Deduction, 38-9, 41, 50
Delcourt, Marie, 70fn
Delhi, 187
Delphi, Delphic Oracles, 70-3, 178, IX, X
Delpierre, Mme., 216fn
Dessoir, Max 130
Determinism, 25, 27-9, 31, 183
Dewey, Thomas A., 173
Dionysius of Syracuse, 43
Divination, 53, 66, 91-2, 113, 123
Dodona, 70
Domitian, 75
Dorn, Dr., 212
Dourdin Inst. (Paris), 176
Dow, Charles, 268
Dreams, 50, 52, 66-7, 90, 113, 119-42
Druids, 76
Du Bois-Raymond, 26
Ducroq, A., 194
Dunne, J. W., 131-41
Dürer, Albrecht, II
Duverger, M., 284fn

Eclipse, 62
Economics, Economists, 34, 42-3, 248-9, 253-5, 259-61, 270, 276-7, 282-6, 293-202: Committee for E. Research, 272-3
Eden, Sir A., 105
Edward VI, 83-5, 20
Egypt, 51-2, 65-8, 104, 145, 149, 151, 266
Ehrlich, Paul, 128
Einstein, A., 26, 140

Eisenhower, Dwight D., 173, 266
Elizabeth I, 157
Elizabeth II, 104-5
Embryo, 76, 102-3, 209-10, 213, 228
Engels, F., 154
Enkidu, 53
Enmeduranki, 53
Entropy, 34
Enzymes, 53
Epidaurus, 90, 133-4, 204.
Equilibrium, 31-3, 35-6, 251-5
E.S.P., 130, 136-9, 141-2
Etruria, Etruscans, 74-5
Eudoxus, 73
Eugenics, 213, 230-3
Euripides, 73
Evolution, 39-40, 154-7
Experience, 40-1, 50, 164
Exta, 74
Eysenck, H. J., 169fn

Faroe Is., 191
Fates, Fatalism, 37, 68-70, 78, 235, 258
Fauque, M., 234fn
Feder, E., 267fn
Fermat, P de, 22, 87
Fidler, A., 208fn
Fortune-telling, 50, 91-2, 117
Fossey, Ch., 56fn
Foster, A. A., 138fn
Fourastié, Jean, 237
Foville, A. de, 270-2, *31*
France, 106, 111-3, 118, 127, 148, 171, 173, 176, 245-6, 266, 270-2, 282-3, 284-6
Freud, S., 121-6, 129fn

Galileo, 22, 88, 181
Galle, J. G., 39
Gallup, George, 169-76, 288
Galton, Sir F., 213, 231
Garcia, Thomas, 237
Gauss, C. F., 123, 240
Genetics, 34, 40, 213-6, 228-9, 251
General Motors, 166, 291
Georgel, Gaston, 148
Gerard, John, 192
Germany, 188-9, 199, 222, 224, 243, 260, 267, 273-5
Gibbs, J. W., 26-7
Gibson, 137
Gilgamesh, 52-3
Goldsmith, F. N., 265-6, V
Gor- and Gosplans, 293, 298
Graunt, John, 228
Greece, Greeks, 35-6, 46, 51-2, 59-60, 68-74, 78, 81
Gregory XI, 148
Guam, 188
Guillaume, A., 52fn
Gurney, E., 132fn
Guthrie, Douglas, 200fn, 205
Gypsies, 91, 120

Hadrian, 75
Hale, 194
Hallucination, 50, 90-1, 135-6
Hamilton, W., 268
Hamlet, 183
Hanau, A., 262fn
Harrison, W. H., 92fn
Haruspices, 74-6
Harvard, 114, 272-3
Hattus, 55
Hegel, 153

Heindl, H., 188
Heine, H., 47
Henri II & IV, 85-6
Heisenberg, W., 25-6, 28
Heliopolis, 67, 145
Hepatosocopy, 53-7, 74-5, 13
Heraclitus, 70, 145
Herodotus, 71
Hertz, 302
Hertzka, T., 44
Hinton, G. H., 140
Hipparchus, 74, 96, 98
Hippocrates, 54, 73, 199, 203
Hitler Regime, 85, 106, 161-2,
    222, 224, 231, 301
Hobbes, Thomas, 46
Hofstatter, P. W., 127fn
Holstein, F. von, 267
Homer, 67, 71, 151
Horoscopes, 60, 78, 83-5, 92,
    100, 102-18, 146, 178-9,
    301
Humbaba, 52, 9
Humphreys, W. J., 187fn
Huter, C. H., 105
Hypnosis, 89-91, 130

India, 52, 163, 227
Induction, 38, 50, 128
Inflation, 252-3, 276-8, 282-3
Inspiration, 36-7, 46-50, 127,
    143
Insurance, 21, 50, 87, 198,
    234-5, 242-7
Intestines, Prophecy from,
    53-7, 74-5, 10, IV
Intuition, 38-41, 48-50, 127,
    143

Isidore of Seville, 147
Israel, 36-7, 63-7, 163, 212,
    266

James, M. R., 131
Jantat, Léon, 89fn
Jeans, J. H., 26, 28
Jevons, W. S., 194
John of Toledo, 80-1, 178
Joseph, 66-7
Josephus Flavius, 146
Jomal, O., 116fn
Juglar, Clement, 257-60, 276
Julius II, 82
Jung, C. G., 127
Jupiter, see also Planets, 74

Kant, I., 119, 139
Kautsky, Karl, 154fn
Kekule, F. A., 128
Kemper, M., 95fn, 128-9
Kepler, J., 83, 104, 25
Keynes, J. M., 249, 253-4,
    277
Khrushchev, Nikita, 298-9
Kierkegaard, S., 91
Kinetic Theory, 26
Kinsey, A. C., 175
Kirchoff, 194
Kitchin, J., 259-60, 276
Koerte, G., 75fn
Kondratieff, N. D., 260-1, 276
Kubie, L. S., 206fn
Kuczinski, R. R., 222fn
Kurski, A., 293fn
Kuznets, S., 260fn

Lamarck, J-B., 182-3
Landon, A. M., 170
Landsteiner, K., 213
Lange, F. A., 26fn
Laplace, P-S., 182-5, 240
Larousse, P., 92
Lavoisier, A-L., 188
Lazareff, P., 170fn
League of Nations, 223-5
Leffler, G., 268fn
Leibniz, G. W., XII
Lenin, V., 293, 295
Leo X, 82
Leverrier, U-J-J-., 39, 185-7
Lewinsohn, R. (Morus),
    210fn, 267fn
Lhermitte, Jean, 127fn
Literary Digest, The, 169-70
Lithology, 69
Lloyd's, 247
Lo King (Chinese Magic
    Disc), 60, VIII
London Soc. Psych. Research,
    131-4
Lotteries, Gambling, 89, 90,
    109, 115, 165-6, 168,
    236-9, 241-2, 248
Louis, J-D., 282
Luther, M., 82

McCombs, R. P., 205fn
McChung, 210
Macbeth, 90
Mackenzie, Sir J., 205
Malthus, T. R. 34, 219-23, 227
Marduk, 59
Martineau, A., 106
Marx, Karl, 43, 153-4, 258-9,
    293-7

Mass Tests, 136-8, 167-75
Maxwell, 302
Medicine, 37, 50, 198-216
    of Probability, 208
Meissner, B., 56fn
Melancthon, 82, 180
Memphis, 67
Mendel, Gregor, 213, 215
Mendeleev, Dimitri, 39
Mendès-France, 106
Mentré, F., 158fn
Méré, Chevalier de, 88
Mersenne, Père, 88
Mesmer, A., 90
Mesopotamia, 51-5, 63, 65,
    74, 76, 80
Meteorology, 30, 50, 58, 67,
    177-97, 255-6, 288-9
    French, 190-1
    German, 188
Minkowski, H., 140
Mirarandola, Pico della, 180,
    189
Misserand, A., 211fn
Moira, 69
Mollet, Guy, 106
Mongols, 105-6
Monnet, Jean, 285-6, 300
Monte Carlo, 237-9
Moore, H. L., 194
More, Sir T. (Morus), 43,
    293
Morgan, J. P., 266
Morgenstern, O., 242fn
Morus, *see* Lewinsohn R. &
    More, Sir T.
Moscow, 188, 296-300
Moses, 63
Moura, Jean, 87fn
Müller, J. H., XIII

Mycenae, 69
Myers, F. W. H., 129, 132

Nabû, 59, 60
Nairobi, 188
Natopa, 67
Necromancy, 50, 65, 85-7
Negro folklore, 95
   sex ratio, 228
   vote, 172
Nelson, S. A., 268
N.E.P., 293-4
Nergal, 58-9, III
Nero, 75
Neumann, J. von, 242fn
New Deal, 170, 253
Newton, Sir Isaac, 27, 31, 38, 51, 140, 171
New York, 107, 168, 212, 266, 268
   City College, 138
Nicepsos of Sais, 51-2
Nietzsche, F., 147-8
Niniveh, 52
Ninurta, 59
Nostradamus, 82-6, 21
Notestein, 237
Notscher, F., 56fn
Numerology, 89-92, 109-10, 116, 145-6

Oberkirch, Baroness, 91
Oblplan, 298
Oedipus, 59
Olympia, 70
Omens, 56-7

Oracles, 70-6, 92
Orestes, 69
Orwell, George, 44
O.T., 36-7, 63-7, 147, 179
Otho, 75

Palamedes, I
Parapsychology, 131-6, 142
Pareto, V., 251-3
Paris: Astrological Monthly, 106, 109
   Musée de Costume, 216
   Nat. Inst. Statistics, 113
Parke, H. W., 73fn
Pascal, Blaise, 22, 87-9, 181, XI
Paul III, 83
Pepin, E., 188fn
Periods, Theory of, 150, 159, 161-3, 211, 240, 253-4, 256-7
Persia, 52, 76
Persons, Warren, 194
Petosiris, 52
Petty, Sir W., 87, 218
Picasso, Pablo, 125, 159
Pinder, W., 158 fn
Planck, Max, 31, 155
Planets, 34, 57, 60-1, 77-85, 99-110, 115-6, 178, 217
   Jupiter, 29, 59, 100, 103, 108-10
   Mars, 59, 100, 107
   Mercury, 59, 100, 108, 110, 23
   Moon, 46, 58-9, 62, 76, 97, 183
   Neptune, 29, 39, 100, 185

Planets—*continued*
  Pluto, 100
  Saturn, 59, 103, 105, 107, 110, *24*
  Sun, 46, 58, 62, 96-7, 100, 193-5
  Uranus, 59, 100, 110
  Venus, 59, 100, 109-10
Planning, 22, 41-2, 49-50, 67, 241, 264, 280, 292-303
Plato, 43, 73, 92, 145-6
Pliny the Elder, 76
Plutarch, 70, 73, 92
Poincaré, H., 248fn
Polo, Marco, 62
Porta, G. della, 84-5
Positivism, 153, 158
Poujadists, 266
Precognition, 30, 50, 130, 134-42
Pregnancy, 98-102, 209-16
Premium Bonds, 241
Princeton, 223-4
Probability, Theory of, 23, 26-30, 50, 87-9, 245-7
Psi-Process, 137
Psycho-analysis, 120-2, 124-9 206
Ptolemy, Claudius, 67-8, 74, 76-7, 96-7, 119
Puységur, Marquis de, 90-1
Pythagoras, 73, 145
Pythia, 70-2

Quantum Theory, 26-8, 31, 155

Raiplan, 298
Raynes, H. E., 246fn

Religion, 36, 46-9, 117, 144-5, 217-8
Renaissance, 82-3, 152, 281
Renan, E., 69
Renouvier, C., 155
Revolution, 31, 33, 156-7, 162, 182, 194, 219, 257, 292
Rhesus (RH) Factor, 213
Rhine, J. B., 130, 136-7
Rhythms, (Cycles), 35, 78-9, 143-6, 148-42, 157-63, 157-63, 193-7, 203, 218, 220, 253-68, 268-78, 301, 306-8
Richet, C., 130
Rio de Janeiro, 116, 188-9
Roll, E., 252fn
Romans, Rome, 54, 74-5, 100, 107-8, 145-7, 149, 280
Romeuf, J., 294fn
Roosevelt, F. D., 85, 169, 170, 253, 287
Roques, F. W., 209fn
Rossby, C-G., 187
Roulette, 235-42
Rowe, J. W. F., 263fn
Rugby, 188
Ruttan, M., 53fn

Sainte-Beuve, C-A., 158
Sartre, J-P., 175
Saul, 64-5
Say, Léon, 282
Scaliger, J. C., 147-8
Scheinfeld, A., 215fn
Scheucher (1734), *15*
Schmeidler, Gertrude, 138
Schnabel, P., 73fn
Schönberg, Arnold, 151

Schopenhauer, A., 91
Schrödinger, 140
Schumpeter, J. A., 260fn
Schwabe, S. H., 194
Science, Scientists, 20, 25, 50,
    93-4, 107, 122, 132, 182-4
Servien, Pius, 240
Sex, 34, 73, 120-6, 175, 210-3,
    220-3, 257
Shamash, the Sun, 58, III
Shakespeare, W., 90, 131
Shaw, G. B., 44
Shaw, Sir Napier, 196fn
Shipton, Mother, 92
Sibyl of Cumae, 74
Siciliano, A., 289
Sin, 58
Sirius-Cycle, 145, 149
Sismondi, S. de., 236
Smith, Adam, 254
Snyder, L. H., 230
Soal, S. G., 130fn, 137fn. 138fn
Socrates, 146
Somnambulism, 90
Sophocles, 69
Sourian, M., 141fn
Spencer, Herbert, 92, 154-5
Spengler, O., 155-7
Spitzbergen, 196
Stalin, J., 294, 297-301
Statistics, 22, 27, 41, 50, 113,
    250, 259, 261-2
Stekel, W., 126
Stern, Curt, 229-30
Stetson, H. T., 194fn
Stöffler, J., 179-80
Stock Exchange, 35, 110, 241-
    2, 255, 264, 267, 274
Stockistic models, 278-9
Stoics, 57, 154

Stravinsky, Igor, 151, 159
Sugermann, Dr., 212
Sulla, 75
Sumerians, 53, 58
Süssmilch, J. P., 217-8
Swedenborg, 135
Symbols, 22, 33, 94-6, 120-6
Syria, 52, 63

Talleyrand, 135, 282
Tannehill, 195fn
Telegony, 98
Telepathy, 91, 128-31, 134
Tell-Hariri, 55
Terman, L. M., 232fn
Tetrabiblos (Ptolemy), 67-8,
    76, 96, 103, 119
Theophilus, 200
Thermometer, 181-2
Thiel, R., 62fn, 180fn
Thothmes,IV, 66
Tiberius, 75
Tinbergen, Jan, 278
Tonti, Lorenzo, 244-5
Torricelli, E., 181, 29
Toynbee, A. J., 155-6, 160-1,
    260
Truman, Harry, 173
Tucker, W., 52fn
T.V.A., 287
Tyrell, G. N. M., 137

Uganda, 53
Ulysses, 65
UNESCO, 115
United Nations, 224, 227

Ur, 53, 58
U.S.A., 111, 117-8, 157, 166-76, 195, 206, 222, 226, 228-9, 230-3, 249, 253-5, 258-9, 266-9, 275-7, 287-92, 298
U.S.S.R., 163, 223-6, 241, 292-303

Vaillant, J. B-P., 185
Valmer, R., 191fn
Vendreyès, P., 25fn
Verne, Jules, 44, 6
Vespasian, 75
Viaut, A., 186fn
Vico, G., 150-3, 155
Vieira, A., 147
Villèle, Pres., 282
Villiaud, Paul, 78fn
Vimont, Claude, 227
Vinci, Leonardo da, 47-8, 7
Virchow, R., 213
Voltaire, 106, 240
Vladivostock, 188

Wagemann, E., 273-4
Wagner, Richard, 151

Wall Street, 35, 168, 265-6, 268-9, 30
Wall Street Journal, 268
Wallenstein, 104, 281, 25
Walsh, W. H., 155fn
Weiss, M., 200fn
Wells, H. G., 44
Wharton, L. R., 211fn
Wiener, N., 302
Winckelmann, 152
Windsor, Duchess of, 107
Winter, P. L., 107fn
Winterstern, A., 122fn, 134fn
Witt, De, 245fn
Wolf, J., 221fn
Woytinsky, 237
Wright Bros., 176

Zaripha, 73
Zener-Cards, 136-7, 26
Zeus, 69, 178
Zinner, E., 61fn, 82fn
Ziqqûrat, 58
Zollner, 194
Zodiac, 58-60, 77, 97, 276, 12, 14, 22, VI
Zweig, F.,